Underground Distribution

D1262747

SECOND EDITION

SYSTEM

DRAWINGS

MATERIALS

INSTALLING

SPLICING

FUSING

MAINTENANCE

TROUBLE

JOB SITE

Additional Publications

Alexander Publications offers a variety of books, manuals, and software for electric utilities. For details, visit www.alexanderpublications.com or request your copy of our latest catalog.

Comments

If you have comments on this book, or suggestions how we might make it more valuable for you or your company, please call or write:

Alexander Publications
104 East Fairview Avenue #406
Meridian, Idaho 83642

Telephone: 1-800-992-3031 or (949)642-0101
Fax: (949)646-4845
E-mail: info@alexanderpublications.com

Warnings

The descriptions, illustrations, tables, and other data in this handbook are intended to be aids for field workers. This material does not replace the extensive training necessary to safely install and maintain underground service.

This handbook describes work practices which are accepted by most utilities, but some might not apply to you. Always follow your company's established safety procedures and work practices.

Notice

This publication is based on work prepared by BC Hydro solely for its internal use. It is made available as-is and without warranty. Neither the author nor the publisher assumes any liability for damages that may result from the use of any information in this publication.

Second edition

Seventh printing: March 2020

Contents

SYSTEM | DRAWINGS | MATERIALS | INSTALLING | SPLICING | FUSING | MAINTENANCE | TROUBLE | JOB SITE

Foreword

For years, the most popular way to deliver electricity was through overhead wires. Construction practices for overhead service became well understood, and this type of service is easier to operate and maintain because equipment is out in the open.

Recently, however, more installations are going underground. Customers prefer underground utilities because, let's face it, electric wires are ugly. And underground service is more reliable because there's no risk of lines going down in storms, or poles being hit by motorists.

But compared with overhead service, underground is more complicated to install and more expensive to repair when that's required. What's more, lineworkers must learn another set of job skills because underground service uses specialized techniques, materials, tools, and equipment. Also, working underground involves additional safety precautions.

This book covers field-proven practices for pulling cables, splicing cables, terminating cables, fusing lines, grounding equipment, and switching circuits. It delivers the special job skills lineworkers and cable splicers need to safely install and maintain underground distribution systems.

Richard Alexander
Publisher

CHAPTER

UNDERGROUND SYSTEMS

DRAWINGS

MATERIALS

INSTALLING

SPLICING

FUSING

MAINTENANCE

TROUBLE

JOB SITE

Historical Background

Power cable technology had its beginnings in the 1880s, when the need for cables became pressing following the introduction of incandescent lighting. With urban growth, it became increasingly necessary to replace some of the overhead lines for power transmission and distribution with underground cables.

The illumination of the larger cities proceeded at such a rapid pace, that under some circumstances, it was impossible to accommodate the number and size of feeders required for distribution using the overhead line approach. In fact, this situation deteriorated so notably in New York City, that in addition to the technical and aesthetic considerations, the overhead line system began to pose a safety problem to the lineworkers, the firemen, and the public.

As a result, the city passed a law in 1884 requiring the removal of the overhead line structures and the replacement of these with underground cables. Similar laws and public pressure were applied in other cities with the consequence, that by the early 1900s, underground electrification via insulated cables was on its way to becoming a well established practice.

The development of early power cables followed closely the extension of the cable techniques which had been developed on low current cables, lines for telegraphy and explosive mine cables. A practical lead press was invented in 1879 and subsequently used to manufacture 2 kV cables for the city of Vienna in 1885. During the same period, vulcanized rubber was used to produce cables on a commercial scale, although gutta-percha was used as early as 1846.

Impregnated paper cables were first put on the market in 1894 by Callender Cables of England, using impregnate mixtures of rosin oil, rosin and castor oil. Only in 1918 were these replaced by mineral oils. In North America, impregnated paper cables were first supplied by the Norwich Wire Company. Varnished cambric cables were introduced by the General Electric Company in 1902; the high temperature behavior of these cables was subsequently improved in 1910 by the addition of black asphalt.

It is interesting to note that some of the earliest cables consisted merely of ducts with the copper conductors insulated from ground by glass or porcelain insulators. In fact, in 1889 the entire city of Paris was electrified using this scheme with sewers serving as ducts.

Some of the more common early insulating materials used in various underground cable installations were: natural rubber, gutta-percha, oil and wax, rosin and asphalt, jute, hemp and cotton. In 1890, Ferranti developed the first oil-impregnated paper cable. Following their manufacture, his cables were installed in London in 1891 for 10 kV operation.

It is most noteworthy that the cables had to be made in 20 foot lengths. As the total circuit was 30 miles in length, about 8000 splicing joints were required. Nevertheless, these cables performed so well that the last cable length was removed from service only in 1933. In 1892, the city of Buffalo, New York, was illuminated with arc lamps and, for this purpose, 7.5 kV rubber insulated cables of the concentric design were placed in service.

Cable installation continued to proceed at a rapid pace so that, by turn of the century, many major cities throughout the world had many miles of underground cable. For example, already by the end of 1909, the Commonwealth Edison Company in Chicago had 400 miles of underground cable operating in the voltage range from 9 to 20 kV.

The city of Montreal had some 4500-foot circuits of three-conductor cables installed in ducts under the canal for 25 kV operation. The same voltage was used for cables traversing the St. Lawrence River in 1906. With some experience behind them, cable manufacturers were increasingly gaining confidence and, during the St. Louis Exposition in 1904, cables developed for voltages as high as 50 kV were put on display.

Prior to the first world war, extensive use was made of oil-impregnated paper cables of the three-conductor belted-type for voltages up to 25 kV. After World War I, the cable design was changed to overcome problems with non-uniform stress distribution. This was done in an effort to accommodate the increased power demand. The problem was solved by shielding each conductor with copper tapes and replacing the belting with a metal bearing binder. The result is that all three shields are at the same potential to ground.

Conductor shapes in three-conductor shielded cables have changed over the years to three basic types. See Figure 1-1.

- Circular

- Oval

- Sectoral

Round
conductors

Oval
conductors

Sectoral
conductors

Figure 1-1. Types of shielded three-conductor cables.

With the individual conductors shielded, it was possible to extend the use of the three-phase cables for voltages as high as 69 kV, though on the average their use has been confined to voltages below 35 kV.

The main reason for this has again been associated with the occurrence of corona discharges which had, in numerous instances, led to the deterioration and failure of the dielectric at the elevated voltages. The corona discharges were found to take place in voids, which were formed either during the manufacturing process or during the load cycling while in service. The problem of void ionization at the higher values of applied voltage required for the transmission of electrical energy was finally and effectively eliminated by the introduction of a low-viscosity oil-impregnated paper insulating system; in this scheme, the formation and ionization of the cavities was avoided by maintaining a pressure slightly above atmospheric on the insulating oil.

Distribution and Transmission Systems

Introduction

There are many factors involved in deciding how the various parts are arranged in an underground system. The actual design is based on future load needs, regulations and by-laws, systems already in existence, customer's needs, and installation costs.

The design of the system will determine the duration and frequency of outages a customer will experience. Some systems have no back-ups in case of an outage, while other systems have several back-ups or sources of power. As a power line technician, you must always try to keep as many customers as possible energized during a fault situation. In order to do this you must be aware of the type of system in which the fault is located.

Upon successful completion of this section, you will be able to describe the generation, transmission system, control center and the different type of underground systems used by electric utilities.

Electric Power System

Most electric energy is generated at a voltage in a range of 7.5 to 13.8 kV. The voltage is raised to transmission levels in a transmission substation located at the generating station. Transmission circuits or lines operating at 138,000 to 500,000 volts deliver the energy to the load area. Transmission substations adjacent to the load area reduce the voltage to sub-transmission levels of 34.5 to 69 kV. The sub-transmission circuits or lines (sometimes referred to as bulk load source) extend through metropolitan areas to distribution substations located in the area of the load to be served. Distribution substations reduce the voltage from sub-transmission levels to distribution levels of 2.4 to 35 kV.

Distribution circuits radiate from the distribution substations to supply the customer's load. Some large industrial customers may be served directly from transmission or sub-transmission circuits. These customers will normally be metered by a high voltage or primary meter installation and have their own substation(s) to reduce the voltage to the desired level for distribution.

Figure 1-2 shows an illustration of an electric system.

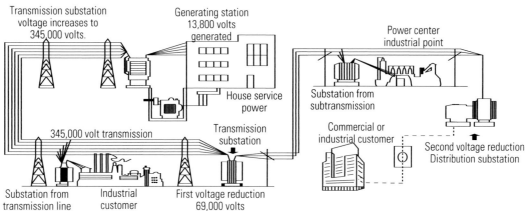

Figure 1- 2. Illustration of an electric system.

System Control Center

Most electric utilities are operated from a system control center. Equipment in the control center is used to continuously analyze and operate the electric system. The output of the electric generators is varied automatically to match the energy supplied with the customer's demand and the purchases and sales to interconnected electric systems.

System control center mimic boards display the entire electrical system. Computers are used to link all parts of the system together. As the circuits and generators are switched in and out of service, the change in electrical energy flows are made automatically by the computer and are displayed at the control center. All work on the equipment is performed in conjunction with the person in charge (PIC) at the area control center (ACC).

Other control centers are usually located throughout the service area.

Transmission System

The distinguishing characteristics of transmission circuits are that they are operated at relatively high voltages (60 kV+), transmit large blocks of electrical power and extend over considerable distances.

Transmission circuits are constructed between transmission substations located at electric generating stations or switching points in the electric system. The transmission circuits may be overhead or underground. A transmission cable system is used to minimize problems with the environmental impact of towers supporting conductors in the middle of an urban area. Each underground circuit consists of three individual cables that are, for the most part, oil-filled paper insulated cables. The splice locations range from 1000 to 2000 feet, depending on the diameter of each cable. The transmission system is normally designed in such a way that there is a backup circuit (alternate feed) for the substations.

Underground Distribution System Design

The designing of underground systems is a complex process that involves many parties, including several regulatory agencies. The system design must ensure that the customers receive the voltage level they require and that the service is reliable and continuous. The type of underground distribution system designs used include:

- Radial system

- Loop radial systems

- Primary loop systems

- Dual radial systems

- Network systems

- 600 Volt primary systems

Radial Systems

Radial systems normally have only one path of power flow. A failure of a component in the power delivery chain will usually result in customers from the fault location onwards being without power. For example, a simple radial system could consist of a power source and a chain of transformers feeding customers. If a fault occurred at the first transformer, all the customers would be without power. If there were five transformers in the chain and a fault occurred at the fourth transformer, then all the customers from the power source up to the fourth transformer would have power, but the customers from the fourth transformer on would have no power. In the most basic radial system there is no back-up.

This type of system is easy to construct and has a reasonable cost. However, it is the most basic form, and does not provide a back-up service for the customers. Many variations of the radial system have been developed to reduce the duration of the outage and to provide more operational flexibility. See Figure 1-3.

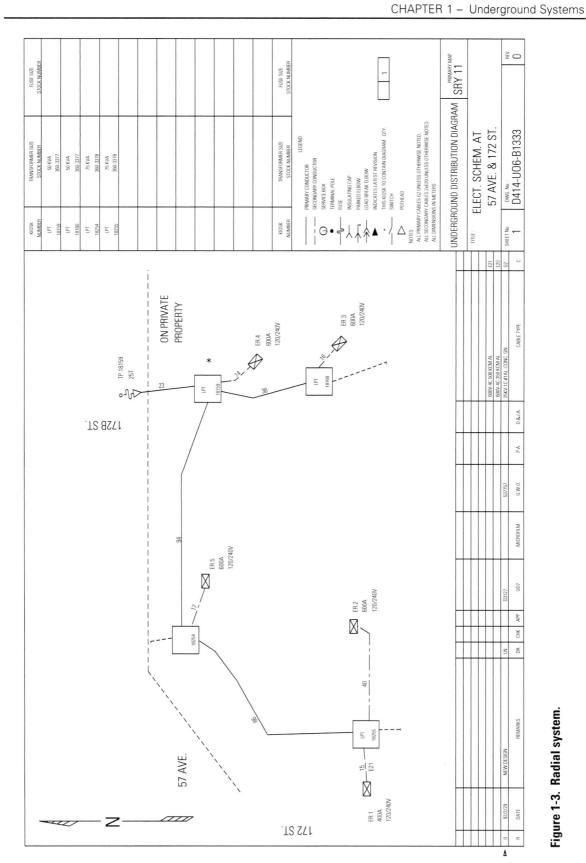

Figure 1-3. Radial system.

DRAWINGS | MATERIALS | INSTALLING | SPLICING | FUSING | MAINTENANCE | TROUBLE | JOB SITE

Loop Radial Systems

The most popular variation of the radial system is the loop system. Basically, this system joins the ends of two radial systems together. It also has a normally open point somewhere in the loop. The normally open point allows part of the system to be fed from one power source and another part to be fed from the other source. If a fault occurs, the feed can be adjusted and switched so that as many customers as possible are still being fed, despite the fault in the system.

For example, if there are five transformers in the loop, three could be fed from one power source and two could be fed from a different power source. For this example, the normally open (NO) is at the middle transformer. If a fault occurred at the second transformer from the first power source, the first transformer could be fed from the first power source and the normally open could be switched to ensure that the other three transformers would feed from the second power source. The damaged transformer could be isolated and repaired. The only customers without power would be the ones fed from the second (damaged) transformer; all the other customers would still have power. See Figure 1-4.

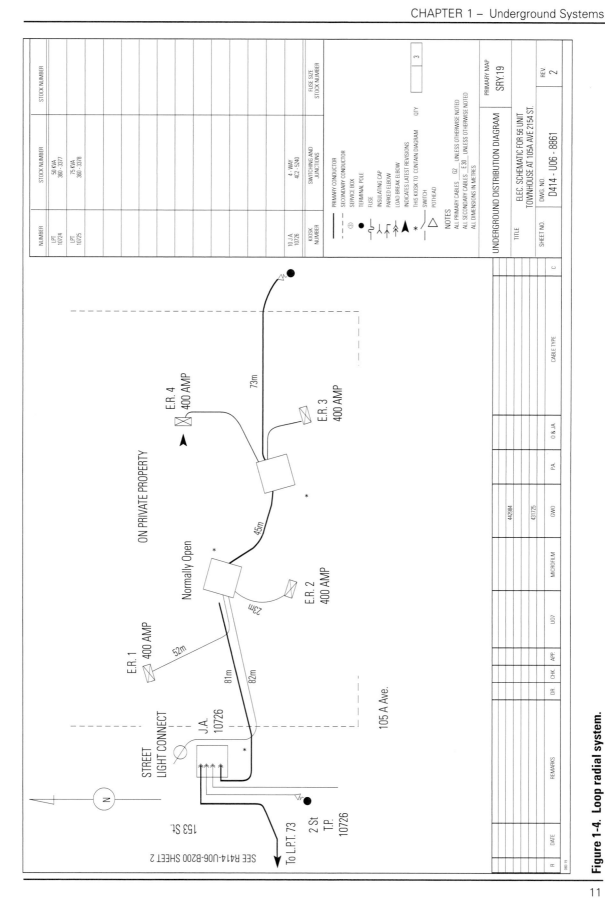

Figure 1-4. Loop radial system.

Primary Loop Systems

Primary loop systems are designed to provide optimum service to large customers, primarily in a downtown area. The system consists of three different circuits in phase from either one or two substations and the customers switch gear. The circuits are configured in a loop feed arrangement with one normally open point to optimize the loading of the circuits. The switch-gear provides a three way Tee tap-off point from the supply system.

The customer's two incoming loadbreak switches and their interlocked disconnect switches comprise this Tee. These switches usually have a unique number permanently assigned to them by the utility. During normal operations, one or both of these branches off the Tee will be closed. In case of a customer fault, cable failure, or routine maintenance, these switches will be operated to either isolate or restore service to the customer.

The utility retains operating authority of these switches. The operator/area dispatcher is the central control operator and person in charge. These switches are defined as Level IV equipment and will only be operated under the specific direction of the person-in-charge. These switches, for protection guarantees, will be locked open and tagged with utility locks and tags.

The main circuit breaker and interlocked loadbreak switch form the third branch of the Tee. The customer retains the operating authority for this equipment and any equipment located downstream from the interlocked loadbreak switch. See Figure 1-5.

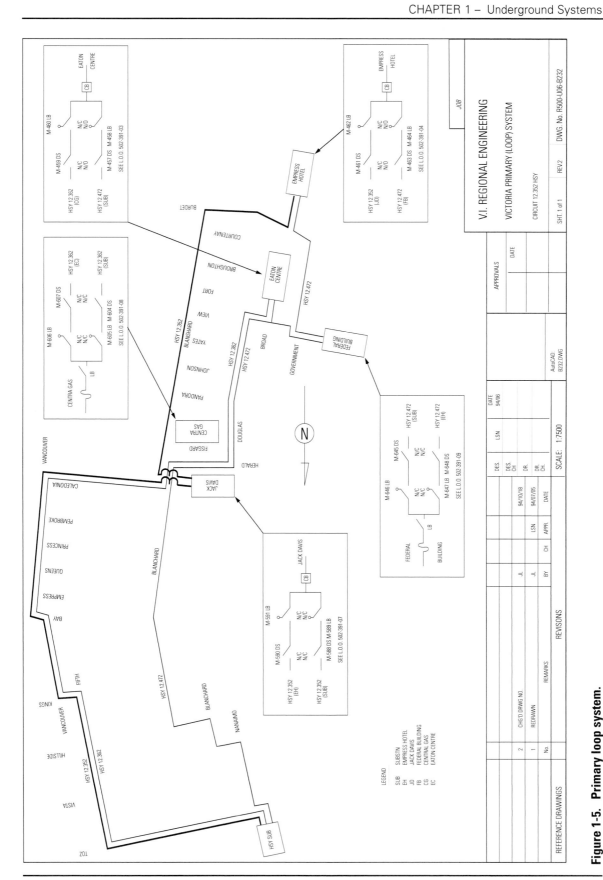

Figure 1-5. Primary loop system.

Dual Radial System

The dual radial and double dual radial vault systems are sometimes used to provide optimum service to large customers, primarily in a downtown area.

A dual radial system consists of a running circuit, which is the normal source of supply and a standby circuit, which is the alternate source of supply. The double dual radial system has two running circuits and one standby circuit. In both systems, the circuits are "in phase" to facilitate switching with no interruption in service. Although usually not thought of this way, the dual radial system is a completely underground multi-branch normally open loop system. Each customer service provides a loop path between two primary feeder sources. The customer's main tap supply is located between two primary selector switches, one of which is normally open. By relocating the normally open point on the loop through selector switch operation, the customer supply is changed to the alternate supply. Customers install and maintain duplicate primary switchgear, protective devices and transformation. The utility maintains the selector switches, one of which is padlocked Normally Open. Only utility personnel are allowed to carry out routine and emergency switching. See Figure 1-6.

The circuits of the dual and double dual radial systems are frequently switched to facilitate maintenance on both utilty and customer-owned equipment. These circuits are isolated by disconnect switches unique to the system located in street vaults.

Note: Lineworkers unfamiliar with the dual radial system must receive training on the operation of the system to ensure their safety, and of others who may be performing maintenance requirements.

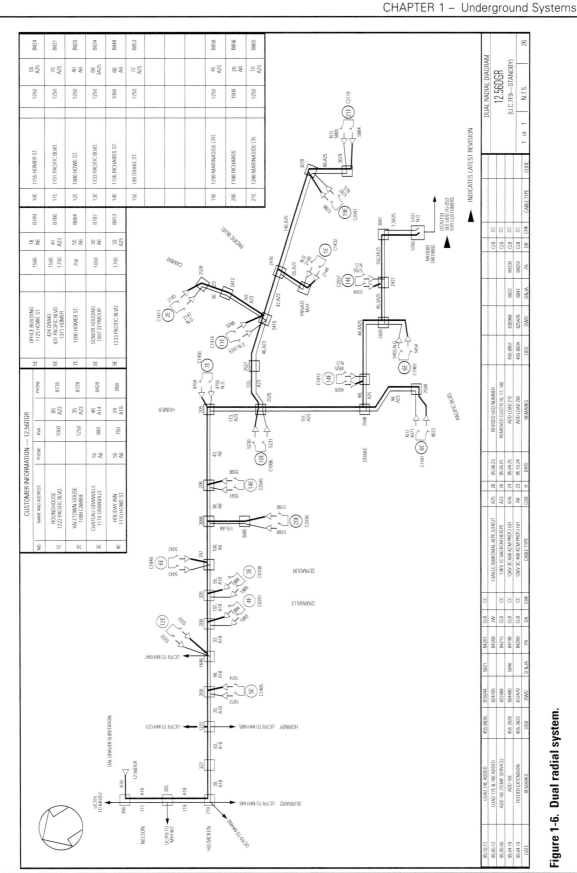

Figure 1-6. Dual radial system.

Network Systems

These systems use at least two separate primary feeds and several transformers connected together to ensure continuous power in case of a feeder or component failure.

These systems are constructed in such a way that single failures can occur in the primary system, transformers or individual secondary cables without interrupting the power flow to customers. They are constructed completely underground and provide a very high quality of service.

Dedicated primary feeders are routed to street vaults which contain up to three submersible three-phase transformers. The submersible transformers in each vault are tapped from a different primary feeder. Primary feeders are configured radially to supply a number of transformers. The secondary of each transformer feeds into a network protector, which is a large reverse current sensing circuit breaker. The protector outputs are hard-wired together to a network bus located in each vault. For integrated network systems, all network buses are interconnected via paralleled secondary mains. For spot network systems, individual network buses operate independently of each other.

When a primary cable or transformer fault occurs, the substation breaker clears the fault jointly with the network protectors, which backfeed the fault from the secondary bus. Sufficient capacity is provided in other network feeders and transformers to continue to supply the load. Parallel runs of secondary have cable limiters installed at both ends. These are high rupturing capacity fuses which both clear if there is a fault on the cable. Parallel secondary runs have sufficient capacity to handle the extra load placed on them when one cable is out.

The network systems are not used very frequently, as they are expensive to construct and only secondary voltages (services) are available. See Figure 1-7.

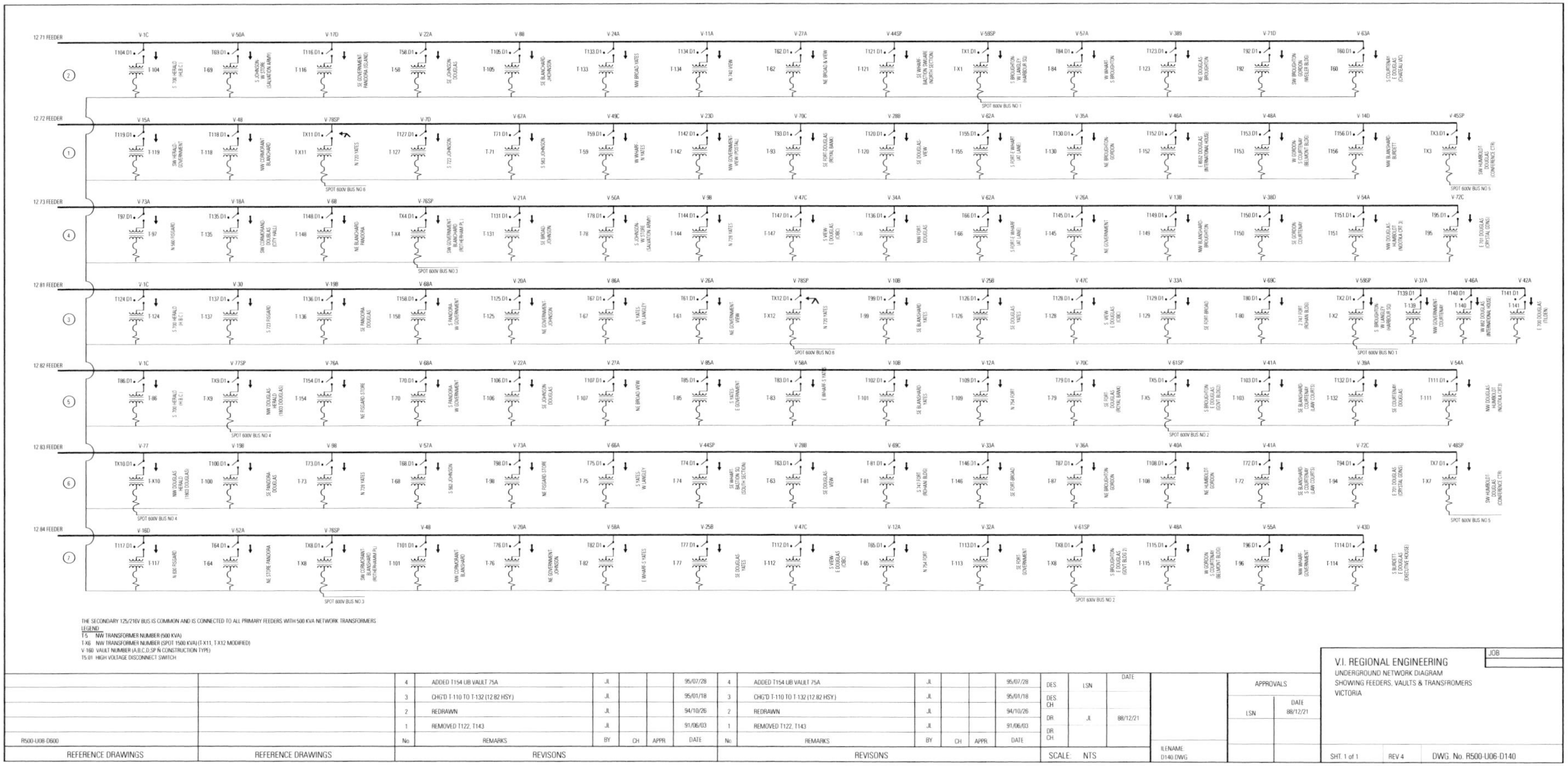

Figure 1-7. Network system.

600 Volt Primary

Figure 1-8 shows a 600 volt primary system designed as part of a downtown beautification project. The system is fed from a substation and transformed via deadfront transformers (DFTs) to 347/600 volts. The DFTs 600 volt secondary now becomes the primary voltage for the 120/240 volt and 120/208 volt transformers and the 240 volt delta transformer. In one area, the 120 volt secondary from transformer vault 2058 becomes the primary voltage for transformer vault 2059. The 120 volt primary is stepped up to 240 volts for street lighting.

Each transformer is protected by a cable limiter spliced inline on the 600 volt primary cable. Transformer vaults 2058 and 2059 are both protected by a single cable limiter. The 25 kV tap pole feeding the DFTs is fused with expulsion and current limiting fuses.

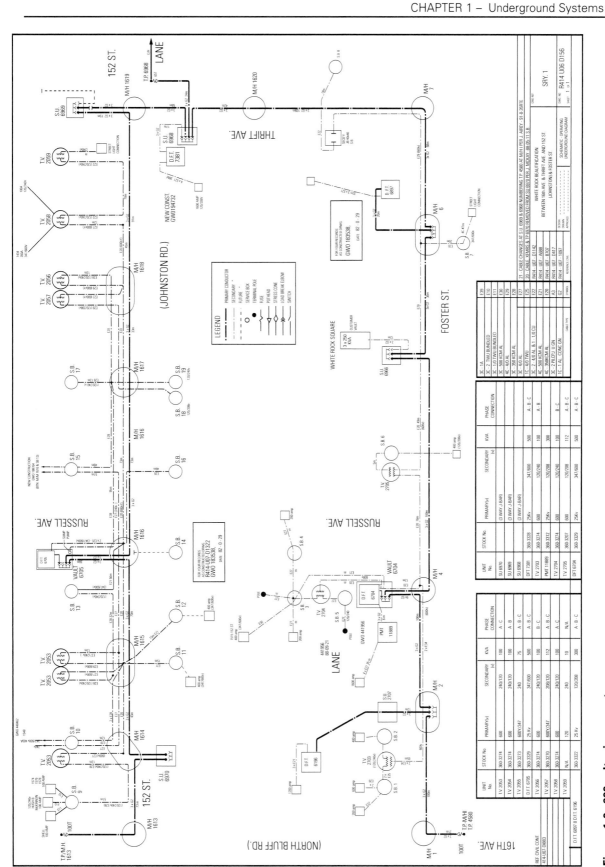

Figure 1-8. 600 volt primary system.

SYSTEM

DRAWINGS

MATERIALS

INSTALLING

SPLICING

FUSING

MAINTENANCE

TROUBLE

JOB SITE

CHAPTER

2

CONSTRUCTION DRAWINGS

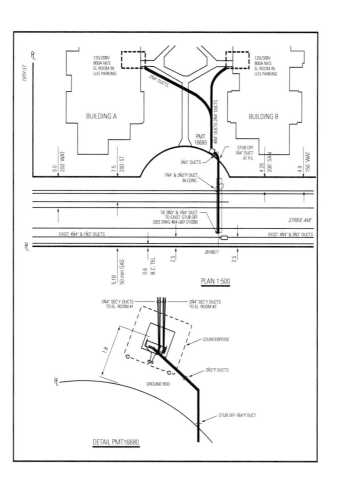

SYSTEM

DRAWINGS

MATERIALS

INSTALLING

SPLICING

FUSING

MAINTENANCE

TROUBLE

JOB SITE

Note: The construction drawings and work practices presented in this chapter are examples only, and may be different from the practices followed by your company.

Civil Drawings

Introduction

Civil drawings show the details of grades, terminal poles, pads, boxes, grounding standards, notes, and reference literature. Typically, this work is performed by contractors.

While the civil drawing is the working map for the installation at the civil stage, it is also vital for future reference of cable and apparatus location, offsets, trouble shooting (dig-ins) damage to equipment, and any landscape changes etc.

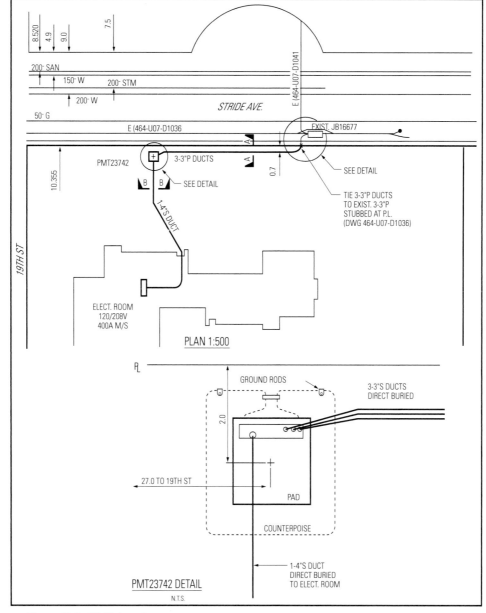

Figure 2-1. Civil drawing.

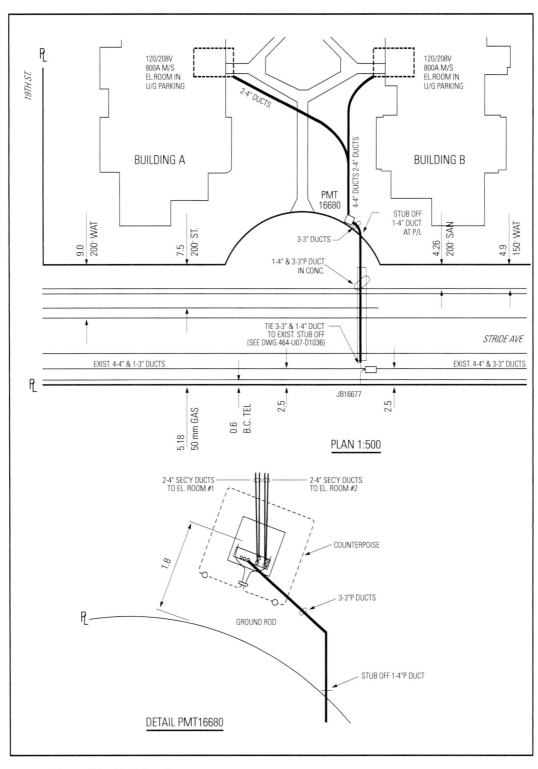

Figure 2-2. Civil drawing.

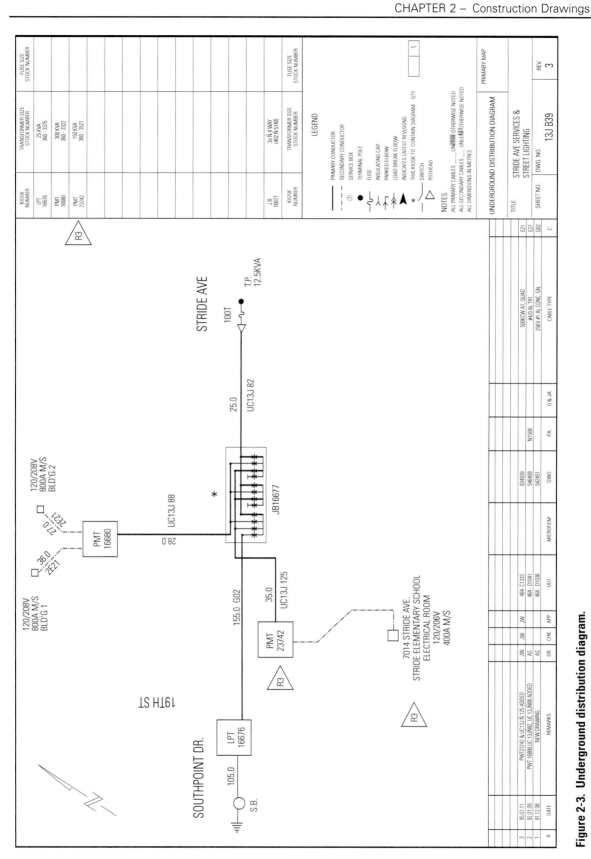

Figure 2-3. Underground distribution diagram.

GFIS

Civil and electrical drawings are often done on a Geo-Facilities Information System (GFIS). GFIS is a database that stores all the map information that the utility has on computer file. It enables the electrical system to be updated once and then to produce many different type of maps that are updated at the same time (i.e. primary, secondary, distribution, operating, joint venture, underground, street lights, etc.). Other features of having this information on a computer file are:

- It allows computer studies to be run directly on the data (load studies, voltage studies, etc.)

- It allows ties to other computer systems (customer information, trouble reporting, estimating, etc.)

It is important that any field changes be noted on the "As Constructed" print in the field. This information is used to create an "As Built" record in the database of the Geo Facilities Information System.

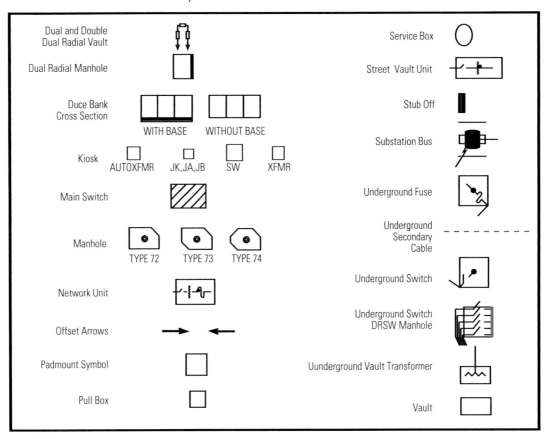

Figure 2-4. GFIS symbols.

Electrical Drawings

Introduction

The first step when working on the underground system is to obtain and read the relevant operating diagrams (one-line diagrams or one-lines). The operating diagrams for underground are the Underground Distribution Diagrams (UDDs). They are also known as Underground One-Line Diagrams and Underground Operating Diagrams. An up-to-date UDD is essential for safe operation of the system. Each source and open point on primary feeds are shown. On the UDD, one-lines are continually updated and must be available to you at all times.

Upon successful completion of this section, you will be able to interpret UDD symbols and terms, explain how to use these prints in conjunction with other prints when doing maintenance work and new installations assignments, and list the various types of electrical apparatus on the underground systems.

Underground Distribution Diagrams (UDDs)

UDDs show the primary and secondary underground distribution, but not feeder cables. Equipment that applies to the primary and secondary distribution is also shown. This would include terminal poles, fuses, service boxes, junction boxes, switching kiosks and transformers.

Reading Underground Distribution Diagrams

On every UDD there is a legend that gives the basic symbols used and there are standard notes that give the code indicating the type of primary and secondary cables. The legend and notes are both located on the lower right hand side of the print.

Diagram Orientation

Drawings are always orientated to the north; this means that north will be indicated on the drawing by means of a compass arrow. When reading the drawing, place it so that north is pointing upward.

Underground Facilities Legend

The following is a description of symbols that represent underground facilities on UDDs. However, you may encounter different symbols on existing prints. It is important that you always check the print for a legend and special notes specific to that print.

Dual and Double Radial Vault	This symbol indicates a vault containing a dual radial transformer and associated cables and equipment. It is a system in which two circuits are connected to transformers via switches. This gives an alternated feed if one circuit experiences an outage.
Dual Radial Manhole	Indicates a manhole containing cables and splices for a dual radial system.
Duct Bank	Shown as cross sections. Two symbols are used, one for duct banks with bases and one for those without.
Kiosks	Indicates above ground boxes containing various types of equipment. On a print, there will be words or abbreviations beside the symbol to indicate whether the kiosk is an auto-transformer (AUTOXFMR), a junction box (JB, JA, or JK), a switch (SW), or a transformer (XFMR). Padmount Transformers (three phase) may be labeled PMT, Low Profile Transformers (single phase) may be labeled LPT.
Main Switch	Indicates customer's main switch. These are not owned or maintained the utility and are, therefore, not accessed by utility crews. In most cases, the boundaries of the switch are dotted in if the operating authority is not the utility.
Network Unit	Indicates one transformer in a vault along with a network protector. A network is a type of distribution system in which the secondaries of more than one transformer are connected together. A spot network is a small network system in a localized area. A network protector is a device which operates similar to an unidirectional circuit breaker.
Offset Arrows	Used to indicate the offset of a duct bank from a property line. The distance of the offset will be recorded beside the arrows. These are shown on civil construction diagrams.
Padmount	Used to indicate the location of a padmount transformer.

Pull Box	Indicates location of underground boxes used during the installation (pulling) of cable. The symbol may be labeled.
Service Box	Indicates location of service box, which is used as a junction point for secondary and/or service cables. This symbol may be labeled SB.
Street Vault Unit	Indicates a submersible transformer in a vault.
Stub Off	Indicates a duct that is for use in the future, and therefore, is presently plugged off.
Substation Bus	Located in a substation, and is the distribution system from which feeders are connected.
Underground Fuse	Indicates a submersible fuse located in a manhole. These are not frequent or standard, and are only installed for specific jobs.
Underground Secondary Cable	Indicates location of or presence of an underground secondary cable.
Underground Switch	Indicates a switch location in a subsurface box. These may be labeled SW or US.
U/G Switch DRSW Manhole	Indicates manholes containing submersible switches that Allows a dual radial system to be split into sections creating more flexibility. DRSW stands for Dual Radial Switch.
Underground Transformer	Indicates transformer located in a underground vault.
Vault	Indicates a manhole containing a transformer. It should be identified with a vault number.

Identification of Apparatus

Each kiosk, vault, and manhole is marked with an identification number that is unique. The same number appears next to the symbol for that particular apparatus on the UDD.

Identification of Cables

In the field each cable end has an aluminum tag uniquely identifying the cable. Terminal poles have a plaque. The same identification is used both in the field and on the UDD. One of two types of identification schemes are used:

- **UC Number** (for example, UC 5F 17): The first part is derived from a grid that divides an area of the power system into squares. The number and letter designate the coordinate of the grid square wherein the cable is located and the additional number is its underground circuit number within that grid square.

- **Destination Tags:** Some areas tag each end of the cable with a destination label that corresponds to the designations on the UDD. They do not use UC numbers.

The lines on a UDD that designate cables have code numbers typed above them indicating cabling type and single-or three-phase underground plant.

Kiosks

The term kiosk refers to a live front transformer kiosks. The kiosk listing book refers to single-and three-phase padmount transformers, above and below ground junction boxes, and switchgear. It also gives the the kiosk number, type of apparatus, address, terminal pole location, civil and primary maps, electrical or UDD drawings, the kVA, and the manufacturer's serial number.

Primary Map Symbols

Underground transformers are labeled LPT (Low Profile), PMT (Padmount), or Kiosks (Livefront) Transformers. The size of these transformers are shown in a square located to the side of the actual symbol. (In some areas, these designations may vary.)

Junction boxes may be labeled JA or JK for an above ground junction kiosk, or JB for below ground box. If the junction box is a three phase, a 3 will be written before the label. The symbols used for junction boxes are a triangle for above ground units and a hexagon for below ground units.

Read Primary Maps

The primary map will have the following shown:

- Circuit designation number and substation

- Municipal grid, if used

- Switch designation

- Fused laterals

- Underground terminal poles and PMTs

- Overhead transformers

- Private lines

CHAPTER 2 – Construction Drawings

SYSTEM

DRAWINGS

MATERIALS

INSTALLING

SPLICING

FUSING

MAINTENANCE

TROUBLE

JOB SITE

Terminology for Transformer Types

Padmounted Transformers

Deadfront Transformer, Single Phase	Up to 100 kVA; primary fuse. Common term used: Low Profile Transformer (LPT).
Deadfront Transformer, Three Phase	Up to 750 kVA; primary fuses and loadbreak switches. Common term used: Padmount Transformer (PMT), and sometimes referred to as Deadfront Transformer (DFT).
Deadfront Auto-transformer	1,000 kVA and over; primary switches and fuses; secondary side is still primary, high voltage. Common term used: Step Down Transformer.
Livefront Transformer Kiosk, Single or Three Phase -	Containing one or three overhead type single phase transformers; optional solid blade or fused disconnect switches. Common term used: Kiosk (also Padmount Livefront, and Doghouse).

Transformers in Vaults

These are found on the underground system:

Vault	A manhole containing a transformer.
Underground vault transformer	A transformer in an underground vault.
Street vault unit	A vault below ground with a submersible transformer.
Customer vault	A transformer vault inside the customer's building, usually fed by underground cables.

Terminology for Switching Unit Types

The following apparatus can be used for switching primary voltage:

Switchgear

Padmounted Switchgear (called a Mark II)	A three phase live front kiosk containing gang-operated solid blade switches and fuses, divided into separate compartments and fed by a common bus.
Underground Switch (SU)	A switching unit in a subsurface box.

Junction Boxes

A junction is where lines come together or cross. Junction boxes contain junction bars into which loadbreak elbows are inserted. They also work as a switching point to allow isolation of a section of cable. Switching on underground is very commonly done on these junction boxes:

Junction kiosk (JK, or JA for junction box above grade)	Single or three phase (junction bars in line).
Junction vault (JV, or JB for junction box below grade)	Single or three phase (junction bars in line).
Switching unit	

Work Orders

Introduction

Work orders contain detailed information that you must review and understand before going to the job site. There are usually drawings accompanying the work orders. These drawings can, at times, look very complicated. However, if you carefully review the legend (key to symbols) and check for the cable(s) that you are to work on, the drawings become easier to understand. Sometimes there are many parties involved in a job and all the relevant information is contained on the drawing. It is easier to interpret the work order by reviewing it to determine exactly what you must do and then refer to the drawing.

Upon successful completion of this section, you will be able to identify and apply the different type of work orders used.

The various types or work orders are:

- Local Work Order (LWO)

- Field Work Order (FWO)

Local Work Order (LWO)

The Local Work Order (LWO), is used for all types of maintenance work, such as:

- Repairing terminations

- Replacing kiosks and LPTs

- Repairing faulted cables and terminations

The LWO is issued or designated in order of priority. Cable faults and terminations always have top priority. The supervisor for the underground department fills out the form and then gives it to the line crew to do the job. Once job is completed, the form is signed-off as completed, the date of completion is filled in and returned to the supervisor.

SYSTEM

DRAWINGS

MATERIALS

INSTALLING

SPLICING

FUSING

MAINTENANCE

TROUBLE

JOB SITE

When a repair job is necessary, the LWO form is completed as follows:

From	Name of the supervisor.
To	Name line crew assigned to do the job.
Date issued	Date that supervisor fills in the form.
Charge number	Supervisor indicates what cost center will be charged for the repair job.
Description of work	Supervisor indicates what has to be done.

Once the work is completed, the following two areas are completed:

Completed as described by	The LWO is signed off when the job is competed.
Date	The date of completion is recorded.

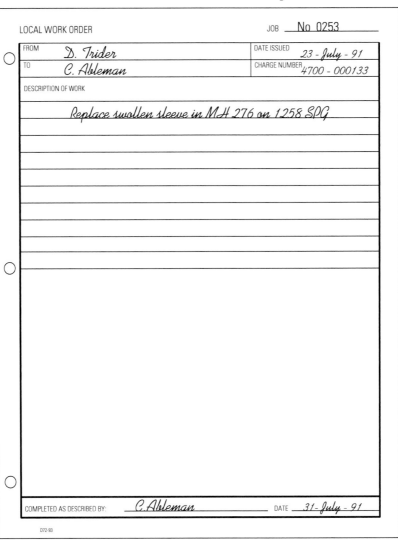

Figure 2-5. Local work order.

Field Work Order (FWO)

The Field Work Order (FWO) is issued for any new work, such as a new installation or new construction. The FWO is a one-page form and is generated by the System Designers or Project Engineer when a circuit has to be upgraded (or expanded) or when a new circuit is needed due to increased load forecasts.

The FWO contains the following information:

Project number	This number is generated in sequence of jobs. Used for tracking purposes.
Number	This is the plant alteration number. It is generated in sequence of jobs. The first character is a letter that identifies the area.
Reference drawing number	With every FWO, a drawing is given. This number identifies the drawing to be used. The drawing shows the job location and supplies other information such as number of cables, type of cable, cable identification number and termination points.
FWO number	This is actually the FWO number. The first four digits identify the cost center and the next six digits are generated by a computer.
Circuit number	This identifies the cable or circuit involved. The power line technician uses this information to either locate the cable or tag the cable once it is installed.
Substation	This identifies the substation from which the circuit originates. This is important for de-energizing the circuit so it can be worked on or for energizing when the work is complete.
Particulars	In this area, the particulars for the job are given in detail along with other reference materials. Other reference materials might include other drawings that may have a bearing on the job or some overhead work that will be occurring along with the underground work.
Approvals and completion	The bottom area of the form is used for signatures of approval and completion, as well as dates. This section is completed by both the engineer or designer and the supervisor of the line department.

When a work order is issued, a FWO form and reference drawings are received by the parties involved in the project. Sometimes, besides the FWO and drawings, other computer-generated forms are received. These usually contain the same information as the FWO but can also contain additional costing information and a list of parties involved in the project. There will also be a computer generated materials list that gives the equipment and materials needed to do the job.

The information you will need is contained on the FWO, the reference drawing(s) and the materials list. Any other information is usually relevant to other parties involved in the project, such as construction crews and overhead crews.

The sequence of events that take place for the completion of a project involving a cable job is as follows:

1. When the FWO is issued, three copies are received by the line department along with the associated drawings.

2. One set of the information is used by the supervisor for recording work in progress, one set is put in a file and one set is given to the crew assigned to the project.

3. As the project progresses, completed work is recorded and checked off.

4. When the project is completed, the field and progress copies of the FWO are discarded. The final set is signed off by the supervisor and returned to the office staff.

5. The office staff return the sign-off forms to the original designer. The designer then gets the associated circuit updated to include the completed alteration.

6. Once the circuit drawing has been updated, copies of the drawing are forwarded to the office staff, to the line department and to the control center (CC). The office staff and line department keep the drawing for future references. The mimic circuit board is updated at the appropriate control center.

As circuits are added or altered, the control center updates the mimic board to include the new circuit or alteration. Any time work has to be done on a circuit, the control center must be involved. Its role is to ensure the circuit is properly de-energized and the appropriate safety permit is issued.

JAN 26 1996

B5R2520E

```
* * * * * * * * * * * * * * * * * * * * * * * * * * * * * *          CIC2        25 NOV 16
*                                                       *                        11:17:57
*                    FIELD WORK ORDER                   *       * * * * * * * * * * * * * *
*                  -----UNDERGROUND -----               *       *  JOB#: 4610-645620    *
*           DCS-ELEC EXTN'N EWO - SERVICES - SECONDARY  *       *  REV#: 00             *
* * * * * * * * * * * * * * * * * * * * * * * * * * * * * *       * * * * * * * * * * * * * *
```

WORK DESCRIPTION: TO PROVIDE AN U/G SEC'Y DIP TO A ROGERS FIBER OPTIC KIOSK
120/240V 100AMP

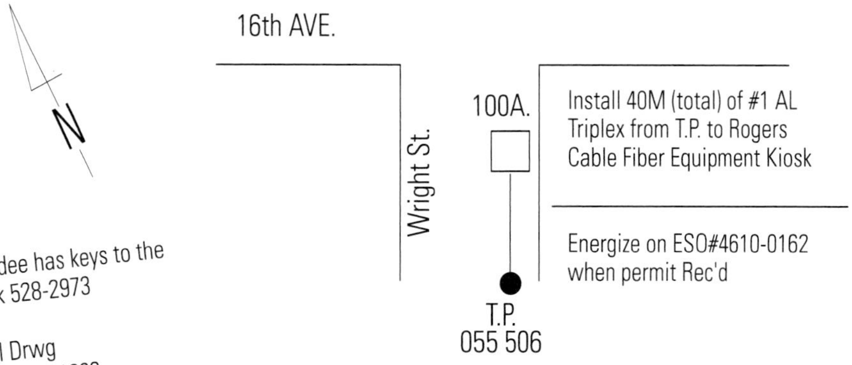

16th AVE.

N

Wright St.

100A.

Install 40M (total) of #1 AL
Triplex from T.P. to Rogers
Cable Fiber Equipment Kiosk

Energize on ESO#4610-0162
when permit Rec'd

T.P.
055 506

Cresdee has keys to the
kiosk 528-2973

Civil Drwg
464-007-B1369

COMPLETED: DATE _____ BY _____

CHANGES: _____

_____

_____

_____

_____

DATE INITIATED: 95 NOV 16
DATE REQUIRED BY: 96 JAN 10

PLAN/DRAWING# _____   DATE STARTED: _____
PLANNER: JH CRESDEE   DATE EST. COMPLETE:

STANDARD   JOB TYPE: EWO   WORK CODE: U1EXSS001

AREA: LM / BURNABY   REVISION DATE:
FROM : CUST SRVC & DES-LMN   MASTER JOB#:
TO: O/H & U/G CONST   HYDRO PO#:   CAR#:
BILL   CUSTOMER PO#:
 TO   CAPITAL DISTRICT: 4021
N&A
                                            BILL ON:

FILE: 16TH AVE WRIGHT WORK LOCATION: WRIGHT ST AT 16TH AVE., BBY
TITLE: U/G DIP FOR ROBERS FIBER
STAKED BY: _____   PHONE: _____   JOB#: 4610-645620
                                                                         REV#:

Figure 2-6. Field work order.

CHAPTER

MATERIALS

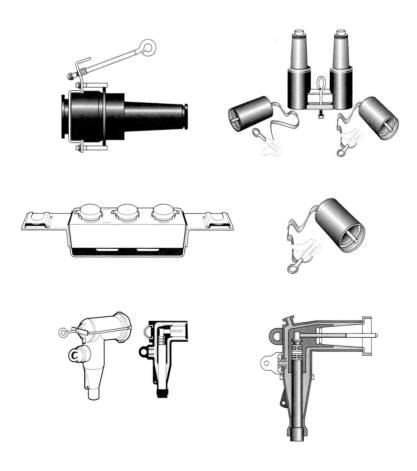

SYSTEM

DRAWINGS

MATERIALS

INSTALLING

SPLICING

FUSING

MAINTENANCE

TROUBLE

JOB SITE

Introduction to Cables

Cable Construction

Power cables are constructed in many different ways and are generally classified as unshielded or shielded cables. Unshielded cables normally consist of a conductor, conductor strand shielding, insulation and a jacket. The use of unshielded power cables is limited to the lower primary voltages, which normally operate below 7200 volts.

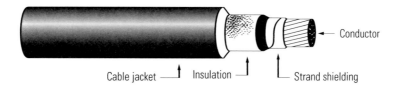

Cable jacket —— Insulation —— └ Strand shielding

Conductor

Figure 3-1a. Unshielded cable.

Shielded power cables are generally manufactured with a conductor, conductor strand shielding, insulation, semi-conducting insulation shielding, metallic insulation shielding and a sheath. If the sheath is metallic, it may serve as the metallic insulation shielding and be covered with a nonmetallic jacket to protect the sheath.

Shielded cables are commonly used on circuits operating above 7200 volts.

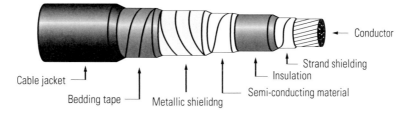

Cable jacket —— Bedding tape —— Metallic shielidng Semi-conducting material Insulation └ Strand shielding

Conductor

Figure 3-1b. Shielded cable.

Cables can be single-conductor or multi-conductor. Multi-conductor cables consist of three single conductors wrapped in a common sheath and/or jacket.

Conductors

Cable conductors are made of either copper or aluminum. Copper is more popular as it has a higher conductivity than aluminum and it is easier to work with and handle.

Aluminum is lighter in weight but the conductors must be larger than copper conductors (due to aluminum's lower conductivity) to supply a given load. Also, the surface of aluminum conductors oxidizes quickly and can be damaged by galvanic action when touching other metals (with moisture present).

The size of the conductor is designated by American Wire Gauge (AWG) units. The AWG numbers for power cables normally start at 6 AWG and decrease with increasing conductor size to 1 AWG. Then, as the size continues to increase, the numbers increase from 1/0 to 4/0 AWG.

For conductor sizes greater than 4/0, the sizes are given in thousand circular mils (kcmil). A circular mil is the area of a circle one mil (1/1000 in.) in diameter.

Power cables with a conductor size smaller than 2 AWG use a solid conductor, while power cables with a conductor size of 2 AWG and larger are stranded. This allows the cable to be as flexible as possible. The stranded conductors come in a variety of shapes.

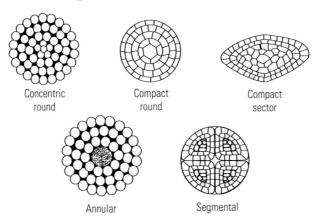

Figure 3-2. **Common shapes of stranded conductors.**

The concentric round, compact round, and annular are all used for single-conductor cable. The segmental is composed of three or four segments which are electrically separated from one another. This type is used to create single-conductor, small-diameter cable with high current-carrying ability and lower AC resistance.

The sector shape is used in multi-conductor cables where all three phases are in one sheath. Each sector must be insulated from the others to withstand the phase-to-phase voltage. Concentric round can also be used for this application, but the use of the sector shape results in a smaller overall diameter, less weight and lower cost.

CHAPTER 3 – Materials

SYSTEM

DRAWINGS

MATERIALS

INSTALLING

SPLICING

FUSING

MAINTENANCE

TROUBLE

JOB SITE

Conductor Sealing

The space between the conductor strands can be filled with a semi-conducting compound during the manufacture of the cable conductor. The filling compound is designed to prevent water from penetrating the stranded conductor during manufacture, storage, installation, splicing (joining the two conductors together) and terminating (putting a device on the end of the cable conductor) of the cable. Water in between the strands can result in premature cable failure due to electrochemical reactions between the water, electricity and the insulation.

Strand Shielding and Cable Insulation

If the insulation is applied directly to the conductor, tiny air voids will exist between the conductor strands and the insulation.

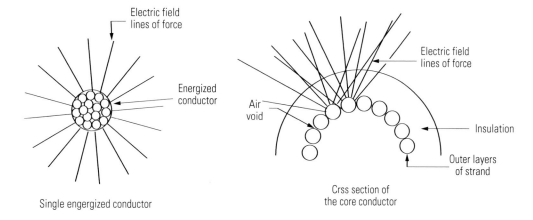

Figure 3-3. Electric field around an energized conductor.

The energized conductor gives off lines of force that extend radially from the conductor to create an electric field around the conductor. In Figure 3-3, it can be seen that some of these lines of force pass through existing air voids and subject them to an electric field. At 13 kV, the electric field would be strong enough to cause the air to ionize and break down. When the air in the voids breaks down, small arcs occur, resulting in burning of the insulation.

Since the lines of force originate from only the surface of any energized conductor, the way to prevent them from passing through the air voids is to provide a smooth conducting surface all around the conductor. This is accomplished by wrapping the conductor with a tape which is impregnated with particles of carbon, thus causing the tape to be electrically conductive. This type of tape is known as semi-conducting tape. When the conductor is wrapped with semi-conducting tape, the lines of force originate from the tape instead of the conductor strands, and thus none of them pass through the air voids; therefore, the air will not break down. This semi-conducting tape is called the strand shielding (Figure 3-4).

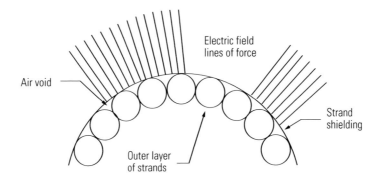

Figure 3-4. Effect of strand shielding on electric field energized conductor.

The insulation is applied over the strand shielding. The three most common materials used as insulation for power cables are:

- Taped insulation such as oil-impregnated paper and varnished cambric

- Rubber or rubber-like synthetic compounds such as butyl rubber

- Thermoplastics such as:

  - Polyvinyl chloride (PVC)

  - Polyethylene (PE)

  - Cross-linked polyethylene (XLPE)

The insulation used depends on several factors, such as:

- Operating voltage

- Current load

- Ambient temperature

- Type of installation

- Type of outer covering

Insulation Shielding

If the insulated conductor is placed on a grounded surface and energized, the lines of force of the electric field will be concentrated in the lower section of the cable.

This means that the electric field in the lower section of the cable is much stronger than the electric field in the upper section of the cable; therefore, the lower section of the cable insulation is in danger of breaking down if the cable is energized at a sufficiently high voltage.

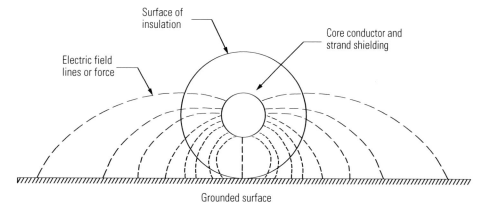

Figure 3-5. Effect of grounding surface on the electric field of unshielded cable.

The electric field can be uniformly distributed by placing a grounded surface around the exterior of the insulation. This grounded surface is known as the insulation shielding.

Insulation shielding can be either a metallic tape or a semi-conducting tape with a metallic shield over it. The metallic shield over the semi-conducting tape may consist of copper wires or strips. If these copper wires or strips have sufficient cross-section areas, they may be used as a concentric neutral to carry the return current from the core conductor.

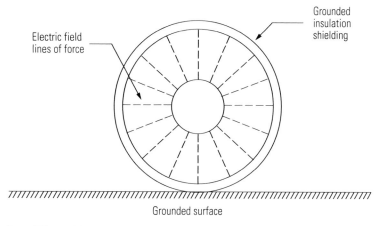

Figure 3-6. Effect of insulation shielding on electric field of shielded cable.

Bedding Tapes and Filler Tapes

Bedding tapes are generally used in a cable to add mechanical strength. They are located in various places by different manufacturers: under the sheath, under the shielding and between the conductor and insulation.

Filler tapes of suitable materials generally are used in spaces between the cables, where necessary, to give the completed assembly a nearly circular cross-section. Fillers are normally either treated hemp rope, synthetic rubber compound or thermoplastic material.

Sheaths, Jackets and Armors

The insulated conductor (the cable) must be able to withstand the physical conditions which it will encounter when in operation. Some of the means used to protect the cable are the use of sheaths, jackets or armors, or a combination of these.

Metallic sheaths provide mechanical protection to the cable and may also function as a current return. Lead sheaths are used with varnished cambric and paper-insulated cables as mechanical protection and to prevent entrance of moisture or loss of insulation impregnate.

Lead is particularly suited for this application although aluminum has also been used. Lead forms a flexible covering which allows the cable to be bent easily during handling and installation. Experience has shown that an intact lead sheath is the most effective protection for insulation against moisture, weather and oxidation.

Plastic and rubber jackets are used to seal the cable from moisture and to protect it from a moderate amount of physical damage. The lead sheaths are protected from corrosion by applying a jacket over the sheath. Polyvinyl chloride (PVC) has excellent resistance to acids, alkalis, cutting, flame, moisture, oils, ozone, sunlight and weathering.

Armors are used to protect cables against severe physical damage. Armors are found on submarine cables. The metallic armor (steel tapes or wires) is usually applied over a jute bedding, jacket or lead sheath for mechanical strength and mechanical outer protection.

Grounding of Cable Shields and Sheaths

The insulation shielding of a cable must be effectively grounded. The proper functioning of the shield is based upon it being grounded. If the shield is not properly grounded, it not only fails to accomplish its purpose, but it may actually increase the hazard to both the cable and the operating personnel.

An ungrounded shield may have an induced voltage that may be very nearly equal to that of the conductor. This potential, in the case of jacketed cables, could be sufficient to arc through the jacket to ground.

Generally, a cable shield should be grounded at both ends, and should be grounded more frequently on long cable runs. The accessibility of grounding points usually determines the number of grounds on a long cable run (that is, the cable would be grounded at such places as manholes, junctions, terminations, etc.).

In cases where a cable carries a large current, it is sometimes necessary to ground the shield or sheath at only one end due to the large magnitude of the currents which would be induced if it were grounded at both ends. These currents cause excessive heating of the shield or sheath and also result in appreciable losses in carrying capacity.

Conclusion

The components used to make a cable depends on how the cable will be used, the voltage needed and the environment in which it will exist. There are a variety of power cables that are able to meet all types of needs. Consult your cable manufacturer's data sheets, for specific details.

Handling Cables

Cables in Service

Caution should be used when moving any energized cable. If the cable is damaged, it must not be moved, especially high voltage cables, as the disturbance of the cable may distort the insulation while it is under electrical stress and could result in an insulation failure. Also, the sheath (metal sheath cables) is usually grounded at only one end and moving the cable may ground the sheath at another place permitting ground currents to flow in the sheath. If the ground currents are excessive, they could damage the sheath at the point of ground contact. Stress coned cables are usually grounded at only one point but cones are usually bonded to the sheath at both ends.

Cables carrying current are subjected to expansion and contraction due to temperature changes caused by loading and ambient temperature. This can create problems on metal sheathed cables by fatiguing the sheath so that it may crack. In oil filled cables, this may allow the oil to seep out and moisture to seep in.

Excessively cold temperatures may cause some thermoplastic insulated cables to fracture if moved or jarred. This is becoming uncommon as the manufactures improve the manufacturing process. Cables that are exposed to mechanical damage should be adequately protected.

De-energized Cables

Before hand contact is made on the de-energized conductor of a cable, the required safety permit must be in place and it should be grounded to discharge any static charge. The charge on the conductor is due to capacitive effect of the cable and could be several thousand volts.

Storing Cable

Cables to be stored should be rolled up on cable reels. Both ends of the cable must be properly sealed to prevent the entry of moisture. Cables should be stored in a dry location and protected from mechanical damage.

CHAPTER 3 – Materials

SYSTEM

DRAWINGS

MATERIALS

INSTALLING

SPLICING

FUSING

MAINTENANCE

TROUBLE

JOB SITE

Secondary Cables

Secondary and service cables are available in aluminum and copper conductors and sizes ranging from number 8 AWG to 750 kcmil. The secondary cables are available in four different configurations:

- One conductor cable

- Three conductor cable

- Four conductor cable

- Concentric neutral service cable with two conductors

While all these cables are used in the underground system, the most common ones used today are the three and four conductor aluminum cables. Copper is still used in some areas of heavy load centers.

Service cable size is based on the current (amps) the cable will cary. Adequate size must be used to prevent excessive voltage drops.

Secondary Connectors

The most common secondary connectors used are insulated secondary multi-connectors, commonly referred to as "squids." These connectors use a rubber insulating sleeve to protect each bolt-on connection and are rated from 1000 to 2000 amps. After the rubber sleeve is slid on the conductor, the conductor is cleaned and prepared for splicing. Two-slot compression lug connectors are compressed on the conductors and bolted to the multi-connector. The rubber sleeve is slid up over the bolted connection to protect and waterproof the connection.

The concentric or bare neutral conductors are connected with a spade terminator connector. The neural is connected to the spade connector with a copper C-type pressed connector. The connection is sealed with a mastic pad or self-amalgamating tape and then covered with electric vinyl tape.

The multi-connectors are used in service boxes to connect the house services to the secondary run. When connecting the multi-connector to the secondary run, the run is usually connected to the inside position, leaving the outer positions accessible for the service connections.

It is important to remember, that where more than one service box is being fed in one direction from the transformer or where the design includes provision for future secondary tying, the source conductors at the intermediary connection points should terminate at the second position from the end. The load side secondary (extension) main run must connect to the first position. Refer to Figure 3-7.

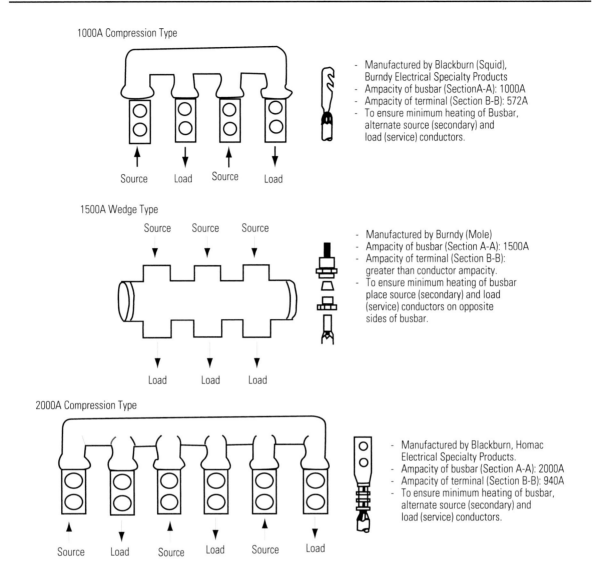

1000A Compression Type

- Manufactured by Blackburn (Squid), Burndy Electrical Specialty Products
- Ampacity of busbar (Section A-A): 1000A
- Ampacity of terminal (Section B-B): 572A
- To ensure minimum heating of Busbar, alternate source (secondary) and load (service) conductors.

Source Load Source Load

1500A Wedge Type

Source Source Source

- Manufactured by Burndy (Mole)
- Ampacity of busbar (Section A-A): 1500A
- Ampacity of terminal (Section B-B): greater than conductor ampacity.
- To ensure minimum heating of busbar place source (secondary) and load (service) conductors on opposite sides of busbar.

Load Load Load

2000A Compression Type

- Manufactured by Blackburn, Homac Electrical Specialty Products.
- Ampacity of busbar (Section A-A): 2000A
- Ampacity of terminal (Section B-B): 940A
- To ensure minimum heating of busbar, alternate source (secondary) and load (service) conductors.

Source Load Source Load Source Load

Figure 3-7. Secondary connectors.

The wedge-type multi-connector is designed for 1500 amps. The source ball is connected to one side of the bus bar and the load to the opposite side. The wedge-type multi-connector is designed for copper secondary conductors and referred to as a "mole." The multi-connector uses a specific cone (depending on the size of conductor used) and is inserted in the nut assembly. After the rubber sleeves is slid on the conductor, it is cleaned and prepared for connecting to multi-connector. The copper conductor is slid into the nut assembly and tightened. This compresses the cone and makes a solid connection. The rubber sleeve is then slid over the nut assembly to protect and waterproof the connection. Refer to Figure 3-8.

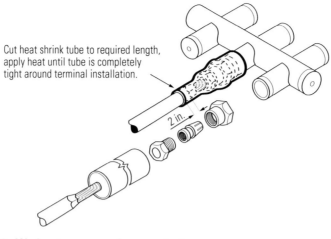

Cut heat shrink tube to required length, apply heat until tube is completely tight around terminal installation.

2 in.

Figure 3-8. Wedge-type secondary conductor.

SYSTEM

DRAWINGS

MATERIALS

INSTALLING

SPLICING

FUSING

MAINTENANCE

TROUBLE

JOB SITE

Cable Terminations

Underground primary cables connect overhead lines via terminators to LPTs, switchgear, or directly to the customers equipment. Available in various sizes from No. 1 to 4/0 AWG, (15 and 25 kV Class).

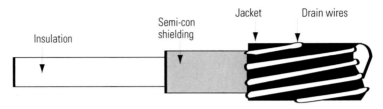

Figure 3-9. XLPE cable, stranded neutral conductor.

15 kV Class Cable Description	25 kV Class Cable Description
1/0 full tension	No. 1 full tension
4/0 full tension	4/0 full tension
4/0 reduced tension (3 phase only)	4/0 reduced tension (3 phase only)

Feeder cables come in two sizes, 500 and 750 kcmil (15 and 25 kV). They usually originate in the substation and connect to the overhead lines via potheads or underground switch gear. Proper phasing is extremely important.

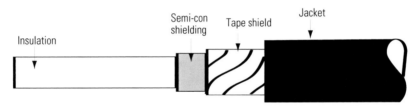

Figure 3-10. Feeder cable, taped neutral conductor.

15 kV Class Cable Description	25 kV Class Cable Description
500 kcmil reduced neutral	500 kcmil reduced neutral
750 kcmil reduced neutral	750 kcmil reduced neutral
500 kcmil taped neutral	500 kcmil taped neutral
750 kcmil taped neutral	750 kcmil taped neutral

Tel-Eyes are tubes with an eye connected to it. They are pressed onto the end of the XLPE cable and used in conjunction with a swivel to pull in the cable.

Figure 3-11. Tel-Eyes.

200 amp deadbreak elbows can be identified by the bail assembly that secures them to the junction rack. It is important to note that they cannot break any current or voltage. During switching, the cable must be de-energized or a flashover will occur. These elbows are usually not used for new installations.

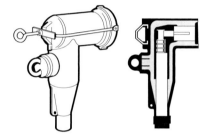

Figure 3-12. 200 amp deadbreak elbow.

200 amp loadbreak elbows provide a connection from the cable to the electrical apparatus and is capable of breaking loads up to 200 amps. They can be ordered in various line voltages and sizes. A white band around the elbow body identifies it as a loadbreak elbow.

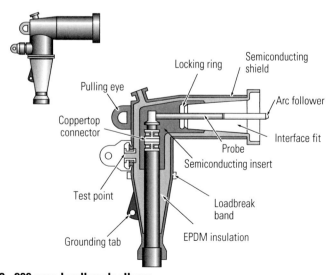

Figure 3-13. 200 amp loadbreak elbow.

Feed-thru bushing inserts most commonly used to add a second or third cable to a transformer. The feed-thru screws directly into the bushing well provided in the transformer and accepts two loadbreak elbows. Switching on a feed-thru bushing insert is not recommended. Due to the depth of these, they are limited to use in 25 kV equipment only.

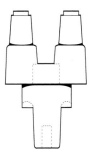

Figure 3-14. Feed-thru bushing insert.

200 amp loadbreak junction bars with universal bushing well are available as 3 or 4 points and installed in above and underground junction boxes. They are used in conjunction with load break elbows for switching and providing an isolation point. Stand-off plugs can be installed on either side of the junction bar for parking cables. The bushing inserts can be replaced if defective. Insulating caps are used to cover the exposed bushing inserts.

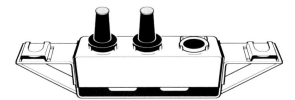

Figure 3-15. 200 amp loadbreak junction bar.

200 amp loadbreak with integrated bushings, are available as 3 or 4 points and installed in above and underground junction boxes. They are used in conjunction with load break elbows for switching and providing an isolation point. Stand-off plugs can be installed on either side of the junction bar for parking cables. The bushing inserts cannot be replaced if defective. Insulating caps are used to cover the exposed bushing inserts.

Figure 3-16. 200 amp loadbreak with integrated bushings.

600 amp deadbreak/200amp loadbreak junction bars are available as 3 or 4 points and installed in above and underground junction boxes. They are used in conjunction with loadbreak elbows for switching and providing an isolation point. Stand-off plugs can be installed on either side of the junction bar for parking cables. The bushing inserts can be replaced if defective. Insulating caps are used to cover the exposed bushing inserts.

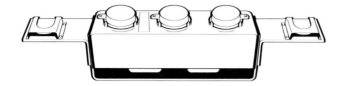

Figure 3-17. 600 amp deadbreak/200 amp loadbreak junction bars.

The junction bar comes in various configurations:

2 - 600 amp bushings and 1 - 200 amp bushing well
2 - 600 amp bushings and 2 - 200 amp bushing well
3 - 600 amp bushings and 1 - 200 amp bushing well

Bushing well inserts are used in conjunction with the junction bar to provide an interface between the elbow and the junction bar. The insert should be torqued to 18 foot-pounds.

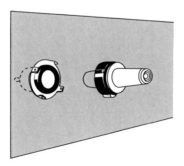

Figure 3-18. Bushing well inserts.

Insulated stand-off plugs are used to park energized (and de-energized) elbows in transformers and junction boxes.

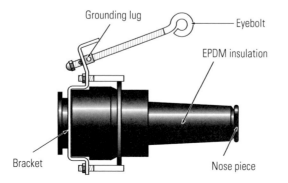

Figure 3-19. Insulated stand-off plug.

Insulating caps are used to cover unused live bushing inserts. The insulating caps grounding lead must be connected to ground before being installed on the bushing insert.

Figure 3-20. Insulating cap.

Feed-thru tools are mounted on the transformer case or junction bar similar to an insulated standoff. This allows the current to flow from the feed elbow to the load elbow without an electrical connection to the transformer.

Feed-thrus can be used to:

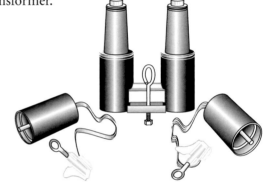

- Provide a temporary bypass

- Test for full line tension

- Isolate a cable

- Phasing

- Provide a grounding interface

Figure 3-21. Feed-thru tools.

600 amp deadbreak elbows are used mostly on feeder cables. It is important to note that they cannot break any current or voltage. During switching, the cable must be de-energized or a flashover will occur.

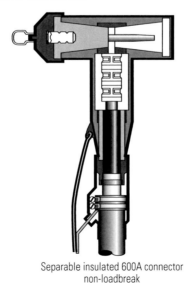

Separable insulated 600A connector
non-loadbreak

Figure 3-22. 600 amp deadbreak elbow.

Multi-connector bus bars (squids) are made by Blackburn and Burndy. They are designed for aluminum conductors and pressed connectors. The source secondaries are connected to the middle terminals of the bus bar and the load secondaries are connected to the outside terminals. The connectors are then bolted to the bus bar and covered with a rubber insulating sleeve (squid). Unused terminals are also covered with a rubber insulating sleeve. The bus bar is rated for 1000 amps and the terminals are rated for 572 amps.

1000A Compression Type

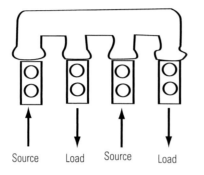

- Manufactured by Blackburn (Squid), Burndy Electrical Specialty Products
- Ampacity of bus bar (SectionA-A): 1000A
- Ampacity of terminal (Section B-B): 572A
- To ensure minimum heating of Bus bar, alternate source (secondary) and load (service) conductors.

Figure 3-23. Multi-connector bus bars.

Multi-connector bus bars (squids) are made by Blackburn and Homac. They are designed for aluminum conductors and pressed connectors. The source secondaries are connected to the middle terminals of the bus bar and the load secondaries are connected to the outside terminals. The connectors are then bolted to the bus bar and covered with a rubber insulating sleeve (squid). Unused terminals are also covered with a rubber insulating sleeve. The bus bar is rated for 2000 amps and the terminals are rated for 940 amps.

2000A Compression Type

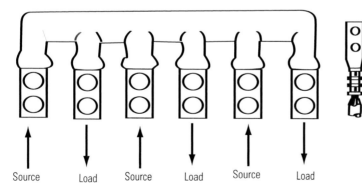

- Manufactured by Blackburn, Homac Electrical Specialty Products.
- Ampacity of bus bar (Section A-A): 2000A
- Ampacity of terminal (Section B-B): 940A
- To ensure minimum heating of bus bar, alternate source (secondary) and load (service) conductors.

Figure 3-24. Multi-connector bus bars.

Multi-connector bus bars (mole) are made by Burndy and designed for copper conductors. A socket and nut assembly clockwise compression cone is threaded into the bus bar and a piece of heat shrink is pushed over the conductor. The copper conductor is pushed into the compression cone and tightened. The heat shrink is slid over the nut assembly and heated, forming a watertight seal. Unused terminals are sealed with a terminal plug. The source and load secondaries are connected on opposite sides of the bus bar. The bus bar is rated for 1500 amps.

1500A Wedge Type

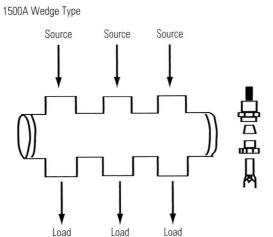

- Manufactured by Burndy (Mole)
- Ampacity of bus bar (Section A-A): 1500A
- Ampacity of terminal (Section B-B): greater than conductor ampacity.
- To ensure minimum heating of bus bar place source (secondary) and load (service) conductors on opposite sides of busbar.

Figure 3-25. Multi-connector bus bars (mole).

Loadbreak Connectors

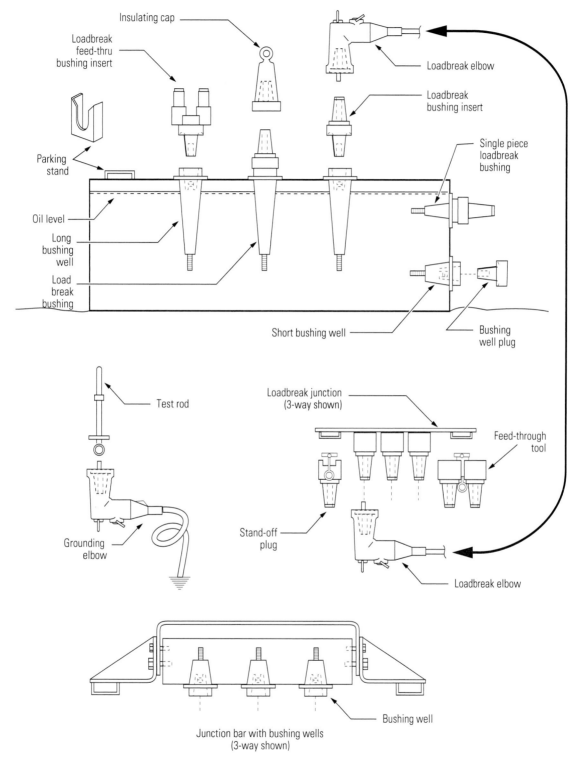

Insulating cap

Loadbreak feed-thru bushing insert

Loadbreak elbow

Loadbreak bushing insert

Parking stand

Single piece loadbreak bushing

Oil level

Long bushing well

Load break bushing

Short bushing well

Bushing well plug

Test rod

Loadbreak junction (3-way shown)

Feed-through tool

Grounding elbow

Stand-off plug

Loadbreak elbow

Bushing well

Junction bar with bushing wells (3-way shown)

Figure 3-26. Loadbreak connectors.

SYSTEM

DRAWINGS

MATERIALS

INSTALLING

SPLICING

FUSING

MAINTENANCE

TROUBLE

JOB SITE

Deadbreak Connectors

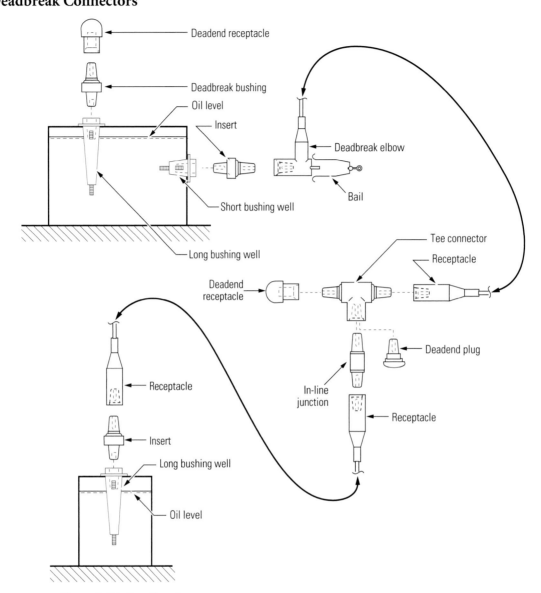

Figure 3-27. Deadbreak connectors.

Tools

Cable cutters are used to cut aluminum and copper conductors. They are not designed to cut ACSR. The 20-1/2 inch cutter comes with insulated handles and is designed to cut conductors up to 350 kcmil. The 31-1/4 inch cutter come with insulated handles and is designed to cut conductors up to 1000 kcmil.

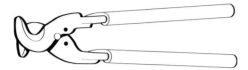

Figure 3-28. Cable cutter.

Raychem torches are used for heat shrink splices and terminations. The FH-2606 Raychem torch has a regulator setting of 5 psi, while the FH-2629 Raychem torch has a regulator setting of 15 psi.

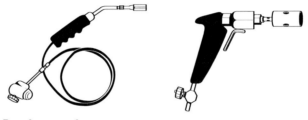

Figure 3-29. Raychem torches.

Regulators are used to regulate the amount of propane entering the Raychem torch. Propane can be regulated from 1 to 30 psi. Raychem torches are regulated at either 5 or 15 psi.

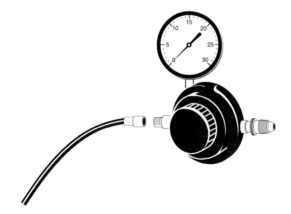

Figure 3-30. Regulator.

Connecting hoses come in approx. 30 feet lengths and connect the torch to the regulator.

Figure 3-31. Connecting hose.

Key loadbreak probe/torque wrench is designed to provide operating personnel a means of preventing probe arc follower contamination and other damage. It holds the probe and acts as a handle during positioning and installation of the probe into the threaded eye of the elbow connector. The Tor-key tool has a pre-set torque of 100 inch-pounds. The tor-key clicks when the set value (100 inch-pounds) has been reached.

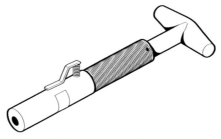

Figure 3-32. Key loadbreak probe/torque wrench.

Hotstick loadbreak probe/torque wrench is designed to be used in a shotgun and provides a means of re-tightening elbow probes while they are energized. Both the loadbreak probe and the actuating sleeve of the tool are made of insulated material. The tool will click when the pre-set torque (100 inch-pounds) is reached.

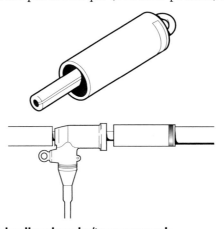

Figure 3-33. Hotstick loadbreak probe/torque wrench.

SYSTEM | DRAWINGS | MATERIALS | INSTALLING | SPLICING | FUSING | MAINTENANCE | TROUBLE | JOB SITE

Feed-thru insert tool is designed to facilitate the installation of a feed-thru bushing insert into a bushing well. Well stud breakage is prevented due to a integral torque limiter that is built into the tool. The tool will click when the pre-set torque (100 inch-pounds) has been reached.

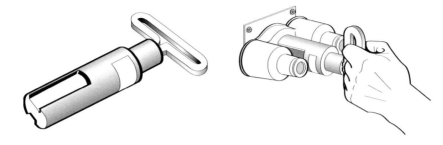

Figure 3-34. Feed-thru insert tool.

Bushing insert tool is designed to provide an effective and reliable means of installation and removal of bushing well inserts without any damage to insert interface. A Tor-key is attached to the rear of the tool and has a pre-set torque (100 inch-pounds) that provides a consistent tightening of the bushing insert. It also prevents breakage of the stud.

For bushing insert removal, the tool has a integral hexnut for use with a wrench.

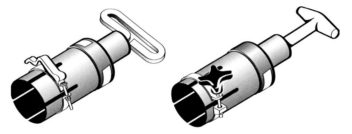

Figure 3-35. Bushing insert tool.

Semi-con stripper is used to remove the layer of unit 1 semi-con from the insulation on the XLPE cables. The semi-con stripper starts with straight cut and then spirals to the end.

Figure 3-36. Semi-con stripper.

SYSTEM | DRAWINGS | MATERIALS | INSTALLING | SPLICING | FUSING | MAINTENANCE | TROUBLE | JOB SITE

Insulation stripper is used to remove the inner insulation without damaging the conductor. It has various depth settings and also makes a straight cut at the end.

Figure 3-37. Insulation stripper.

Lid lifters for manhole covers are used to easily slide the cover from the manhole. The hook is inserted into the hole on the cover and the cover is slid up and off the manhole.

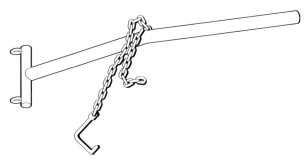

Figure 3-38. Lid lifter for manhole covers.

Lid lifters for box lids are used to raise the heavy lids on street vaults and junction boxes.

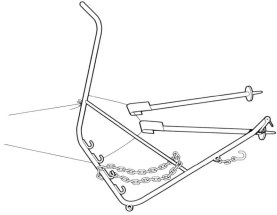

Figure 3-39. Lid lifter for box lids.

Lid lifter for vault gratings are used to pull the grating off the vault, and to remove service box lids.

Figure 3-40. Lid lifter for vault graters and service box lids.

Elbow pullers are used to break the seal on the elbow and safely remove or install it. Gripalls (shotgun) must not be used for pulling elbows but may be used once the seal is broken by the elbow puller.

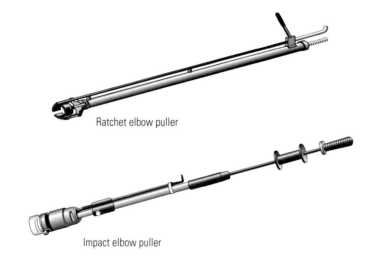

Ratchet elbow puller

Impact elbow puller

Figue 3-41. Elbow pullers.

CHAPTER

INSTALLING CABLE

SYSTEM

DRAWINGS

MATERIALS

INSTALLING

SPLICING

FUSING

MAINTENANCE

TROUBLE

JOB SITE

Pulling Cable

Introduction

There are many factors to consider when pulling cable through ducts such as tension on the cable, size of ducts, bends, and inclines. Proper design and cable size, as well as lubricants, rigging, and pulling equipment can assist in making a successful pull, a pull without damaging the underground cable.

Upon successful completion of this section, you will be able to describe the various steps required to prepare and successfully pull in underground cable.

The topics covered are:

- Pulling tension

- Duct preparation

- Fishwiring

- Equipment and set-up

- General considerations when pulling cable

- Cable pulling procedures using the portable power puller

- Cable pulling by hand procedures

- Cable racking, cutting and capping

Pulling Tension

Pulling tension is the tension exerted on a cable during the pulling process. In a straight pull situation, every type of cable has a maximum pulling tension. This should not be exceeded as the cable may be damaged by the extra forces exerted on it.

The length of cable that can be safely pulled into a duct system depends on the following factors:

- Size and type of conductor (copper or aluminum)

- Maximum pulling strain allowed on conductors

- Method of pulling cable (e.g. pulling eye or cable grip)

- Number of bends in conduit

- Radius of bends

- Bend angle

- Coefficient of friction

- Cable pulled dry or lubricated

Some utilities use an interactive mainframe computer program that calculates the total pulling tension on a cable as it is pulled through a duct. The duct layout is entered in sections and the cumulative cable tension out of each section is displayed.

If a cable pulling tension program is not available, the pulling tension can be approximately calculated by reducing the layout run into straight and bend sections and then applying these simplified concepts:

Straight Pull Sections

Figure 4-1a. Forces on a straight pull section.

$$T_{OUT} = T_{IN} + T_F$$

where

T_{OUT} = tension at the exit (pulling end), in pounds

T_{IN} = backtension at the entrance, in pounds

T_F = tension added by friction between the cable and the conduit in pounds.
= cable weight per foot × length in feet × C.F.

C.F. = Coefficient of Friction (dimensionless). The coefficient of friction is the ratio between the force needed to overcome friction, and the weight of the object being moved. For example, if a force of 1 pound is required to move a 4-pound book across a table top, the coefficient of friction is 1 divided by 4, or 0.25. The coefficient of friction varies with the different materials involved. For example, the C.F. of a PVC single-conductor cable in a dry PVC conduit is 0.69. The C.F. of a same conductor in a lubricated FRE conduit is 0.20.

		Conduit					
		Dry			Lubricated		
Jacket	Cable	PVC	Transite	FRE	PVC	Transite	FRE
PVC	Single Conductor	0.69	0.73	0.39	0.50	0.60	0.20
	Three Conductor, 3 Single Conductor	0.54	0.68	0.39	0.44	0.72	0.20
PE	Single Conductor	0.46	0.53	0.26	0.34	0.56	0.13
	Three Conductor, Four Conductor	0.56	0.56	0.24	0.46	0.60	0.12

Table 4-1. Coefficients of friction for cables and conduit.

Size	Cable Description	Jacket Dia., Nom. (in.)	Weight (lbs/1000 ft)
1/0 AWG	15 kV Jacketed Concentric Neutral	1063	603
750 kcmil	15 kV Tape Shielded	1688	1438
1/0 AWG	35 kV Jacketed Concentric Neutral	1440	952
500 kcmil	35 kV Tape Shielded	1954	2817

Table 4-2. Physical properties of primary cables.

Note: Table 4-2 presents typical data for comonly used primary cables. For the exact properties of cables used by your utility, contact your cable manufacturer.

SYSTEM

DRAWINGS

MATERIALS

INSTALLING

SPLICING

FUSING

MAINTENANCE

TROUBLE

JOB SITE

Type	Size	Weight (lbs/1000 ft)
Triplex	8 AWG	74
	6 AWG	117
	1/0 AWG	390
	4/0 AWG	713
	350 kcmi	1129
Quadruplex	4/0 AWG	1014
	350 kcmil	1604
	750 kcmil	3111

Table 4-3. Weight of underground secondary cables.

Example:

Cable: 1/0 AWG, single conductor
Jacket: PVC
Conduit: PVC
Conduit length: 80 feet
Lubricated: No
Back-tension at entrance: 100 pounds

$$T_{OUT} = T_{IN} + T_F$$

$$T_{OUT} = T_{IN} + \text{weight/foot} \times \text{length} \times \text{C.F.}$$

$$= 100 + 0.390 \times 80 \times 0.69$$

$$= 100 + 21.5$$

$$T_{OUT} = 121.5 \text{ pounds}$$

Curved Pull Sections

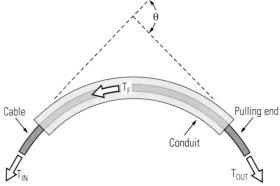

Figure 4-1b. Forces on a curved pull section.

$$T_{OUT} = T_{IN} \times T_F$$

where

T_{OUT} = tension at the exit (pulling end), in pounds

T_{IN} = backtension at the entrance to the conduit, in pounds

T_F = tension added by friction between the cable and the conduit (pounds)

= $e^{C.F. \times \theta}$

e = 2.72, a mathematical constant, the natural logarithm (dimensionless)

C.F. = Coefficient of Friction (dimensionless). For examples see Table 4.1.

θ = angle of the bend (radians). The bend angle in radians can be calculated by dividing the angle in degrees, by 57.3. (57.3° = 1 radian)

Example:

Cable: Triplex 1/0 AWG
Jacket: PVC
Conduit: PVC
Bend: 90 degrees
Lubricated: No
Backtension: 100 pounds

$$T_{OUT} = T_{IN} \times T_F$$
$$= 100 \times e^{C.F. \times \theta}$$
$$= 100 \times 2.72^{0.69 \times 90 / 57.3}$$
$$= 100 \times 2.82^{1.08}$$
$$T_{OUT} = 294 \text{ pounds}$$

Straight *and* Curved Pull Sections

If the installation consists of straight and curved sections, calculate the cable tension by considering each section, one at a time.

The backtension for the first section is the backtension from the cable reel. Calculate the exit tension for the first section.

The exit tension for the first section is the backtension for the second section. Calculate the exit tension for the second section.

The exit tension for the second section is the backtension for the third section. Calculate the exit tension for the third section.

Continue, until you complete the calculation for the last section. This is the tension on the cable puller.

Duct Preparation

Distribution cable ducts are usually installed by the customer's contractor. The ducts must be installed in accordance with the rules set by the utility.

Before cable is pulled in through the duct, it must be checked to ensure that it is unobstructed. If there is a build-up or obstruction, a test mandrel must be drawn through the duct to remove the obstruction and clean the duct before pulling in the cable. Depending on the type of obstruction, the test mandrel can be a wire brush type, a swab type or a cutter type. The diameter of the mandrel used must at least 1/2 inch smaller than the inner diameter of the duct.

If the ducts are too small, the following problems may occur:

- Pulling difficulties

- High cable installation costs

- Cable installation damage

If the ducts are too large, the problem may be high construction costs.

Fishwiring

Fishwiring is the term used to describe the pulling of a fishline through a duct to install the pulling line. The pulling line is used to pull in the cable.

At a new job site, the fishlines are normally pulled into the ducts by the contractors. However, if they are not pulled in, that task must be done first. The fishline must be an approved twine. Each fishline must be firmly attached to either a pulling iron or other rigid object at each duct end so that it is not lost.

For short ducts (up to 100 feet), the steel tape fishing method is recommended to pull in the pulling rope. These tapes must be lightweight, easy to handle, and must wind up into lockable reels that prevent them from spinning loose. The steel tape is fished through the duct, and the pulling rope (called a strawline) is attached to the end.

Note: Due to electrical hazards, the steel tape or fish tape must never be pushed towards energized boxes or kiosks or used in substations.

The vacuum pump method can be used for most fishwiring jobs.

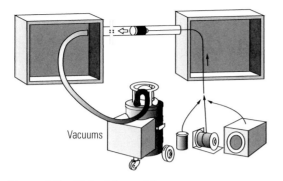

Figure 4-2a. Fishwiring with a vacuum pump.

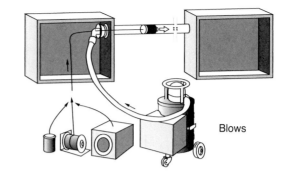

Figure 4-2b. Fishwiring with a blow pump.

The pump can be used either as a vacuum pump or as a blower, depending on the situation. The duct must never be sized by blowing the piston towards energized equipment. Also, if the duct contains water, it is recommended that the pump be used as a blower rather than a vacuum pump, as the pump has limited holding capacity for the water.

The compressor method is used for heavy-duty jobs such as fishwiring of 4 inch and 5 inch feeder ducts over 300 feet in length. The compressor method uses a parachute rather than a polyurethane foam piston for installing the fishline. The parachute is connected to the fishline and blown through the duct.

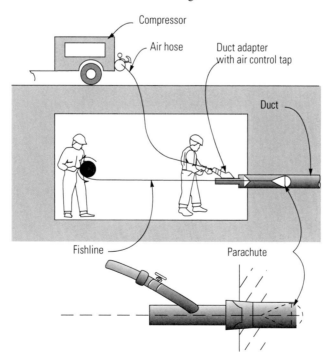

Figure 4-3. Fishwiring with a compressor.

The power dart method is an economical means of rodding, fishing and measuring long PVC duct runs.

To operate the power dart, use the following steps:

1. Locate the end of the blow line.

2. Insert and pull blow line through one of the holes in the drag plate located on the tail end of the seal-off handle.

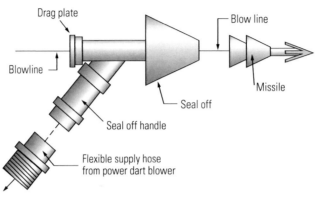

Figure 4-4. Power dart blower.

3. Feed the line through the center of the selected seal and attach the seal to the handle assembly.

4. Connect the line to the selected missile.

5. Attach the flexible hose from the blower to the seal-off handle.

6. Adjust the drag plate to put a slight tension on the blow line. This will minimize excessive blow line build up in the conduit.

Note: When turning on the unit, start one blower at a time to avoid overloading the power supply circuit.

Equipment

The equipment used in pulling cable varies depending on the type of job and the method used. However, the equipment that could be used consists of:

- Line trucks and cable trailers

- Cable reels

- Portable power cable puller, vacuum pumps, compressors

- Ropes, fishwire

- Cable grips, pulling eyes

- Baloney

- Miscellaneous rigging devices such as frames and brackets

A portable power cable puller (capstan) is used for most pulling jobs in underground systems.

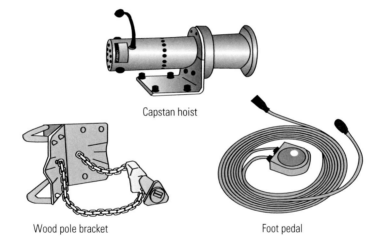

Capstan hoist

Wood pole bracket

Foot pedal

Figure 4-5. Electric-powered capstan hoist.

The capstan in one of the most versatile tools used to pull in underground cables. It operates on 120 volts/15 amps and is controlled by a weatherproof footswitch, which leaves the operators hands free to control the pulling rope and operate the radio. The capstan is capable of pulling 750 pounds at 60 feet per minute and is designed to turn in only one direction. It also incorporates a locking device which holds the tension when the power is turned off. The light weight of the capstan allows it to be easily moved from site to site.

The capstan is also used to pull service cables from the transformer to the service box or the customers panel. Figure 4-6a and 4-6b show a variety of pulling set-ups.

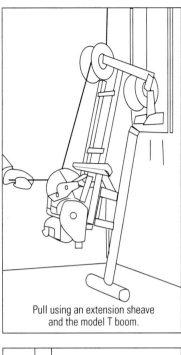

Pull using an extension sheave and the model T boom.

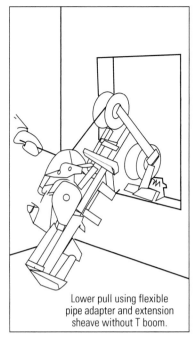

Lower pull using flexible pipe adapter and extension sheave without T boom.

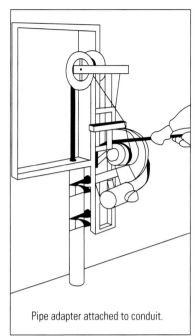

Pipe adapter attached to conduit.

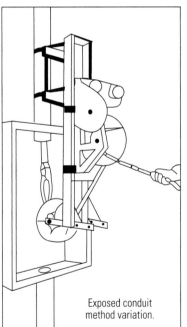

Exposed conduit method variation.

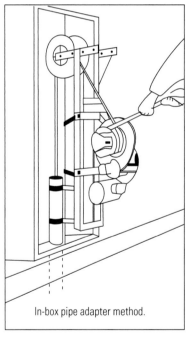

In-box pipe adapter method.

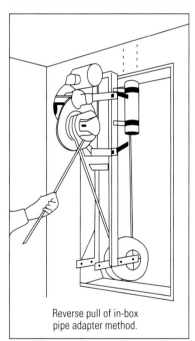

Reverse pull of in-box pipe adapter method.

Figure 4-6a. Cable installation with power puller, and various set-up methods.

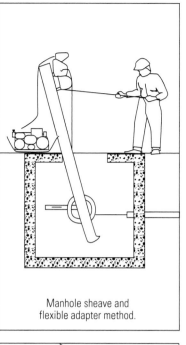

Manhole sheave and
flexible adapter method.

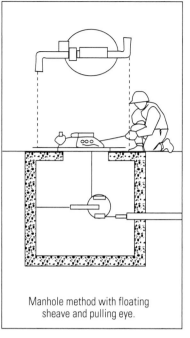

Manhole method with floating
sheave and pulling eye.

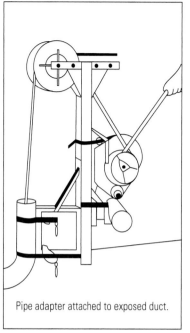

Pipe adapter attached to exposed duct.

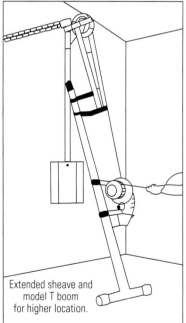

Extended sheave and
model T boom
for higher location.

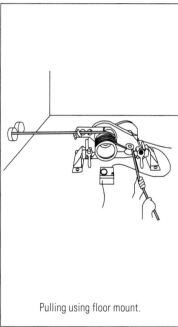

Pulling using floor mount.

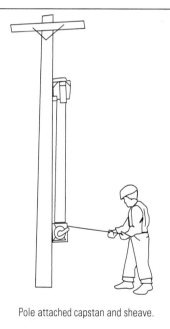

Pole attached capstan and sheave.

Figure 4-6b. Cable installation with power puller, and various set-up methods.

SYSTEM

DRAWINGS

MATERIALS

INSTALLING

SPLICING

FUSING

MAINTENANCE

TROUBLE

JOB SITE

All cable installation equipment such as pulling devices, line trucks, cable trailers and other materials must be set up so as not to interfere with the local traffic flow. At times this may not be possible, but every attempt should be made to reduce interference. Open manholes, cable trenches, kiosks, etc., must be barricaded. Warning signs must be put in place to warn the public of possible dangers.

The pulling equipment and the cable reels are set up to provide such things as:

- the most convenient pulling schedule

- the lowest pulling tensions

- safe operation and low labor costs

A typical set-up is shown below.

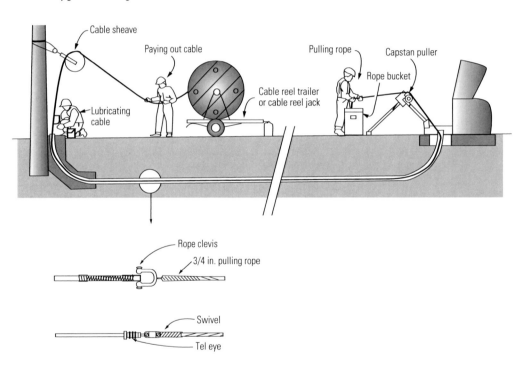

Figure 4-7. Underground primary cable pull from terminal pole to low profile transformer (LPT).

CHAPTER 4 – Installing Cable

SYSTEM

DRAWINGS

MATERIALS

INSTALLING

SPLICING

FUSING

MAINTENANCE

TROUBLE

JOB SITE

General Considerations When Pulling Cables

You should consider the following aspects of pulling cable before setting up and doing the pull.

- Direction of pull

- Pulling cable over bends

- Cable lubrication

- Communications

Direction of Pull

The choice of pulling direction can be affected by several factors. Advantages in reduced pulling tensions can be obtained by considering the location and angle of bends or by considering the duct slope. A bend may be minimized if the cable is pulled so that the bend is nearer to the feed-in end. An incline can be minimized by pulling down the incline. If cable slack is required at one end, pull the cable away from that end. Cable runs consisting of many sections usually require several equipment set-ups that allow pulls in two or more directions. Cable to be terminated should, if possible, be pulled towards the termination (up a terminal pole, into a substation or into a breaker panel of a building).

If cable slack is required in a manhole and no definite pulling direction has been established, the cable reel should be set up at the manhole where the slack is required. This allows the cable to be conveniently cut to the required length, and re-gripping of the cable is not necessary.

Cable Pulling Over Bends

When pulling over bends, sheaves or skid plates are used to prevent the cable and ropes from rubbing against sharp edges and protrusions. These sheaves can be attached to terminal poles using rope slings. The rope slings must be wrapped around the pole at least twice. In the case of manholes or underground vaults, the sheaves can be attached to the pulling irons or to the manhole lid frame. If there are no pulling irons, a temporary rigging system can be used.

Cable Lubrication

The pulling force can be reduced by lubricating the cable before its installation. Lubrication reduces the coefficient of friction between the cable jacket and the duct wall.

Since a number of lubricants are available on the market, careful consideration should be given to its affect on humans and the environment, compatibility with cable jackets, flash point, ease of use, and clean-up. Some lubricants, such as Ideal Yellow 77, leave a residue when dried and become very flammable and should not be used. At times, you may be asked to test the performance of various lubricants being considered.

Cable lubricants are usually applied by hand, although a dispenser can be used. Some lubricant should be placed in the duct ahead of the cable and during the pull. Caution should be used when working with cable lubricants, as they may cause the worksite to become untidy and slippery.

Communications

Communication is an important part of any cable pulling job. There must be a means of communication at the feeding end and at the pulling end of a duct line. Standardized hand signals can be used, but radios or walkie-talkies are more common.

Note: Citizen band radios are not to be used.

Due to possible cross-channel interference problems with radios and walkie-talkies, the commands used are kept short and clear, plus some trade jargon is used. The following gives some examples of commands and their meanings.

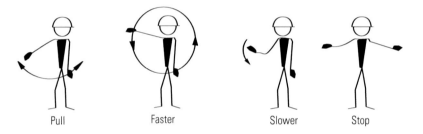

| Pull | Faster | Slower | Stop |

Figure 4-8. Standard hand signals for cable pulling.

Command	Meaning
Stop	Stop the action
Slower	Slow down the action
Ease back	Allow slack in the cable
It's in the duct	Cable is in position; the pulling speed can be increased
Cut-cut-cut	Enough cable received, it can now be cut

All instructions, except **Stop**, must be acknowledged and then carried out.

Cable Pulling Procedures Using the Portable Power Puller

Note: In the following explanation, the lineworker at the cable feeding end will be called the *feeder* and the one at the pulling end will be called the *puller*.

The steps followed when pulling a cable using a portable power puller are:

1. Set up the cable reel at the feeding end and the power puller at the other end of the duct (pulling end). If a pull box is installed in a duct system, the cable reel should, if possible, be set up at the pull box.

2. At the cable feeding end, attach and use the fishline to pull in the heavier strawline. The strawline is approximately 3/8 inch thick.

3. A power puller (capstan) is then used to pull in the heavier cable pulling rope.

4. At the feeder end, the pulling rope is attached to the cable with either a cable grip (sock) or a pulling eye.

Note: To prevent damaging the cable by scrapping on the manhole frame or at the duct opening or in passing over other cables, a feeding tube is sometimes used. This guiding tube, called a baloney, is made of flexible steel tubing about 4 inches in diameter and from 10 to 20 feet in length.

7. When the pulling rope is connected to the cable, a power puller (capstan) is used to pull the cable through the duct.

   When pulling in the cable, wrap two or three loops of rope onto the capstan and keep constant tension (pulling) on the tail of the rope. The pulling action can be interrupted by relieving the tension of the rope and/or by shutting off the power puller motor.

Note: If a pull box was installed, do not attempt to pull cable through it, since this defeats the purpose of the box. Feed the cable from the box in both directions and then splice the cable ends in it.

Cable Pulling by Hand Procedures

Short lengths of light cable can be pulled into a duct either by hand or with a lightweight wire puller. Both methods are timesaving and are used mainly to install service cables.

The hand pulling force should not exceed the value that can be obtained by arm force alone. This means that the body weight must not be used by leaning against the pull.

The steps followed when pulling cable by hand are:

1. Set up the cable reel at the feeding end and the pulling device, if required, at the other end of the duct.

2. Attach the pulling rope to the fishline and pull the rope by hand.

3. Attach the cable to the pulling rope using cable or wire grips, and pull the cable into the duct.

When pulling the cable by hand, remove all material and equipment that could interfere with the pulling. Make sure the surface is dry and provides a safe standing base for the Journeyman. Do not pull while standing on unstable obstructions, ladders, etc.

Cable Racking, Cutting, and Capping

When the cable pulling has been completed, the cable is placed on the racks to keep it off the ground and protect it from possible water contamination. If racks are not present, use rope to secure the cable high off the ground.

Once positioned on the racks, the cable can be cut using a hacksaw or cable cutters. Ensure that an excess amount of cable is left to allow for the splicing process.

If the cable is not spliced or terminated immediately, the cable ends must be capped. The cable left on the reel must also be capped.

The purpose of capping is to prevent the penetration of moisture into the cable interior, which could result in a cable failure.

To cap both primary and secondary plastic cables with heat-shrink end caps:

1. Clean end of cable and slide a heat-shrink end cap into place. Refer to Table 4-4 for the appropriate end cap to use for the cable being capped.

Size	Application
3-3/4 in. to 7-1/2 in.	Triplex and quadruplex secondary cables, #1 to #4/0 AWG
6 in. to 11-1/2 in.	Triplex and quadruplex secondary cables, #4/0 AWG to 500 kcmil
10-1/4 in. to 20 in.	Triplex and quadruplex secondary cables, 750 kcmil Concentric neutral secondary cables Primary cables

2. Use a propane torch to shrink the end cap. Begin shrinking the cap from the closed end and go towards the open end.

3. When the cap has recovered enough so that it assumes the cable shape and sealant flows from the open end, discontinue the heating. These caps are rated 600V and are not to be energized at primary voltages.

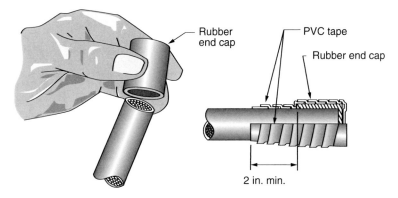

Figure 4-9. Installation of rubber end cap.

To cap secondary plastic cables with rubber end caps:

1. Select the appropriate rubber end cap for the cable being capped.

2. Put the cap on the end of the cable.

3. Apply PVC tape in two half-lapped layers to fully tape over the cap.

4. These end caps are rated 600V and are suitable for energization at secondary voltages:

Duct Sealing

Sealing the cable ducts become very important in areas that are particularly susceptible to heavy rains, water or gases. Also, faulted cables may cause combustible gases to flow into the switching units, manholes, or customers vaults.

Sealing of the ducts can be accomplished by using duct seal or Rayflate Duct Sealing System.

Rayflate Duct Sealing System

The Rayflate Duct Sealing System (RDSS) has been designed for use in conjunction with concrete, plastic, or steel duct to provide a watertight duct seal. With the RDSS, unsealed ducts need no longer cause dampness and flooding in cable vaults, access manholes, and sub-station basements.

Equipment

The Rayflate Duct Sealing System main unit consists of a gas cylinder holder, regulator, flow and pressure controller and the delivery pipe with a tube snap assembly.

The RDSS kit consists of an inflatable bladder of flexible metallic laminate, coated on both side with a sealant strip and a clip used as a seal in-between the cables.

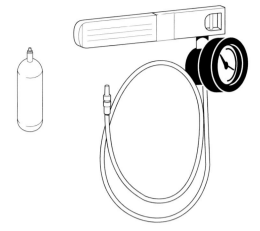

Figure 4-10. Assembled equipment and bladder.

Equipment Preparation

1. Check On/Off lever is in the Off position

2. Unscrew and remove the gas cylinder holder.

3. Check the cylinder, only E7512-0160 cylinders should be used with the TDUX-IT-16 inflation unit.

4. Wipe clean and insert the gas cylinder, neck up, into the gas cylinder holder.

5. Screw the cylinder holder hand tight on to the inflator.

Note: In cold weather, warm the cylinder in a gloved hand.

To identify an empty cylinder, shake the cylinder. A rattling sound indicates an empty cylinder.

Duct Preparation

1. With a wet cloth, clean the duct and cable sheath. Remove as much dirt, mud, rust, etc. as possible.

2. For ease of installation, lubricate the cable sheath.

Figure 4-11. Step 2, lubricate the cable sheath.

3. For 0, 1, or 2 cables, skip to step 14. For 3 or more cables, continue with step 4.

4. Locate and prepare RDSS clip.

5. Remove the protective paper from one side of the clip.

6. Lubricate black sealant immediately after protective paper is removed.

7. Remove the protective paper from the other side of the clip and lubricate. Ensure the entire clip is lubricated.

9. Slide the clip in between the cables. Tie wrap the clip to one of the cables. Do not pull the tie wraps too tight as this will make it difficult to slide the clip into the duct. Use the following diagrams to ensure proper installation of the clip.

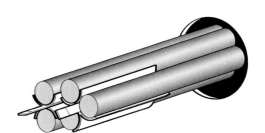

Figure 4-12. Step 7, lubricate the clip.

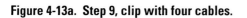

Figure 4-13a. Step 9, clip with four cables.   **Figure 4-13b. Step 9, clips with five cables.**

11. Slide the clip into the duct until the line on the stick is approximately 1 inch (25mm) from the end of the duct.

12. Pull the tie wrap to secure the clip to the cables. Tie wrap may also be used to bundle the cables together and hold the clip in place.

13. Remove the protective paper from the (RDSS inflatable bladder) seal strip. Lubricate the inside and outside of the (inflatable bladder) seal, as well as the filling tube on the RDSS section.

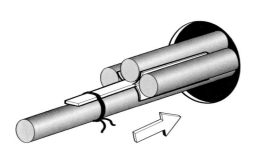

Figure 4-14. Step 12, tighten tie wrap to secure clip.

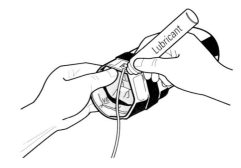

Figure 4-15. Step 13, lubricate the bladder.

SYSTEM | DRAWINGS | MATERIALS | **INSTALLING** | SPLICING | FUSING | MAINTENANCE | TROUBLE | JOB SITE

14. Wrap the RDSS around the cables and slide completely into the duct.

15. In the case of two (2) cables, wrap the RDSS around and inbetween the cables.

16. Connect the filling tube to the tube-snap on the inflation tool. Gently insert the tube until it will not go in any further.

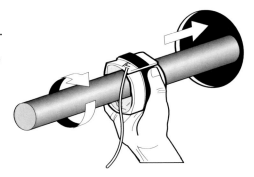

Figure 4-16. Step 14, wrap the RDSS around cable(s).

17. Inflate the RDSS up to the pressure of 45 psi and keep the pressure at 45 psi for 30 seconds. During inflation, hold the inflator so the gas cylinder is pointing up between vertical and horizontal. Do not operate the inflator with the gas cylinder pointing downwards.

Note: Refer to the operating manual for the specific inflation tool being used.

18. Pull the filling tube out of RDSS in one gentle move.

19. Remove the gas cylinder from the inflation unit.

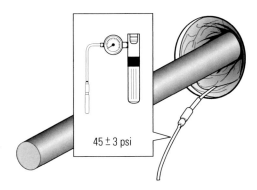

Figure 4-17. Step 17, inflate the RDSS.

Removing the RDSS

1. Deflate the RDSS by piercing with a knife or screwdriver.

2. Release the RDSS from the duct and from the cable sheath with a blunt tool.

3. Remove the RDSS from the duct with a pair of pliers.

Cable Pulling Tips

- The number of bends in the run greatly influences pulling tension. Additional bends must never be added to the designed conduit layout without consulting the design engineer. Field conditions such as obstructions or conflicts with other utility's facilities requiring additional bends might be unavoidable.

- Pulling tension can be affected by the direction of the pull. Usually, the wire feed should start at the end of the conduit that is closest to the first bend.

- Check to be sure there are no nails, staples, or other sharp objects in a location that can damage the cable.

- Inspect cable reels to ensure that reel flange bolts are tight and cable ends secure. Make sure the reel turns freely.

- Don't pull cable until the conduit has been covered with enough dirt to hold it firmly in place. If it moves, the conduit can be damaged. Always backfill before pulling in cable.

- To prevent abrasion and damage to pulling lines and cables, use only guides, rollers, sheaves, and tubes that have smooth edges. Cable and pulling lines should be led over adequately sized blocks, sheaves, or pulling lines. They should never be dragged on the ground or over sharp edges or abrasive surfaces.

- If a difficult cable pull is anticipated, prelubricate the conduit using a duct swab. This lubrication is in addition to lubricating the cable.

- Pulling eyes are recommended for pulling 500 and 750 kcmil cables. Compared with socks, pulling eyes are more compact and ride through bends easier. They attach directly to the stranded conductor.

- Improper pulling line will damage the conduit. Pulling line should have the necessary tensile strength while not stretching or rotating, and it must not burn the conduit. Use synthetic rope. Do not use twine, nylon, or polypropylene pulling lines. These will burn the conduit.

- The lower the force needed to pull a cable, the better, resulting in greater safety, prevention of cable damage, and less equipment wear and conduit damage.

- Keep dirt and rocks out of the conduit. No amount of lubrication can compensate for dirt in the conduit. If you suspect there are problems, there are ways to clean the conduit.

- Cable pulled over curved surfaces will be damaged if the curve is too small. Use sheaves large enough to prevent pinching.

SYSTEM

DRAWINGS

MATERIALS

INSTALLING

SPLICING

FUSING

MAINTENANCE

TROUBLE

JOB SITE

- Excessive tension damages the cable and reduces cable life. The crushing effect of the sidewall pressure experienced at all conduit bends is directly proportional to the pulling tension.

- Lubrication significantly reduces pulling tension, minimizes cable damage, and is mandatory on all long cable pulls.

- Use colored tape for phase identification. Don't use paint because it can damage the cable.

- To allow the cable to pass without snagging, anchor all rigging equipment securely.

- Do not use the collapsible reel ("butterfly") on the line truck to pull cable because it can collapse.

- Don't stop! Once the pulling starts, don't stop unless absolutely necessary. More pulling tension is required to overcome *stationary* friction than *moving* friction.

- To ensure safe operation, the maximum pulling speed is 60 feet per minute. As a reference, the truck capstan should have a maximum speed of 54 feet per minute.

- Pulling tension can be greatly reduced by manually turning the cable reels. Reel stands should be level and well lubricated to ensure easy turning. Braking of the reels should only be done to prevent reel overturn.

- Do not allow any worker to be in the vault or handhole during the actual pull of the conductors. If a worker needs to access the vault or handhole, all pulling operations must stop.

Tagging Cable

Introduction

It is important that every cable and phase be identified and tagged with an identifying mark. This identification tag is in the form of either a metal strip or a plastic circle attached to the termination, cable, or joint.

If a cable is identified incorrectly, the result may be deadly. It is imperative that cables are tagged with the correct identification.

Upon successful completion of this section, you will be able to correctly tag and identify UD, feeder, and secondary cables

The topics covered are:

- Types of tags and attachment

- Feeder identification

- Primary cable identification

- Secondary cable identification

- Phase identification

After a cable is pulled into location, placed on the racks and cut to the required length, it is necessary to identify it. At this point, a temporary tag is put on the cable. This temporary tag can be plain white tape wrapped around the cable with the identification number written on it with a pen or marker. After the cable is spliced and terminated, the temporary tag must be replaced with a permanent tag.

Types of Tags and Attachments

Various types of tags are used for identification purposes.

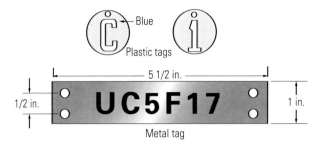

Figure 4-18. Samples of types of tags.

Identification tags are made of either aluminum or plastic. The aluminum tags use a die set to punch the identification number into them. The punched identification number can be highlighted by spraying the tag with paint and wiping off the excess pain with a dry cloth. Aluminum tags are often used to identify feeder circuits and cables.

Circular, plastic tags are used to identify phases. These tags are colored with either letters or numbers stamped on them.

Both types of tags are attached to the cables with cable ties.

Feeder Identification

Feeder cables are identified with a tag that contains the following information:

*   Circuit voltage

*   Circuit number

*   Identification letters for the station

For example, a 12 kV feeder circuit from the substation named Sperling, with cable number 56, the tag might contain the following alphanumeric identification:

12-56 SPG

The work order shows the information required on the feeder cable identification tag. Most substation circuits use 50 as their lowest number and go up from there.

Figure 4-19. Feeder identification tag.

Primary Cable Identification

Primary cables other than feeders are sometimes tagged with an underground circuit, or UC number. The reason for this, is to distinguish them from feeder circuits. The underground circuit number is sometimes obtained from a map on a grid. This grid divides the area into squares. There are numbers running on one side and letters on the other side. Figure 4-19 shows a sample grid. When a cable is labeled, the location of that cable must be found on the map, together with the number and letter that identify the area. Also, the number of circuits installed in that grid section must be known.

The alphanumeric number for the tag could be as follows:

1.   UC for underground circuit

2.   Grid number

3.   Grid letter

4.   Circuit number

This alphanumeric number is usually given on the work order.

For example, notice in Figure 4-18 that square 5F is highlighted. If the cable was located, and it is the seventeenth circuit installed in that area, the cable could be tagged with the following alphanumeric identification: UC 5F 17

Note: Some utilities tag each end of the cable with a destination label that corresponds to the designations on the underground distribution diagram (UDD). They do not use UC numbers.

Cable tagging is done at the ends of each circuit and at all splice locations.

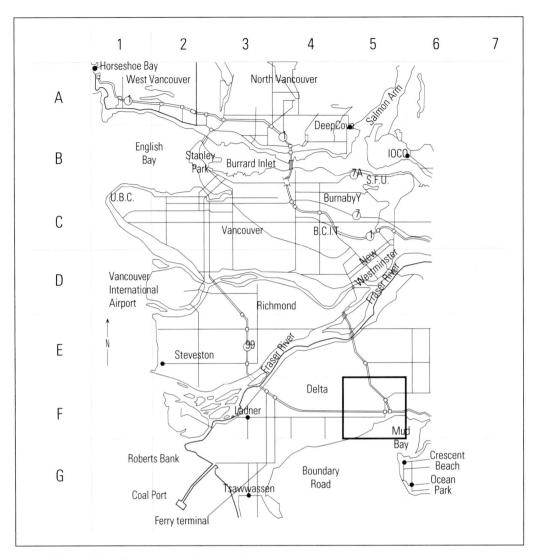

FIgure 4-20. Underground circuit grid system.

Secondary Cable Identification

Secondary cables are usually identified using the aluminum tags. These cables do not have to be numbered or plotted on a schematic, but the tag does have to tell the lineworker what customers are being fed. Because of this, the address of the customer that the cable is servicing is punched into the tag. Sometimes, if it is servicing a large customer or a customer with a recognizable name, such as Safeway or McDonald's, only the customer's name is put on the tag.

A nylon tag of the same dimensions as metal tag can also be used. The address is applied using a special marker that can write on the tag.

Tags are placed at the ends of each circuit and at splice locations.

Phase Identification

Phases are identified along the circuit wherever the cable can be separated. This is usually at the terminal poles, junction boxes, etc.

At the substations, phases are clearly identified, such as A, B and C. Since the cables are secured in place and cannot be moved, the phases can be positively identified as either A-phase, B-phase or C-phase. If you are labeling phases and are not at the substation or positive as to the identification of the phases, label what you think is the A-phase as 1, B-phase as 2 and C-phase as 3. This is normally the case with underground circuits that are fed from overhead circuits. These plastic tags are circular and have the numbers 1, 2 or 3 on them.

When phases are positively identified as A, B or C, colored tags are often used with the A tag red, the B tag yellow, and the C tag blue. Corresponding letters are also present on each tag. Remember, however, that the tags most commonly used in underground circuits are the numbered circular tags.

| Red | Yellow | Blue | | Red | Yellow | Blue |
| Lettered tags | | | | Numbered tags | | |

Figure 4-21. Plastic tags used for labeling phases. Numbered tags are most commonly used.

Phases can be temporarily identified with colored tape until the job is completed. After the job is completed, this tape must be replaced with tags.

Figure 4-21 shows what XLPE cables would look like when both phases and the circuit are identified.

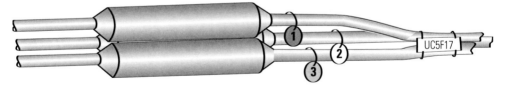

Figure 4-22. Phase and circuit identification of XLPE cable.

SYSTEM | DRAWINGS | MATERIALS | INSTALLING | SPLICING | FUSING | MAINTENANCE | TROUBLE | JOB SITE

Primary Cables

Conductor	Color (Identify by PVC Tape)
A phase	Red
B phase	Yellow or black*
C phase	Blue

Secondary and Service Cables

Single Phase	Three Phase	Color
Cables With Factory Coloring		
X_1	A phase	Red
X_3	B phase	Black
—	C phase	Blue
X_2	Neutral	White
Cables Without Factory Coloring (Identify by PVC Tape)		
X_1	A phase	Red
X_3	B phase	Yellow or black*
—	C phase	Blue
X_2	Neutral	White

* Yellow is the preferred color for a B phase cable, but black may be substituted.

Table 4-5. Cable color code.

Locate Cables on Poles

Introduction

When you are making the transition between underground cables and overhead lines, the location of the cable on the pole is an important consideration. Telephone lines may also exist on the pole and care must be taken not to interfere with this service. Over the years, instructions have been developed regarding where to locate the cables.

Upon successful completion of this section, you will be able to describe the location and procedure for installing cables on wood and cement poles.

The following topics:

- Climbing space

- Pilaster location

- Cable protection

- Installation procedures (wood and concrete poles)

Climbing Space

It is imperative that designers and others involved with power line construction are aware of the necessity to provide adequate climbing space. In general, the climbing space may be considered as a clear column having minimum horizontal dimensions of 30 × 30 inches for conductors or other energized equipment operating at greater than 300 volts, and of 24 × 24 inches if less than 300 volts.

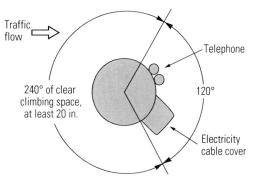

Figure 4-23. Climbing space in relation to service equipment.

This column should be on one side or quadrant of the pole all the way to the top, but where this is impractical the column may shift from one position to another. If this happens, the adjacent columns must overlap by at least 40 inches and there must be no obstruction between the two columns. In addition, a clear climbing space of the appropriate horizontal dimensions must extend vertically at least 40 inches above and below the limiting conductors or energized parts.

The problem of climbing space is particularly acute where cables are attached to the pole. At least 240° of the pole surface must be available for the worker's feet.

Maintenance of adequate climbing space requires coordination with telephone conduits and customer dips and may limit the number of conduits that can be placed on a pole. In order to achieve a 20-inch circumferential climbing space on the pole, a minimum of a 30-inch pole circumference is required. This necessitates the selection of a Class 3 pole or better. It should be noted that a restriction in climbing space at the bottom of the pole where the cable guard expands in size to cover the pilaster is acceptable.

It is the responsibility of the utility designers to ensure that adequate climbing space is maintained.

Pilaster Location

When considering a pole and pilaster location, the pole is divided into four quadrants. A preferred location for both the telephone pilaster and the electric utility pilaster is shown in Figure 4-24.

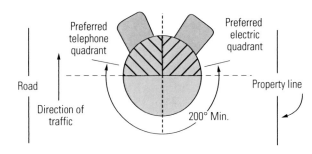

Figure 4-24. Preferred location of pilasters.

The idea is to keep the power cables in the quadrant of the pole that is furthest away from the flow of traffic. This prevents accidents that result in harm to either the cable or the driver of the vehicle.

If the preferred location is not possible, the alternate location is shown in Figure 4-25.

If there is an existing telephone pilaster, the electric utility pilaster must be installed in relation to the existing one, so as not to conflict with the telephone cable training. If possible, install pilaster as shown in Figure 4-26.

The ducts and pilasters usually stop just above grade or ground level.

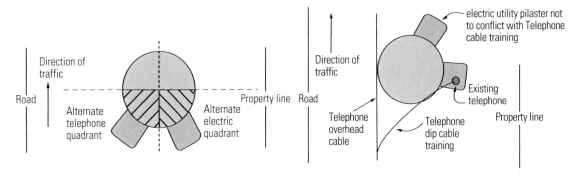

Figure 4-25. Alternate location of pilasters.

Figure 4-26. Location of electric utility pilaster when installed with an existing telephone pilaster.

Cable Protection

All cables on poles must be protected from mechanical damage by vehicles or other objects and must also be protected from probing by a curious public. In general, the lower portion of the cable above the pilaster is encased in a suitable approved plastic or fiberglass cover. In very cold climates, it is advisable to use steel because of the poor low-temperature impact resistance of plastic. The part of the cable above this lower portion is usually covered with a fiberglass cable cover that is firmly lagged to the pole.

Installation Procedures on Wood Poles

To install cable guards and covers on wood poles:

1. Fasten the backing plate to the pole using 2-inch long galvanized nails. Spread the lower ends of extruded type backing plate to adapt to the inside configuration of the cable guards, leaving a gap of approximately 3/8 inch. Fasten the ends to the pole.

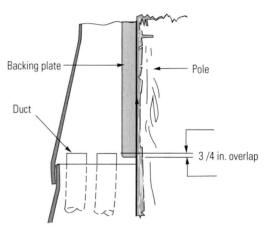

Figure 4-27. Position of backing plate. Side view of bottom of pole.

2. Run the cable(s) up the backing plate and secure it (them) with a cable support grip.

3. Install ground conductor. See Figure 4-29.

4. Install cable guard and fasten it to the pole using 4-inch long lag screw and washers. See Figure 4-29.

5. Install the cable covers and fasten them to the pole using 3-inch long lag screws and supplied neoprene washers in every second hole. See Figure 4-29.

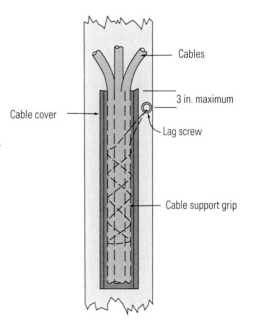

Figure 4-28. Cable support grip used to secure cables.

6. Terminate the cable covers at 6 inches above the line neutral for single-phase and three-phase primary cables. For secondary cables, terminate the cable covers at 2 inches above the neutral level of the secondary rack.

Note: For tape-shielded XLPE feeder cables, two ducts are installed: one for the cables and one for the system neutral. These cables require large guards and large guard to small cover adapters, except on 750 Al kcmil, where a large cover is used all the way to neutral.

Concentric neutral XLPE feeder cables require: one duct, small guard, and small cover.

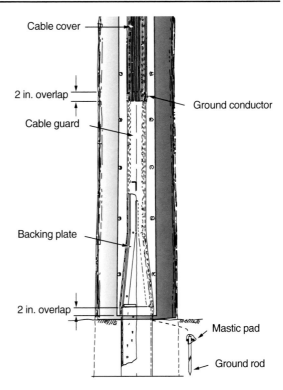

Figure 4-29. Arrangement of cable guard, cable cover and backing plate on a wooden pole.

Installation Procedures on Concrete Poles

To install cable guards and covers on concrete poles.

1. Modify cable protection devices as follows:
   On the backing plate, make 1-inch wide cuts in both flanges at a distance of 1 foot from both ends. These notches will be used to accommodate stainless steel bands.

2. Fasten the backing plate to the pole with stainless steel bands. Position the buckles and clamps on the reverse side of the pole.

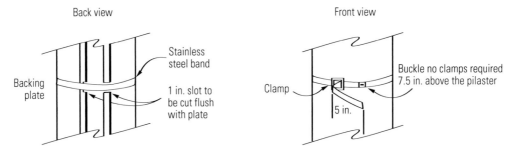

Figure 4-30. Backing plate installation using stainless steel bands. Note notches cut in the side flanges (front view).

3. Run the cable(s) up the backing plate and support it (them) with a cable support grip. There should be a hole located approximately 76 inches from the pole top. If not, use any hole between 104 inches and 122 inches from the top.

4. Install the cable guard and fasten it to the pole using stainless steel bands. Slide the bands under the backing plate then through the notches on the side edges of the guard. Secure the bands on the reverse side of the pole.

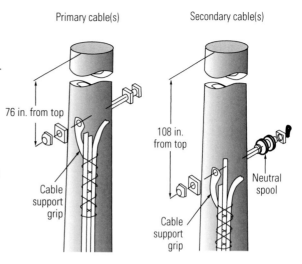

Figure 4-31. Installation of cable support grip.

5. Install the cable covers and fasten them to the pole using stainless steel bands. Repeat procedure used for the guard (Step 4). Use only three bands per cable cover installed over 7.5 feet above the pilaster.

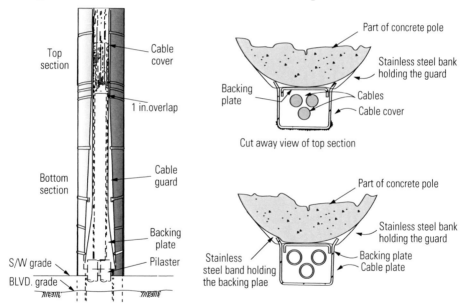

Figure 4-32. Arrangement of backing plate, cable guard and cable cover on a concrete pole.

6. Terminate the cable covers at 6 inches above the line neutral for single-phase and three-phase primary cables. For secondary cables, terminate the covers at 2 inches above the neutral level of the secondary rack.

7. For jointly owned poles, install additional stainless steel bands with buckles and clamps at the following elevations: 4 inches, 93 inches, 152 inches and 211 inches.

SYSTEM | DRAWINGS | MATERIALS | **INSTALLING** | SPLICING | FUSING | MAINTENANCE | TROUBLE | JOB SITE

No holes are to be drilled into concrete poles.

Note: For tape-shielded XLPE feeder cables, two ducts are installed: one for the cables and one for the system neutral. These cables require large guards and large guard to small cover adapters, except on 750 kcmil, where a large cover is used all the way to neutral. Concentric neutral XLPE feeder cables require only one duct, small guard and small covers.

Prepare Underground Apparatus

Introduction

Once the cable has been pulled in, the underground apparatus must be prepared before the cable is spliced and terminated. The underground apparatus is positioned, securely in place and identified with the appropriate markings. Once secured, the apparatus must be prepared for the cable termination and connection. This may involve installing brackets, busbars, bushing well inserts and grounding and bonding of the equipment. This apparatus includes transformers, switchgears, and junction boxes.

Upon successful completion of this section, you will be able to describe and prepare for installation, the various types of underground apparatus.

The topics covered are:

- Standards and specifications

- Preparation of transformers

- Preparation of switchgears

- Preparation of junction boxes

Nameplate Data

Transformer nameplates must contain the following information:

- Name of the manufacturer

- Transformer technical data

- Schematic diagram of the electrical circuits

- Assurance of non-PCB contamination

- Date of manufacture

SYSTEM

DRAWINGS

MATERIALS

INSTALLING

SPLICING

FUSING

MAINTENANCE

TROUBLE

JOB SITE

Preparation of Transformers

There are three steps in preparing a transformer for termination and connection of cables:

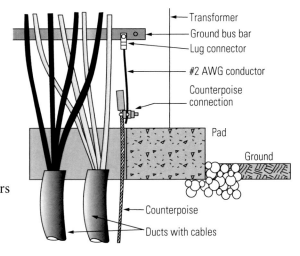

1. Install grounding connections

2. Install bushing well inserts

3. Check fuses

The first step in preparing transformers is to connect the counterpoise to the ground bus bar. Press a "bolt-on lug connector" onto a piece of #2 bare copper wire and connect to the grounding bus. Measure from the

Figure 4-33. Close up showing grounding of counterpoise to the ground busbar.

grounding bus to the counterpoise and cut the #2 bare copper to length. Connect the #2 bare copper to the counterpoise with a U-bolt connector.

Note: If the counterpoise is a copper cable, use a compression tap connector instead of a U-bolt.

The second step is to install the bushing well inserts. These inserts come with a set of instructions that must be reviewed before doing the installation. Basically the inserts (short end) are cleaned with isopropanol, greased with silicone and then screwed, by hand, into the bushing wells located on the front panel of the transformer. Using a bushing insert tool (See Figure 3-41), tighten the inserts to the specified torque (100 inch-lbs). Do not over-tighten, as the stud may break.

Once installed, the bushing well inserts must be bonded. To bond the insert, cut a piece of #14 AWG copper wire (approx. 6 inches in length) and attach one end of it to one of the holes in the insert collar, and attach the other end to one of the metal tabs around the bushing well. Connect the wire by simply twist-tying it.

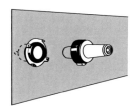

Figure 4-34. Bushing well and bushing well insert on a transformer.

The third step is to check the fuses to ensure that they are ready for operation. Since the transformer is not energized, you can manually pull out the fuse holders and check whether there is a correct-sized and continuous fuse element inside. Depending on the type of fuse, you may be able to confirm the presence of the element by visually looking or you may have to unscrew the end of the bayonet and look inside. If you suspect that the fuse element is not continuous, perform a continuity test. Some transformers have an interlocking device over the fuses, which has to be removed first. This is done by turning the load break switch handle.

The transformer is now ready for the cables to be terminated and connected.

Preparation of Switchgear

To prepare the switchgear for the termination and connection of cables:

1. Install terminator support channel

2. Install ground bus

3. Check fuses

The switchgear sits on a manhole or pit, where the terminator support channel are installed and the preparatory work is done. Before the cables are installed, attach the terminator support channels (using the existing holes in the pit's wall) to the side of the pit closest to the switches.

There are two sides to the switchgear, the side that contains the switches and the side that contains the fuses. The fuse side is used for lateral cables. Also, there are terminator support brackets mounted under the fuse compartment that were installed by the manufacturer.

Next, a ground bus is installed by placing a 4/0 AWG bare copper wire around the perimeter of the pit (close to the top). The copper wire is connected to one of the switchgear's frame clamps and then placed around the pit and connected to the other side of the frame. Using a U-bolt connector, connect both ends of the counterpoise to the ground bus.

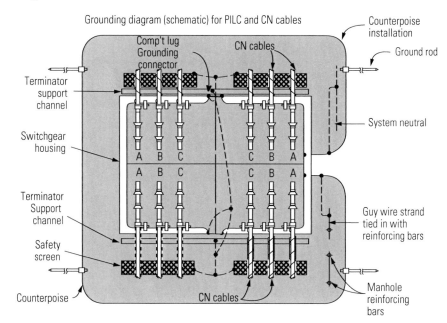

Figure 4-35. Grounding schematic of the switchgear grounding bus.

The last step is to check the fuses to ensure that they are ready for operation. The procedure is the same as that used for checking the fuses in the transformer.

The switchgear is now ready for the cables to be installed and terminated.

Preparation of Junction Boxes

Junction boxes may be below-grade vaults or above-grade kiosks. For explanation purposes, we will call them below-grade and above-grade junction boxes.

The following topics are covered for above grade and below grade junction boxes.

1. Install junction bar (J-bar) brackets.

2. Install junction bars and parking stands.

3. Do bonding and grounding.

4. Install bushing well inserts.

Below-Grade Junction Boxes (JB)

To prepare the below-grade junction boxes for terminations and connection of the cables, the J-bar brackets must be installed. C-channels located near the top of the box in the concrete wall are used for holding the J-bar bracket. The bracket is galvanized and has openings for two bolts in the back. Install the bolts through the bracket and attach a spring nut to each bolt. Turn the nut sideways so it can be installed in the C-channel. After tightening the spring nut, turn the nut to secure it in the C-channel.

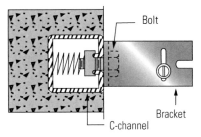

Figure 4-36. J-bar bracket attached to C-channel.

An alternate method of mounting the J-bar is to install the spring nuts into the channel and then put the bolts through the brackets and thread them into the spring nuts. In three-phase installations, three brackets must be installed and evenly spaced across the wall.

The next step is to install the junction bar on the J-bar bracket. Most J-bars come with a parking stand at each end. If not, they must be bolted to the bracket at each end of the J-bar. Each bracket and J-bar must be tilted so the elbows can be easily removed with a shotgun from outside the vault.

The J-bar brackets are bonded with No. 2 AWG copper conductor, bonding one bracket to the next. Compression lugs are crimped onto the end of the conductor and attached to the bracket with the same bolts holding the J-bar or parking stand.

A 2/0 copper conductor is installed on the wall opposite the J-bars to form the ground bus. A compression lug is crimped on each end of the measured conductor and connected to the C-channel with a bolt and spring nut. A clamp is used to support the middle of the conductor.

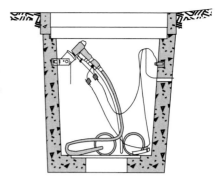

Figure 4-37. Complete J-bar mounting with an elbow in place.

To ground the junction box, connect the No. 2 AWG copper conductor (that extends from the ground rod through the concrete wall into the junction box) to the ground bus with a compression tap connector. See Figure 4-38.

The J-bar bracket assembly must be bonded to the ground bus on each side of the junction box. Two measured lengths of No. 2 copper with crimped lug connectors are attached to the
J-bar bracket and the ground bus. This procedure is performed at each end of the bracket (vault).

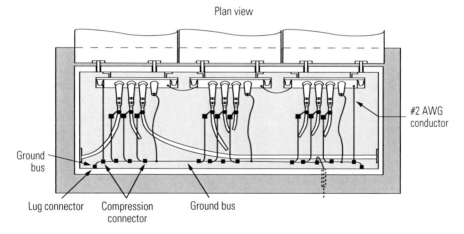

Figure 4-38. Grounding and bonding of the below-grade junction box, viewed from the top.

The next step is to install and bond the bushing well inserts. (Some J-bars come equipped with the integrated bushings, making this step unnecessary.) The inserts come with manufacturer's instructions which should be reviewed before installing the inserts. Grease the short end of the insert and then manually screw it into the bushing well on the junction bar. Using a torque wrench, tighten the inserts to the specified torque. The bushing well inserts are bonded to the bushing wells with a piece of No. 14 copper wire.

Above-Grade Junction Kiosks (JK)

To prepare the above-grade junction kiosks for termination and connection of cables:

1. Install grounding by connecting the counterpoise

2. Install the junction bar

3. Install bonding by connecting bonding conductors

The first step is to connect the counterpoise to the kiosk ground bus with a U-bolt connector.

Next, install the J-bar. Using two hose clamps, fasten the J-bar to the channels that are already present in the kiosk. The clamps should fit snugly around the junction bar and the steel channel. Wood wedges can be used to adjust the angle of the J-bar for proper hot stick operation.

To bond the junction bar to the ground bus, measure and cut a length of No. 2 copper conductor (bonding conductor) to reach from the J-bar to the ground bus. On one end of the bonding conductor, crimp on a compression lug and connect to the junction bar with a nut and bolt. On the other end of the bonding conductor, use a compression tap connector and crimp it to the ground bus.

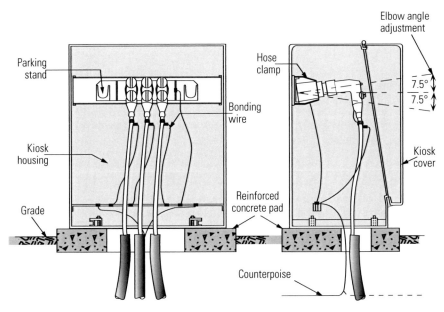

Figure 4-39. Above-ground junction kiosk with junction bar and grounding connections.

The junction kiosks (both types) are now ready for the cables to be terminated and connected.

Install Underground Apparatus

Introduction

This section covers the initial installation or placement of transformers, switchgear and junction boxes. To install apparatus, means to position the apparatus and secure it in place.

Upon successful completion of this section, you will be able to identify and install the various types of underground apparatus.

The topics covered are:

- Low profile transformers (LPT), single-phase
- Three-phase, padmount transformer, deadfront, deadbreak (PMDFT)
- Transformer design
- Install or place the transformer
- Switchgear
- Install switchgear
- Junction box
- Install junction boxes
- Markings

Low Profile Transformers (LPT), Single Phase

Commonly used low profile transformers are 37-1/2, 75, and 100 kVA. These units have dead-front, load break elbows on the primary connections. Deadfront means that the exposed primary connections are at ground potential. The primary is fed through a 200 amp primary bus inside the transformer, terminating on two bushing wells. Bushing inserts are screwed into the wells and the elbows connect to the inserts. These elbows are designed to be operated under load (200 amps maximum) to make and break connections. Although the manufacturer says Bay-O-Net Fuses can break load, it is not the practice of most utilities to break load with padmounted transformer fuses. New transformers have a decal, "Do Not De-energize with Fuse." You must first de-energize the transformer by standing off the elbows or by opening the primary switch.

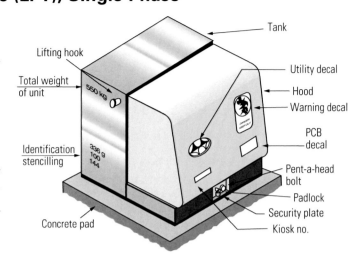

Figure 4-40. Typical single phase radial feed padmount transformer. This is a low profile transformer (LPT).

Three-Phase, Padmount Transformer, Deadfront, Deadbreak (PMDFT)

Most of these units are intended to be radial-fed, although there are some that have an extra set of bushing wells similar to a LPT, for a loop feed to another transformer. They also have hot-stick-operable load break switches to de-energize the transformer on the secondary coils.

Padmount transformers usually have a load break switch. Bayonet type or dry type fuses must not be pulled when the transformer is energized. The following procedure should be followed:

1. Break load (stand to side)

2. Check secondaries (back feed)

3. Remove fuses after tests show that the transformer is de-energized

The three-phase, padmount transformer has a transformer tank and cable compartment built as a unit with hinged doors for access to high and low voltage bushings. The unit is sized from 75 to 1000 kVA. It is oil immersed and air cooled.

The transformer is completely weatherproof, tamperproof, and self-contained. The hinged doors are designed to provide maximum access and can be secured in either a 90° or a 120° open position. The doors are bonded to the cable

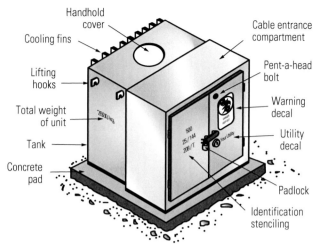

Figure 4-41. Three phase, padmount, deadfront transformer.

enclosures by a strap. They have a single padlocking feature so that high-voltage doors cannot be opened without opening the low-voltage doors. In addition, a special safety screw, called a penta bolt, locks both doors.

The three phase unit is equipped with the following features:

- Emergency knockouts

- Lifting lugs

- A hand hole cover with a built-in automatic relief valve

- An external off-load tap changer with four 2.5% taps located on the front part of the transformer. Two taps are full capacity above normal (FCAN) and two are reduced capacity below normal (RCBN). Provisions for locking in each position is provided.

- The transformer is protected by three externally accessible, oil-immersed, load-break and load-sensing isolating links.

- A manual pressure relief valve which must be operated prior to drawing out the bayonet fuse holder

- Oil level gauge

- Thermometer

- Oil spill tray pan with drain

- Three oil immersed, group-operated switches (two for loop feed and one for the transformer). The switches are rated 23 kV, 125 kV BIL, 200 amp continuous and interrupting with 9000 amps on momentary close and hold. The switch compartment is connected to the main tank by two filters to reduce contamination migration.

Transformer Design

The three-phase padmount transformer has six clamp type, high voltage bushing wells which accept dead break bushing inserts. It also has six parking stands for dead break accessories. The ground (H_0) comes out of the primary compartment through a bushing. The compression lugs are connected to the four low-voltage bushings with spade-type terminals.

The ground bus extends through the high voltage and the low voltage compartments located on the front of the tank at the top of the sill. The H_0 and X_0 bushings are solidly grounded by a grounding strap to a short ground bus extending into each compartment. It is then connected to the main ground bus located at the bottom of the transformer. The figure below shows the general layout and wiring details of a three-phase padmount deadfront transformer.

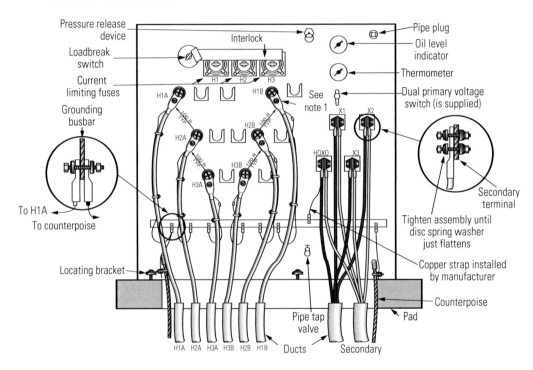

Figure 4-42. General layout and wiring of a three-phase padmount deadfront transformer.

Installation of Transformers

Before a transformer is installed, the following work is usually done by the customer's contractor. For this example, we will explain the steps based on the installation of a low profile transformer.

The transformer support box must be installed below grade as a base for the transformer.

After the concrete lid is installed on the transformer support box, the box must be grounded. This is accomplished by connecting two 3/4 inch × 10 foot ground rods with bare copper counterpoise to form a continuous ground around the box. The primary function of this is to reduce the touch potential under fault conditions and to reduce step potential. The placement of the rods are to provide protection for personnel driving the rods through other utility lines, such as television or telephone. The 2/0 bare copper is connected from the ground rod to the box. It is also connected to itself using a 2/0-2/0 copper ampacts. Figure 4-43 shows the final result of the work that is usually performed by a contractor.

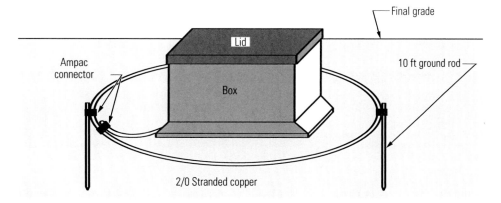

Figure 4-43. Padmount grounding.

To install the transformer on the padmount:

1. Use proper hoisting techniques to lift the transformer

2. Align and level the transformer for ease of operation on the platform provided

3. Secure it to the padmount using bolts

The transformer is now in place and ready for cable installation and termination

The distribution transformer should be handled with care as bushings and other equipment on the transformer can be easily damaged. The windings of the transformer may be damaged if the transformer is dropped or severely jolted.

Switchgear

A switch is used to disconnect (open) or connect (close) circuits. High voltage switches are operated remotely or with a live line tool.

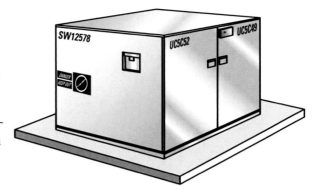

Switches for underground distribution circuits are usually installed in padmounted switchgear. The switches are operated with the cabinet doors closed to provide protection for the lineworker.

Figure 4-44. Switchgear unit shown is a S&C padmounted switchgear called a MKII.

Some underground systems use S&C padmounted switchgear units which are commonly referred to as MK II's. These are composed of two mini-rupter, 600 amp, loadbreak switches (incoming feed) and two 200 amp outgoing feeds protected by sectionalizing fuses. This type of switchgear can be ordered with any combination of mini-rupter switches and/or sectionalizing fuses. The fuses can be opened under load by using the S&C load buster tool.

These units are used for:

- Sectionalizing and protection of distribution feeders and laterals

- Switching and protection of individual single phase and three phase transformers

Install Switchgear

Before the switchgear can be installed, the customer's contractor must install a platform, a cement pad or a manhole, on which the switchgear is placed.

To install the switchgear:

1. Use proper hoisting techniques to lift the switchgear

2. Align and level the switchgear for ease of operation on the platform provided

3. Secure it to the platform using bolts

4. Remove the lift tabs

The switchgear is now in place and ready for cable installation and termination.

Junction Box

A junction is the place where lines come together or cross. Junction boxes are either steel kiosks situated on padmounts (above grade) or underground vaults. Both the kiosks and the vaults contain junction racks into which load break elbows are inserted. These junction bars provide loadbreak switching up to 200 amps. Their only drawback is on three phase, where loads are dropped one phase at a time.

Junctions boxes usually feed a transformer and provide a switching point to allow the isolation of a line or section of cable. Since they are less expensive, they are sometimes used in place of the MK II switchgear.

Install Junction Boxes

Before a junction box can be installed, the customer's contractor must install either a platform on which the junction box is placed or a junction vault (underground). If a platform is installed, the contractor must also install perimeter grounding around the platform. This grounding reduces step-and-touch potential under fault conditions.

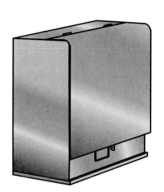

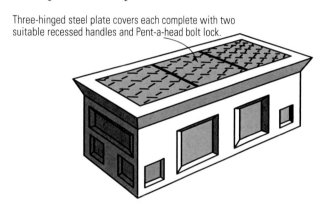

Three-hinged steel plate covers each complete with two suitable recessed handles and Pent-a-head bolt lock.

Figure 4-45. Above-grade junction box.   **Figure 4-46. Underground junction vault.**

To install the junction box on a platform:

1. Use proper hoisting techniques to lift the junction box.

2. Align and level the junction box for ease of operation on the platform provided.

3. Secure it to the platform using bolts.

The junction box is now in place and ready for cable installation and termination.

In the case of a junction vaults, the civil contractor installs the vault underground. The ducts are complete with the pull strings installed. It is now ready for cable installation and termination.

Markings

Every transformer, switchgear and junction box is marked to identify the apparatus in the system and to warn the public of high voltage danger.

These makings can be placed on the apparatus after they have been installed (positioned and secured) or after the cable has been pulled, spliced and terminated. Normally, the lineworker applies the markings to the apparatus after the rest of the cable installation job has been completed.

The markings applied to a transformer, switchgear and junction box are:

* Warning decal indicating high voltage

* Decal indicating property of the electric utility

* Kiosk number

* Cable ID

The kiosk number is obtained from the work order on the construction drawing. Figure 4-47 shows the arrangement of the markings on a transformer.

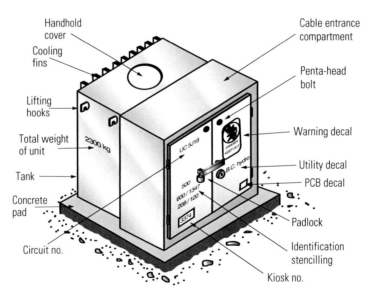

Figure 4-47. Markings on a transformer.

Other markings on the apparatus were applied by the manufacturer. These include weight, voltage and size.

The transformer should already have a PCB inspection decal on it, which indicates that it has been checked for PCBs and has been deemed to be acceptable for use. If there is no PCB decal on the transformer, it must not be used.

CHAPTER

SPLICE, TERMINATE CABLES

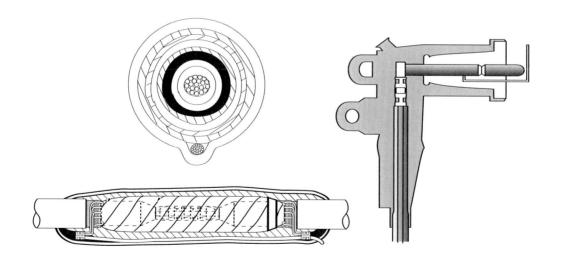

SYSTEM

DRAWINGS

MATERIALS

INSTALLING

SPLICING

FUSING

MAINTENANCE

TROUBLE

JOB SITE

CHAPTER 5 – Splice, Terminate Cables

SYSTEM
DRAWINGS
MATERIALS
INSTALLING
SPLICING
FUSING
MAINTENANCE
TROUBLE
JOB SITE

Splice XLPE Feeder Cables

Introduction

The procedures for splicing and terminating XLPE feeder cables are similar to the splicing procedures for primary underground cables. The main differences between primary underground cables and feeder cables is, most feeder cables originate from a substation and connect to primary overhead lines and underground cables. Since they originate from a substation and paralleling with other circuits may be required, correct phasing is extremely important. Underground cables come in sizes up to 4/0 AWG (212 kcmil). XLPE feeder cables typically come in two sizes, 500 kcmil and 750 kcmil (15 and 25 kV). Feeder cables can have either concentric neutrals or copper tape-shielded neutrals.

The topics covered here are:

- Tools and materials

- Splice XLPE feeder cable

- Terminate XLPE feeder cable using a heat shrink terminator

- Mount the terminator

- Terminate XLPE feeder cable using an elbow

- Bond the cable

- Energize feeder cables

Tools and Materials

The type of kit used when splicing or terminating an XLPE feeder cable depends on the job being done, the type of cable, and the size of cable being spliced or terminated. Each has specific instructions for the components in them. Always check the kit to ensure that all the components and instructions are present.

The tools and materials needed to splice or terminate a XLPE feeder cable are the same as those used to splice and terminate primary underground distribution cables. The one exception is the power connector, which is a new type of connector that gives a better connection. It is not a compression connector that is crimped, but is heavier and contains solder. It is installed and then heated to release all the solder to ensure that no voids exist. Its correct application is extremely important to the success of the job.

Raychem XLPE Feeder Cable Heat Shrinkable Splice

Before starting any splicing job:

- Ensure that the appropriate isolation and grounding procedures have been followed.

- Prepare the work area.

- Visually inspect the kit components.

- Read the manufacturer's instructions to familiarize yourself with the splice.

- Make sure that the proper tools are on hand and that cleanliness is observed throughout the procedure.

The steps to follow when doing a heat shrinkable 25 kV copper *tape-shielded* XLPE feeder cable splice are:

1. Straighten the cables and train them to their final positions. Using a cable cutter or power hacksaw, cut the cables so the ends of the conductors meet. Clean the cable jacket and slide on all the heat shrinkable tubing. See Figure 5-1.

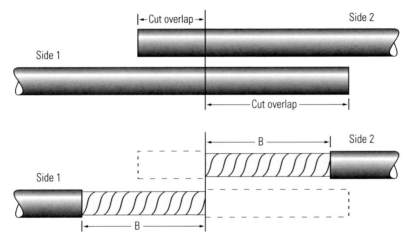

Figure 5-1. Steps 1-2, determining centerline, cutting cable, and removing jacket.

2. Using a skinning knife, remove the jacket and any bedding material on Sides 1 and 2 to dimension B.

Note: The kit contains the instructions and measurements required for each splice. The measurements depend on the cable size and kit being used. See Figure 5-2 for an example of the dimensions required for this splice.

Kit Number	Conductor Size	Jacket Cutback (B)	Semicon Cutback (C)	Connector	Insulation Cutback (D)
SMOC 1270	500 kcmil, 15 kV	10 in	5-1/8 in.	ATC-400	3 in.
SMOC 1270	750 kcmil, 15 kV	10 in	5-1/2 in.	ATC-600	3-3/8 in.
SMOC 1270	500 kcmil, 25 kV	10-5/8 in	6-1/4 in.	ATC-400	3 in.
SMOC 1270	750 kcmil, 25 kV	10-5/8 in	6-5/8 in.	ATC-600	3-3/8 in.

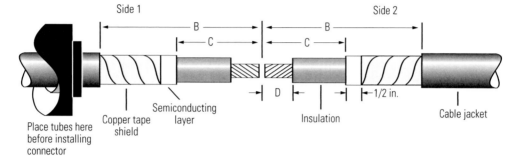

Figure 5-2. Steps 2-6, dimensions for copper shield, semi-con, and insulator removal.

3. Remove the copper tape shield to dimension C plus 1/2 inch. Secure the copper tape with the adhesive-backed copper tape supplied with the kit.

4. Remove the cable semi-con to dimension C. When removing the semi-con, make a clean cut with no jagged edges. Do not nick or cut the cable insulation.

5. Remove cable insulation to dimension D. These dimensions include the allowance for the offset and the required gap needed for the power connector (power sleeve). Do not nick the conductor.

6. Clean the cable jacket for 30 inches on the side where you will store the shrinkable tubes. Slide all heat shrinkable splice tubes onto the cable.

7. Prepare conductors for the connector. On compact conductors, loosen the strands slightly with pliers to help with solder penetration. Immediately before putting on the connector, wire brush the aluminum conductors.

8. Bend both cable ends up. Push or tap the connector (power sleeve) onto one cable end. Insert the second cable end and push down until the splice is straight. Ensure that the second cable end bottoms out (hits against the inside section of the connector).

9. Apply fireclay (solder-retention compound) to both ends of the connector (fireclay is in a sealed bag in the kit). Do this by pinching off small pieces of the fireclay and pushing it tightly into the opening all around both ends of the connector (use your fingertip). Don't leave any holes or gaps.

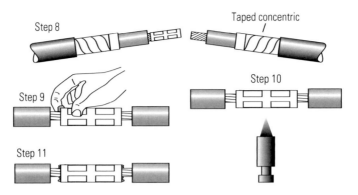

Figure 5-3. Steps 8-11, installing a power sleeve (connector).

10. Heat the connector with a torch to activate the solder. Point the flame at the center (middle) of the connector.

11. For aluminum conductors, heat until 5 to 10 drops of solder drip down. Observe both ends of the connector. As soon as solder appears at one end, move the torch toward the other end. Continue heating until solder appears at that end, then stop heating.

12. Let the connection cool for about one minute without disturbance. This will allow the solder to set. After one minute, the cooling can be accelerated by wrapping a wet cloth around the connection.

13. Once cooled, chip off all of the fireclay. Check connector and remove any rough spots with aluminum oxide cloth.

14. Clean the insulation with an aluminum oxide cloth to remove all traces of semi-conducting shield. Solvent clean the insulation surface. Always wipe from the cable end toward the semi-con.

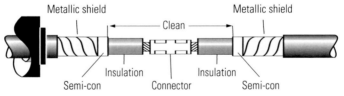

Figure 5-4. Step 14, cleaning.

15. Apply stress relief material (SRM), also referred to as mastic. Remove the release paper from the short angle-cut piece of SRM and place 3 to 4 tight wraps at each semi-con cutback. The SRM must be tapered to overlap the semi-con and the insulation by approximately 1/4 inch. Note that the kit usually contains more SRM than required.

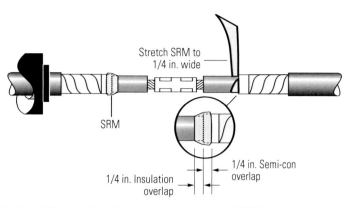

Figure 5-5. Step 15, applying short angle-cut piece of SRM.

16. Now remove the release paper from one side of the long strip of SRM and roll into a convenient size. Using half-laps, tightly wrap the SRM around the connector, filling all voids.

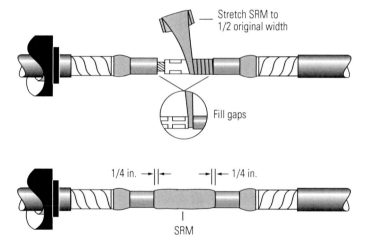

Figure 5-6. Steps 16-17, splice with stress material applied.

17. Tightly fill all gaps with the SRM up to the level of the cable insulation. The SRM should overlap onto the cable insulation at least 1/4 inch but not more than 1/2 inch.

18. Center the stress control tube over the connector. Do not touch the SRM with the inside of the tube, as it might adhere to it. Using a propane torch, begin shrinking at the center of the tube. With a smooth brushing motion, move the torch around the entire circumference of the tube. See Figure 5-7. After the center portion shrinks, move the torch towards one end to shrink it and then to the opposite end. Do not point the flame at the semi-con layer.

Note: Some of the kits (older ones) may contain an insulating tube. If the kit you are using has one, center it over the stress control tube. Shrink it down following the procedure used to shrink the stress control tube.

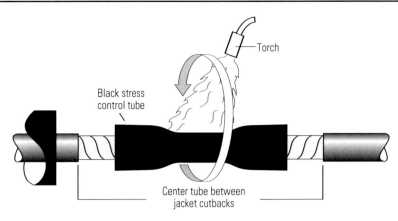

Figure 5-7. Step 18, heating shrink tube.

19. Apply the sealant strip, also referred to as mastic. Remove the release paper from the sealant strip and place two wraps around the cable. These wraps must be butted up against the edge at each end of the stress control tube.

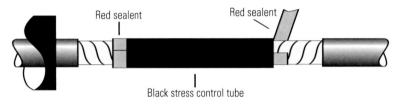

Figure 5-8. Step 19, applying the mastic.

20. Center the dual layer insulating/shielding tubing over the splice area. Using a torch, shrink the tubing starting at the center. Shrink toward one end and stop approximately 3 inches from the end of the tubing. Do the same at the other end, then finish shrinking the first end. Repeat for the second end. Post-heat the tubing for 45 seconds.

Note: Steps 21-22 apply when splicing two ends of copper tape-shielded XLPE feeder cable, using an external braid. For other grounding options refer to the section on grounding braids located after the next splice.

21. The kit contains a bonding braid with a solder or moisture block area close to one end. The solder block is preformed to follow the contours of the outside of the cable.

   Using the GCA ground clamp spring, attach the moisture-blocked braid to the copper tape shield. Flare the end of the braid that is farthest from the moisture block and butt it up against the installed splice tubes on one side of the splice. Apply two wraps of the spring clamp over the braid close to the cable jacket. Fold the braid back over the spring clamp and wrap the remainder of the spring clamp over the braid.

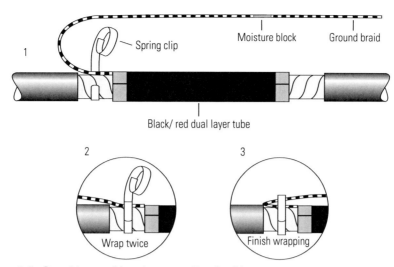

Figure 5-9. Step 21, attaching the grounding braid.

With your fingers, tighten the clamp over the braid, then secure it with a small piece of the copper foil tape (supplied). Run the braid lengthwise along the splice towards the other end, and secure the braid to the copper tape shield in a similar fashion to the first end. A piece or tail of the braid will remain (containing the moisture block). It will be used for bonding.

22. Build a waterstop by wrapping two wraps of sealant (mastic) over the cable jacket directly underneath the moisture-blocked portion of the braid. Place the braid over the sealant and wrap an additional two wraps of sealant over the moisture-blocked portion so that it is totally embedded in and covered by the sealant.

23. Center the overall rejacketing tubing over the splice. Ensure that the tail of the bonding braid extends outside the tubing. Shrink the sleeve beginning in the center, and work towards one end then the other. Continue to heat until a bead of the hot-melt adhesive forms at each end of the tubing.

Note: Look for dimples in the tube. Hot melt appears long before the tube is completely shrunk. The tail of the bonding braid will be used to bond the splice.

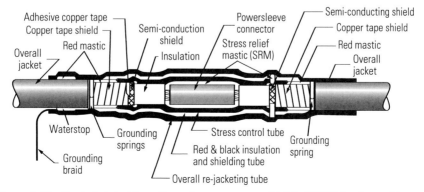

Figure 5-10. Heat shrinkable splice of copper tape-shielded XLPE feeder cable.

Raychem Extruded Dielectric XLPE/EPR Feeder Cable Splice (Kit No. SMOC 1272)

Before starting any splicing job:

- Ensure that the appropriate isolation and grounding procedures have been followed.

- Prepare the work area.

- Visually inspect the kit components.

- Read the manufacturer's instructions to familiarize yourself with the splice.

- Make sure that the proper tools are on hand and that cleanliness is observed throughout the procedure.

The steps to follow when doing a heat shrinkable 500 kcmil 25 kV copper *tape-shielded/concentric neutral* XLPE feeder cable splice are:

Note: Concentric and metallic tape are explained at the end of these instructions.

1. Straighten the cables and train them to their final positions. Using a cable cutter or power hacksaw, cut the cables so the ends of the conductors meet. Clean the cable jacket and slide on all the heat shrinkable tubing. See Figure 5-11.

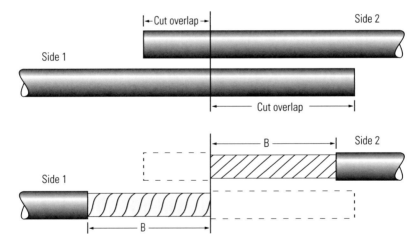

Figure 5-11. Determining centerline, folding neutral strands and cutting cable.

2. Remove the jacket 10-5/8 inches to dimension B as specified in the manufacturer's instructions for a 500 kcmil/25 kV cable.

Note: The kit contains the instructions and measurements required for each splice. The measurements depend on the cable size and kit being used. See Figure 5-12 for an example of the dimensions required for this splice.

Kit Number	Conductor Size	Jacket Cutback (B)	Semicon Cutback (C)	Connector	Insulation Cutback (D)
SMOC 1270	500 kcmil, 15 kV	10 in	5-1/8 in.	ATC-400	3 in.
SMOC 1270	750 kcmil, 15 kV	10 in	5-1/2 in.	ATC-600	3-3/8 in.
SMOC 1270	500 kcmil, 25 kV	10-5/8 in	6-1/4 in.	ATC-400	3 in.
SMOC 1270	750 kcmil, 25 kV	10-5/8 in	6-5/8 in.	ATC-600	3-3/8 in.

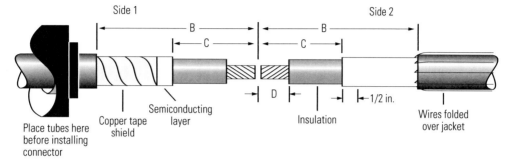

Figure 5-12. Steps 2-7, dimensions for jacket, metal shield, semi-con, and insulator removal.

3. Remove the copper tape shield 6-3/4 inches to dimension C plus 1/2 inch. Secure the copper tape with the adhesive-backed copper tape supplied with the kit. Fold the concentric neutral back over the jacket.

4. Remove the semi-con 6-1/4 inches to dimension C. When removing the semi-con, make a clean cut with no jagged edges and don't nick the conductor.

5. Remove the insulation 3 inches to dimension D.

6. Abrade the insulation as necessary to remove imbedded semi-con. Clean the insulation, wiping toward the semi-con.

7. Clean the cable jacket for 30 inches on the side where you will store the shrinkable tubes. Slide all heat shrinkable splice tubes onto the cable.

8. Install the connector on the conductor and press with the appropriate die. Remove excess inhibitor from the connector and file off any sharp ridges. Clean the insulation with an aluminum oxide cloth to remove all traces of semi-conducting shield and solvent-clean the insulation surface. Always wipe from the cable end towards the semi-con.

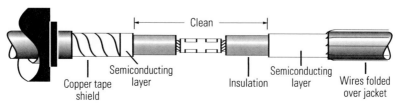

Figure 5-13. Step 8, install connector and clean.

9. Remove the backing from the short angle-cut piece of SRM. Place the tip of the SRM at the semi-con cut back and tightly wrap to fill semi-con step. Overlap semi-con and insulation and taper SRM down to meet the insulation.

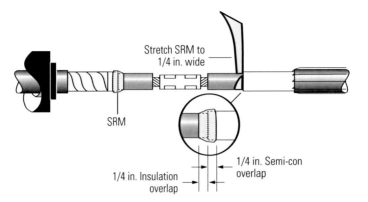

Figure 5-14. Step 9, applying short pieces of stress relief material.

10. Remove the release paper from one side of the long strip of SRM and roll into a convenient size. Remove the remaining backing strip and tightly wrap the SRM around the connector and exposed conductor, filling the gaps and low spots around the connector.

11. Tightly fill all gaps with the SRM up to the level of the cable insulation. The SRM should overlap onto the cleaned insulation at least 1/4 inch but not more than 1/2 inch. Discard any excess SRM (long strips).

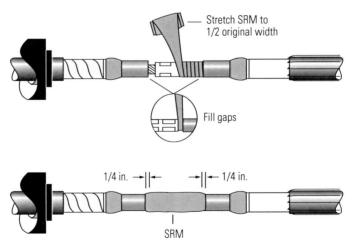

Figure 5-15. Steps 10-11, applying long piece of SRM over connector.

Note: Do not over apply. The finished SRM should only be slightly larger than the cable insulation.

CHAPTER 5 – Splice, Terminate Cables

SYSTEM

DRAWINGS

MATERIALS

INSTALLING

SPLICING

FUSING

MAINTENANCE

TROUBLE

JOB SITE

12. Center the black stress control tube over the connector. Begin shrinking at the center of the tube, working the torch with a smooth brushing motion around the tube. After center portion shrinks, work the torch towards one end, then towards the opposite end. Apply sufficient heat to ensure softening of the SRM, indicated by a smooth surface profile.

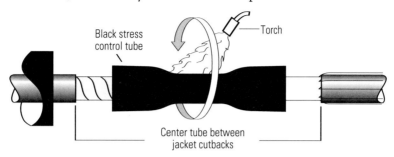

Figure 5-16. Step 12, heating the stress control tube.

13. Remove backing from the red sealant. Using light tension, wrap the sealant over the cable butted against the tube. Build the sealant to the level of the black stress control tube.

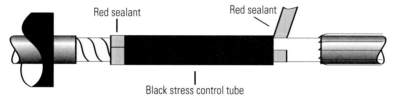

Figure 5-17. Step 13, wrapping the sealant.

14. Center the black/red dual layer tube over the previously shrunk tube. Begin shrinking at the center of the tube, working the torch around all sides of the tube. Before moving away from the center, make sure that the tube has fully shrunk onto the underlying tube, by twisting gently and feeling for resistance.

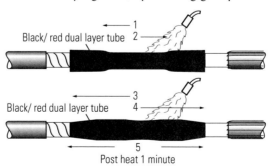

Figure 5-18. Step 14, shrinking the black/red dual layer tube.

Note: The dual layer tube requires more heating time, especially the underside and hard to reach parts. The ridges should be completely smooth. Post heat the entire tube for one minute after fully shrunk to ensure tube is completely recovered.

Note: Step 15 applies when splicing copper tape-shielded XLPE feeder cable to concentric neutral feeder cable using an internal braid. For other grounding options refer to the section on grounding braids located after this splice.

15. Connecting the ground braid internaly between the copper tape and the concentric neutral.

    1. Flare the end of the ground braid and place onto the metallic tape butted up to the installed splice tubes.

    2. Attach the braid to the metallic tape by placing two wraps of the spring clamp over the braid.

    3. Fold the braid back over the spring clamp wraps. Continue to wrap the remaining clamp over the braid. Tighten the clamp by twisting it in the direction it's wrapped and secure with the copper foil tape provided. Lay the ground braid across the splice tube.

    4. Pigtail the concentric neutral and crimp the ground braid to the pigtail with a suitable connector.

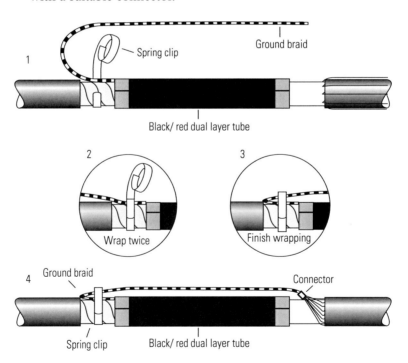

Figure 5-19. Step 15, connecting the ground braid.

16. Remove or tape over all sharp points to prevent puncture of the wrap around sleeve. Remove backing from the wraparound sleeve and center sleeve over the splice. Slide metal channels onto the butter rails. If external grounding, ensure the end or tail of the braid extends outside the sleeve.

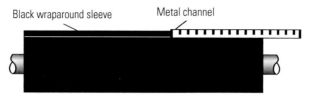

Figure 5-20. Step 16, applying the wraparound sleeve.

17. If two channels are needed, connect the channels with the short channel retention clip. Use pliers to install the clip. Channels must overlap sleeve edge by 1/4 inch minimum.

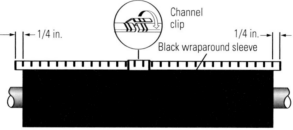

Figure 5-21. Step 17, applying the channel retention clip.

18. Using a torch, preheat evenly along both sides of the rails/channel area until this area begins to shrink. Begin shrinking the wraparound sleeve at the center and working towards the ends. Apply heat until the sleeve is fully shrunk and the heat-sensitive paint is completely converted. Post heat the entire sleeve, concentrating on the metal channel area, for 30 seconds after the sleeve has completely shrunk.

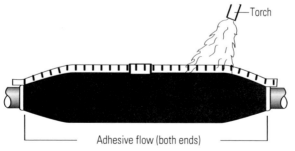

Figure 5-22. Step 18, heating the wraparound sleeve.

19. Allow the splice to cool before moving or placing in service.

Install Ground

The procedure you chose will depend on the types of cables you are joining and if you need an internal or external grounding braid. The exact procedure may varey depending on the kit you are using. Always refer to your kits instructions befor installing the braid. After installing the braid follow the previous examples and finish the splice. following the instructions of your particular kit.

Internal ground braid installation

Metalic tape — metalic tape:

1. Flare one end of the ground braid and place it onto the metallic tape shield butted up to the installed splice tubes.

2. Attach the braid to the metalic shield by placing two wraps of the spring clamp over the braid.

3. Fold the braid back over the spring clamp wraps. Continue to wrap the remaining clamp over the braid. Tighten clamp by twisting it in the direction it is wrapped and secure with copper foil tape provided.

4. Lay the braid across the splice tube and onto the exposed tape shield on the other side.

5. Wrap the clamp twice over the braid. Fold the remaining braid back over the clamp and finish wrapping the clamparound it. Tighten and secure the clamp with copper foil tape.

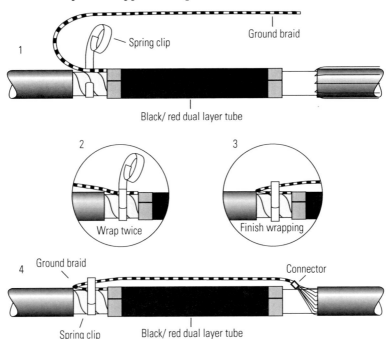

Figure 5-23. Metalic tape — metalic tape, internal ground braid.

Metalic tape — concentric neutral:

1. Perform steps 1-3 as above for attaching the braid to the metalic tape shield.

2. Pigtail the concentric neutral wires.

3. Lay the braid accross the splice tubes and crimp it to the pigtail with the appropriate connector. Trim the pigtailed wires.

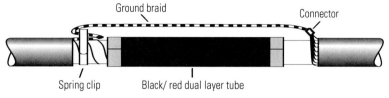

Figure 5-24. Metalic tape — concentric neutral, internal ground braid.

Concentric neutral — concentric neutral:

1. Pigtail the neutral wires on each side.

2. Crimp the ground braid onto one pigtail with with the appropriate connector.

3. Lay the braid across the splice tubes and attach it to the pigtail on the other side with the appropriate connector. Trim the pigtailed wires.

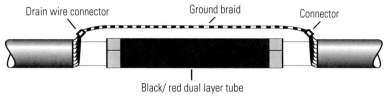

Figure 5-25. Metalic tape — concentric neutral, internal ground braid.

External ground braid installation

Kits for external grounding contain a bonding braid with a solder or moisture block area close to one end. The solder block is preformed to follow the contours of thecable.

1. First consider the type of cables you will be grounding and choose the appropriate procedure for attaching the braid from the internal procedures above.

2. If atleast one of your cables has a tape shiled, it is easiest to attach the braid to this cable first. Start with the end of the braid furthest from the moisture block and attach both ends in the manner described above.

3. Train the remaining braid over the cable jacket. Place two wraps of red sealing mastic over the cable jacket directly under the moisture block. Lay the braid over the mastic, and wrap twice more with the sealing mastic.

Wye Splice

Note: This procedure makes use of the 30MA and 31MA grounding devices. If these devices are not used, a waterstop must be made after the wye splice module has been installed.

Splice Cable With Metallic Tape Shield

1. Train the cable ends and straighten them in their final position. Measure so the cables are 15 inches apart and cut the ends square. Wipe the outer jacket clean for a distance of 38 inches.

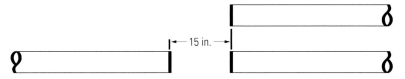

Figure 5-26. Step 1, measure and cut.

Note: Steps 2-13 should be performed on all three cable ends and in the same order as presented.

2. Apply the supplied lubricant or Elastimold approved lubricant to the inside of the 30MA grounding device. Slide the grounding device onto the cable 38 inches. This procedure and following procedures are done for each cable.

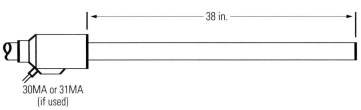

Figure 5-27. Step 2, lubricate and apply grounding device.

3. Slide the receptacle housing onto the cable a distance of 30 inches.

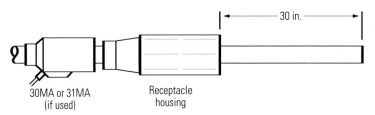

Figure 5-28. Step 3, apply housing.

4. From the end of the cable, measure 12-7/8 inches and carefully remove the outer jacket, leaving a clean straight edge. Do not cut or damage the tape shield.

5. Measure 10-7/8 inches and remove the tape shield. Wrap two turns of tape over the end of the tape shield, with the edge of the tape 1-3/4 inches from the end of the outer jacket. The tape serves as a marker and retainer to keep tape shield in place.

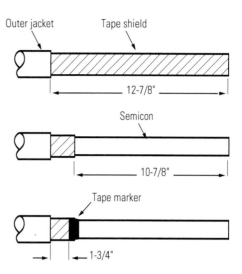

Figure 5-29a. Steps 4, 5.

6. Measure 10-1/8 inches and remove the semi-con with a straight, smooth, squared cut. Do not nick or cut the insulation. Bevel the insulation 1/4 inch from the end.

7. Thoroughly clean the insulation with an aluminum oxide cloth to remove all traces of semi-conducting shield. Solvent-clean the insulation surface. Always wipe from the cable end towards the semi-con.

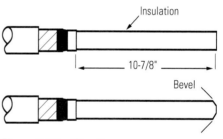

Figure 5-29b. Step 6.

8. Apply the supplied lubricant or approved Elastimold lubricant sparingly to the cable as shown and to the inside of the adapter. Slide the adapter, small end first, over the cable with a twisting motion until the end of the adapter is flush with the end of the tape marker.

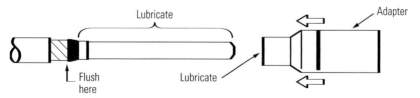

Figure 5-30. Step 8.

9. Select the aluminum holding collar and thread the proper size set-screws part way in. Position the holding collar over the insulation and flush against the cable adapter. Using the enclosed hex wrench, tighten each set-screws one or two turns at a time to keep the collar centered over the insulation. Continue to tighten the set-screws until they are below the surface of the collar.

SYSTEM | DRAWINGS | MATERIALS | INSTALLING | **SPLICING** | FUSING | MAINTENANCE | TROUBLE | JOB SITE

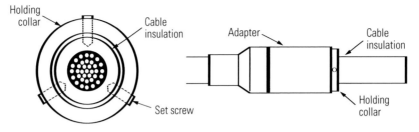

Figure 5-31. Step 9.

10. Measure the inside of the crimp connector plus 1/2 inch for expansion. Apply this measurement and remove the insulation. Do not nick or cut the conductor. The measurement should be between 4-5/16 inches to 4-5/8 inches max.

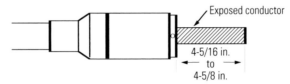

Figure 5-32. Step 10.

11. Remove the protective cap from the crimp connector and insert the conductor into the crimp connector (if using aluminum conductor, brush with inhibitor). Make sure the crimp connector is fully seated.

Note: Take a preliminary measurement from the end of the crimp connector to the aluminum collar. The measurement should not exceed 7-1/8 inches.

Repeat the above steps for the remaining cables to be joined.

12. Before crimping the crimp connector, a final check should be made. All components on all three cable should be positioned as shown.

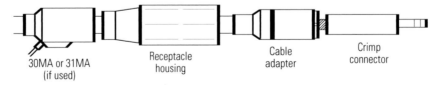

Figure 5-33. Step 12.

Note: Check that the bolt holes in the crimp connectors are positioned properly to align with the bolt holes in the wye section of the splice.

13. Crimp the connector, rotating the Burndy MD-6 tool 90° after each crimp.

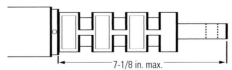

Figure 5-34. Step 13.

Note: After crimping, measure the distance from the end of the connector to the aluminum holding collar. If the distance is over 7-1/8 inches do not proceed. Recheck all previous work.

14. Position the wye section between the cables and assemble the washers as shown. The flat washer should be against the spade contact and the bevel washers next the the bolt head. After the cables are in their final position and hand tightened, do not attempt to move or reposition any part of the assembly. Using a torque wrench, tighten all bolts from 50 to 60 feet-pounds.

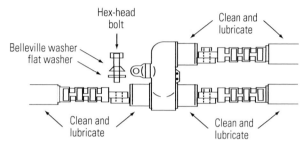

Figure 5-35. Step 14, assemble the wye.

15. Apply the supplied lubricant or Elastimold approved lubricant generously to the outside of the cable adapter and the area of the wye section.

16. Slide the receptacle housing over the cable adapter and up to the position shown. Insert the nylon venting rod (supplied).

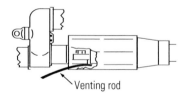

Figure 5-36. Step 16, insert the nylon venting rod.

17 Attach the 650ATY assembly tool. Make sure the U shaped yoke is over the wye section and the C shaped yoke is over the receptacle housing. With the assembly tool in place, slowly raise the handle to slide the receptacle housing over the wye section. Remove the venting rod.

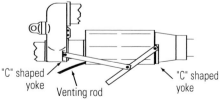

Figure 5-37. Step 17, install receptacle housing.

18. Check all the cable adapters to make sure they are located properly and remove all vinyl tape markers.

19. Obtain the 30MA corrugated contact and remove the wooden plug. Wrap the corrugated contact over the exposed metallic tape, making sure the contact butts up against the cut end of the outer jacket. The ground lead must face away from the wye section.

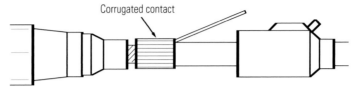

Figure 5-38. Step 19, installing corrugated contact.

20. Cut the rubber sheet to the proper size (according to the insulation diameter) and wrap it over the corrugated contact.

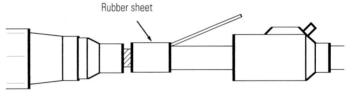

Figure 5-39. Step 20, cover with rubber sheet.

21. Place the clamps (one for Burndy clamp sizes GB to HA and two for sizes HAB to PA) over the rubber sheet and tighten them sufficiently so they will stay in place. Continue to tighten the clamps in stages so that the corrugated contact is tight against the metallic tape but not under excessive pressure. Between stages, test the tightness by rotating the assembly back and forth approximately 1/8 inch turn. When a definite drag is felt, the clamps are tight enough. No not over tighten.

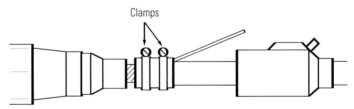

Figure 5-40. Step 21, installing clamps.

22. Apply the lubricant supplied to the hole in the 30MA housing and slide the housing over the corrugated contact making sure the ground lead goes through the small hole. The 30MA housing should be within 1/2 to 3/4 inch of the taper on the wye section.

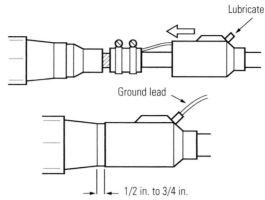

Figure 5-41. Step 22, lubricate and apply housing.

23. Connect a short length of No. 14 AWG copper to each of the grounding eyes of the housings and the eye of the wye section. Make a small loop and twist tightly, using care not to damage the eye.

24. Connect these wires and the ground leads from the 30MA or 31MA devices together using suitable connectors. Ground lead from the 30MA and 31MA is No. 6 or copper. Jumper ground should be equivalent.

Note: For three-phase installations, all grounds from all three phases must be tied to a common ground.

25. Make sure the protective cap is in place over the voltage detection point in the wye section.

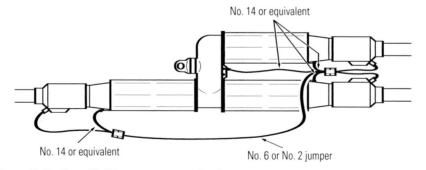

Figure 5-42. Step 23-25, connect ground wires.

Note: If the 30MA grounding devices is not used, the metallic shield of the cable must be grounded through an alternative method.

Note: It is also recommended that the jacket of the cable be waterproofed at this point to prevent moisture from entering under the cable jacket (water stop).

Splice Cable With Concentric Neutral

1. Train the cable ends and straighten them in their final position. Measure so the cables are 15 inches apart and cut the ends square. Wipe the outer jacket clean for a distance of 30 inches.

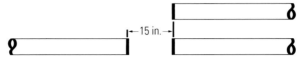

Figure 5-43. Step 1, trim and clean cable ends.

Note: Steps 2-12 should be performed on all three cable ends and in the same order as presented.

2. Apply the supplied lubricant or Elastimold approved lubricant to the inside of the grounding device. Slide the grounding device onto the cable 38 inches. This procedure and following procedures are done for each cable.

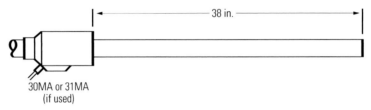

Figure 5-44. Step 2, lubricate and apply grounding device.

3. Slide the receptacle housing onto the cable a distance of 30 inches.

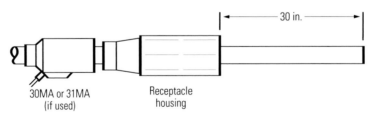

Figure 5-45. Step 3, apply housing.

4. Measure 12-7/8 inches from the end and remove the outer jacket. Make a straight, smooth and squared cut. Take care not to nick or damage the concentric neutral. Unwrap the neutral wires and fold back over the cable.

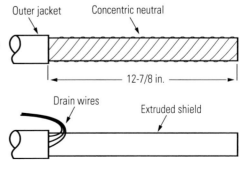

Figure 5-46. Step 4, fold back neutral wires.

5. Measure 10-1/8 inches and remove the semi-con with a straight, smooth, squared cut. Do not nick or cut the insulation.

Measure 1-3/4 inches from the end of the outer jacket and wrap two turns of PVC tape for a marker.

Figure 5-47. Step 5.

6. Bevel the insulation 1/4 inch from the end. Thoroughly clean the insulation with an aluminum oxide cloth to remove all traces of semi-conducting shield. Solvent-clean the insulation surface. Always wipe from the cable end towards the semi-con.

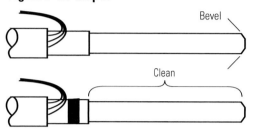

Figure 5-48. Step 6, bevel and clean.

7. Apply the supplied lubricant or approved Elastimold lubricant sparingly to the cable as shown and to the inside of the adapter. Slide the adapter, small end first, over the cable with a twisting motion until the end of the adapter is flush with the end of the tape marker.

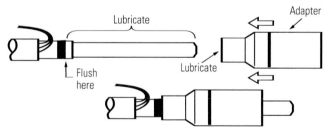

Figure 5-49. Step 7, applying lubricant and installing adapter.

8. Select the aluminum holding collar and thread the proper size set-screws part way in. Position the holding collar over the insulation and flush against the cable adapter. Using the enclosed hex wrench, tighten each set-screws one or two turns at a time to keep the collar centered over the insulation. Continue to tighten the set-screws until they are below the surface of the collar.

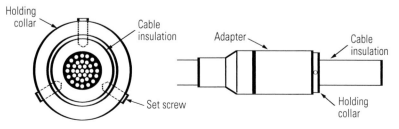

Figure 5-50. Step 8, install aluminum collar.

9. Measure the inside of the crimp connector plus 1/2 inch for expansion. Apply this measurement and remove the insulation. Do not nick or cut the conductor. The measurement should be between 4-5/16 to 4-5/8 inches max.

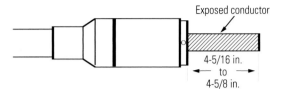

Figure 5-51. Step 9, measure and remove insulation.

10. Remove the protective cap from the crimp connector and insert the conductor into the crimp connector (is aluminum conductor, brush with inhibitor). Make sure the crimp connector is fully seated.

Note: Take a preliminary measurement from the end of the crimp connector to the aluminum collar. The measurement should not exceed 7-1/8 inches.

11. Before crimping the crimp connector, a final check should be made. All components on all three cable should be positioned as show.

Note: Check that the bolt holes in the crimp connectors are positioned properly to align with the bolt holes in the wye section of the splice.

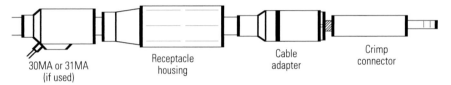

Figure 5-52. Step 11, checking component position.

Repeat the above steps for the remaining cables to be joined.

12. Crimp the connector, rotating the Burndy MD-6 tool 90° after each crimp.

Note: After crimping, measure the distance from the end of the connector to the aluminum holding collar. If the distance is over 7-1/8 inches do not proceed. Recheck all previous work.

Figure 5-53. Step 12, crimp the connector.

13. Position the wye section between the cables and assemble the washers as shown. The flat washer should be against the spade contact and the bevel washers next the the bolt head. After the cables are in their final position and hand tightened, do not attempt to move or reposition any part of the assembly. Using a torque wrench, tighten all bolts from 50 to 60 feet-pounds.

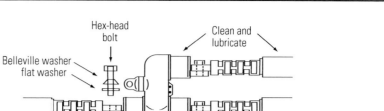

Figure 5-54. Step 13-14, assemble the wye.

14. Apply the supplied lubricant or Elastimold approved lubricant generously to the outside of the cable adapter and the area of the wye section as shown in Figure 5-56.

15. Slide the receptacle housing over the cable adapter and up to the position shown. Insert the nylon venting rod (supplied).

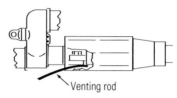

Figure 5-55. Step 15, insert the nylon venting rod.

16 Attach the 650ATY assembly tool. Make sure the U shaped yoke is over the wye section and the C shaped yoke is over the receptacle housing. With the assembly tool in place, slowly raise the handle to slide the receptacle housing over the wye section. Remove the venting rod.

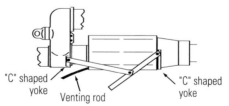

Figure 5-56. Step 16, install receptacle housing.

17. Check all the cable adapters to make sure they are located properly and remove all vinyl tape markers.

18. Build a waterstop at the jacket cutback. Form a tail with the concentric neutral strands and attach the bonding jumper with a copper tap connector. Leave one strand of the concentric neutral unbundled.

19. Wrap 1/2 layer of semi-con tape over the receptacle housing and adapter, starting at 3/8 inch below the grounding eye and extending to 1 inch over the semi-con of the cable.

20. Apply 1/2 lapped layer of self amalgamating tape and 1/2 lapped layer of PVC tape as per taping detail.

21. Bond the wye section, receptacle housing and concentric neutral strands.

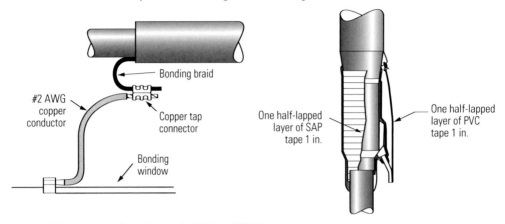

Figure 5-57. Step 21, apply SAP and PVC tapes.

22. Gather the drain wires together and twist to form a pigtail and wrap one turn around the cable. Position the crimp connector over the drain wires.

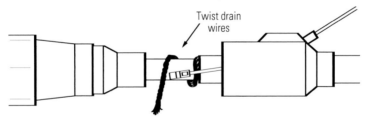

Figure 5-58. Step 22, gather drain wires.

23. Cut the twisted drain wires to length to fit into the crimp connector and crimp. Using PVC tape, tape the twisted wire and the crimp connector to the cable as shown.

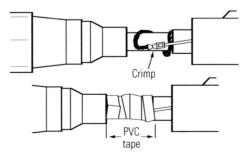

Figure 5-59. Step 23, crimp drain wires and wrap with PVC tape.

24. Slide the 31MA housing forward until it is within 1/2 to 3/4 inch of the start of the taper on the wye section.

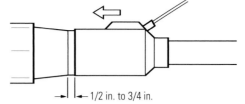

25. Connect a short length of No. 14 AWG copper to each of the grounding eyes of the housings and the eye of the wye section. Make a small loop and twist tightly, using care not to damage the eye.

Figure 5-60. Step 24, slide housing.

26. Connect these wires and the ground leads from the 30MA or 31MA devices together using suitable connectors. Ground lead from the 30MA and 31MA is No. 6 or copper. Jumper ground should be equivalent.

Note: For three-phase installations, all grounds from all three phases must be tied to a common ground.

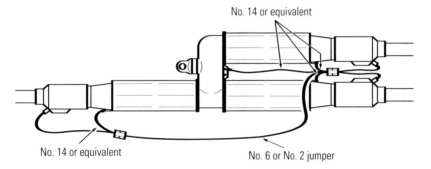

Figure 5-61. Step 25-26, connect ground wires.

27. Make sure the protective cap is in place over the voltage detection point in the wye section.

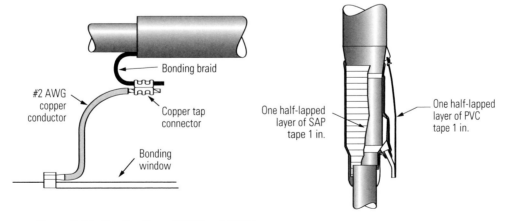

Figure 5-62. Application of SAP and PVC tapes.

Note: It is recommended that the jacket of the cable be waterproofed at this point to prevent moisture from entering under the cable jacket (water stop).

Elbow Wye Splice

Many areas have stopped using the molded wye splice and gone to the elbow wye splice. Refer to the manufacturer's instructions for splicing details. The following illustration shows an exploded view of the elbow wye splice.

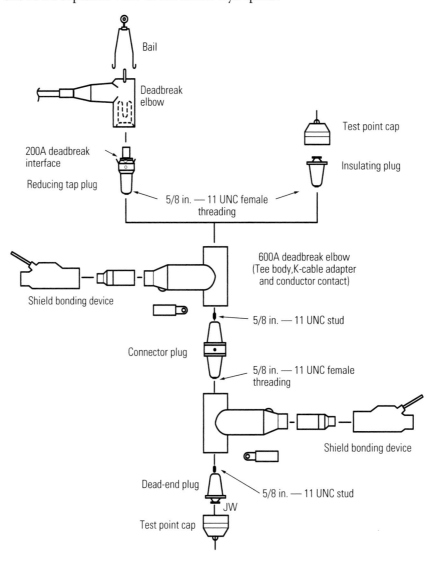

Figure 5-63. Elbow wye splice, 13 kV and 25 kV concentric neutral and copper tape shield XLPE feeder cables.

Terminate XLPE Feeder Cables

Terminate XLPE Feeder Cable Using a Heat Shrink Terminator

Before starting any terminating job:

- Ensure that the appropriate isolation and grounding procedures have been followed.

- Prepare the work area.

- Visually inspect the kit components.

- Read the manufacturer's instructions and the instructions to familiarize yourself with the termination.

- Make sure that the proper tools are on hand and that cleanliness is observed throughout the procedure.

To terminate a 13 kV/25 kV copper *tape-shielded* XLPE feeder cable using a heat shrinkable terminator:

1. Phase the cable to be terminated and check the temporary tag to determine where the cable will be connected or mounted.

   Train the cable so that you have sufficient length to reach the termination point. Leave slack if required.

2. Remove the cable jacket and any bedding material to a dimension of 11 inches plus L from the cable end. L is the strip length required for the connector plus 1/4 inch for application of fireclay. Each connector has to be measured to determine what L equals.

3. Remove the copper tape shield to a distance 1-1/2 inches from the jacket cutback. Use a piece of adhesive-backed copper tape to secure the copper tape shield in place. The copper tape shield edge must be smooth not jagged.

4. Remove the semi-conducting shielding layer (semi-con) to a dimension of 9 inches plus L from the cable end (see Figure 5-66). Make a clean cut with no jagged edges. Do not cut into the cable insulation.

5. Remove the insulation to L (see Figure 5-66). Do not nick the conductor.

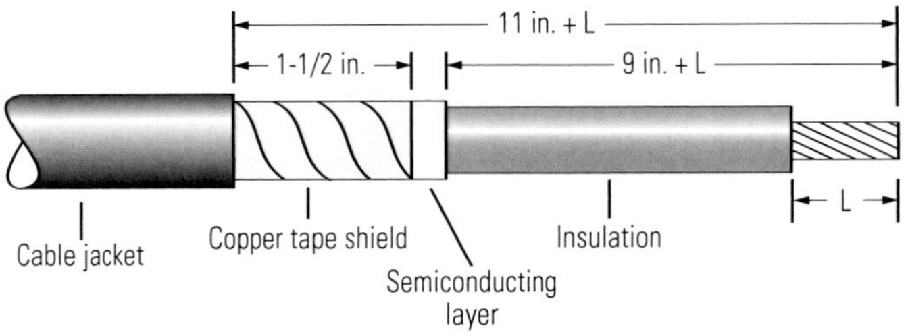

11 in. + L

1-1/2 in.

9 in. + L

L

Cable jacket

Copper tape shield

Semiconducting layer

Insulation

Figure 5-64. Cable dimensions for terminating copper tape-shielded cable.

6. Install the power lug connector. Do this by first slightly loosening the conductor strands with pliers. Before putting the connector on, position it so that the flat surface faces the apparatus. Now push it straight onto the cable end. Do not twist. Ensure that the cable end bottoms out in the lug (hits the inside plate).

7. Apply fireclay (solder-retention compound) into the opening between the connector and the conductor (fireclay is in a sealed bag in the kit). Pinch off small pieces of fireclay and use your finger to push it tightly into the opening at the end of the connector that is in contact with the conductor. Don't leave any holes or gaps.

8. Heat the connector with a torch to activate the solder. Point the flame at the end of connector close to the flat part (palm or tang).

9. Allow 5 to 10 drops of solder to drop down, then stop heating.

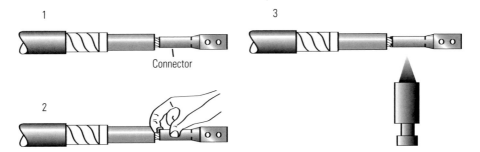

1

Connector

3

2

Figure 5-65. Steps involved in installing a power sleeve (connector).

10. Let the connection cool for about one minute without disturbance to set the solder. After one minute, the cooling can be accelerated by wrapping a wet cloth strip around the connector. Once cooled, chip off all of the fireclay and continue with the termination.

11. Clean the cable insulation with an aluminum oxide cloth to remove all traces of the semi-con shield. Solvent-clean the insulation surface. Always wipe from the connector towards the semi-con.

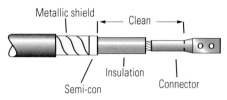

Figure 5-66. Step 11, cleaning.

12. Install the bonding braid using the ground spring clamp (grounding spring). Do this by flaring the end of the braid nearest the moisture block (solder block) and butt against the cable jacket cutback edge.

Now apply two wraps of the spring clamp over the braid (around the cable). Fold the braid back over the spring clamp so the moisture block is positioned on the cable jacket. Then wrap the remainder of the spring clamp over the braid, tighten with you fingers and secure with a small piece of the copper foil tape (supplied).

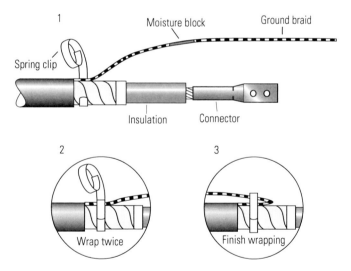

Figure 5-67. Step 12, attaching the grounding braid.

13. Solvent-wipe the jacket and ground braid for 2 inches below the jacket cut back to ensure that the surface is clean.

14. Lift the braid and wrap one layer of sealant (mastic) around the cable jacket (at the location where the moisture block lies on the cable jacket). Put the braid back down so that the moisture block portion is on the sealant. Press the moisture block into the sealant. Wrap two or more layers of the sealant over the braid. Ensure that the moisture block is embedded in and covered by the sealant. This provides a waterstop.

15. Remove the release paper from the short angle-cut piece of stress relief material or mastic (SRM). Place the point of the SRM at the edge of the semi-con cutback so that it is angled away from the cutback. Pull the SRM to half its original width while wrapping it around the cable. Apply two or three wraps so that the edge of the cutback is tapered towards the insulation. The edge of the cutback must be filled in, and the slope of the tape is towards the insulation. The idea is to smooth out the edges or steps and control the electrical stress at that point. The SRM should overlap onto the cable insulation and semi-con by 1/8 inch to 1/4 inch. The kit may contain more SRM than is required to do this part.

16. Install the stress control tube. Do this by squeezing the tube so that it is rounded, then sliding it over the connector. Position it so that it butts against the spring and grounding braid. Shrink the stress relief tube using a torch. Start at the ground end and heat all around the tube. Move towards the connector end as the tube shrinks.

    Inspect the surface of the tube to ensure that it is evenly shrunk and conforms to the cable under it. Extra heat may be required to smooth out any ridges. Check for flat spots by running your fingers over the surface. These are caused by insufficient heating and can be remedied by reheating that spot.

17. Solvent-clean and then wrap sealant around the connector barrel. Use sufficient sealant to build up the connector diameter to that of the insulation. Overlap the sealant onto the insulation by 1 inch.

18. Install the red insulating tubing (HVTM). Position it so that it covers the sealant.

    Shrink it into place starting at the ground end. Apply extra heat at the ground and connector ends to soften the sealant. Heat the bare portion of the connector for 10 seconds.

    Inspect the surface to ensure that the tube has been evenly shrunk and that no flat spots exist. The entire tube should be wrinkle-free, with the profile or image of the inner components clearly defined. To correct flat spots, reheat the tubing.

    If the tube surface has been burned or blistered, allow the tube to cool and then clean it off with a solvent wipe.

    If the tubing extends onto the contact area (flat surface) of the connector, that excess must be removed by ring cutting after the tube has cooled.

The contact area must be cleared of any obstructions since these will result in a poor contact.

19. Install the skirts. Position the first skirt 4-1/2 inches from the bottom of the red insulating tubing (HVTM). Hold the edge of the skirt lightly with pliers, ensure that it is straight then shrink it in place by brushing the flame tip around the outside of the skirt collar. Only the collar will shrink. Position the second skirt 4-1/2 inches above the first skirt.

Note: One skirt is used for 13 kV and two skirts are used for 25 kV.

Figure 5-70 shows a completed heat shrink termination for 25 kV copper tape-shielded XLPE feeder cable.

Feeder cables can also be terminated using pre-molded terminators and elbows. For information on these terminations, refer to the manufacturer's instructions in the various kits.

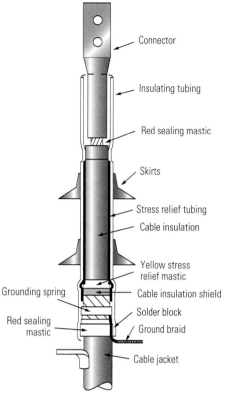

Figure 5-68. Heat shrinkable termination of copper tape-shielded XLPE feeder cable.

Mount the Terminator

Once the terminator has been installed on the cable end, it must be mounted. Depending on the job, it may be mounted in a switchgear or on a terminal pole.

The terminator requires a bracket attached to it so it can be installed as required. Attach the mounting bracket to the cable just under the terminator with hose clamps. Tighten the clamps firmly over the cable jacket. Be sure not to over-torque.

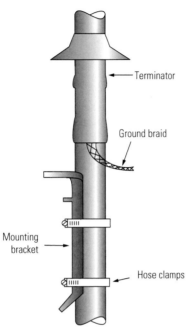

Figure 5-69. Mounting bracket attached to terminated copper tape shielded XLPE cable.

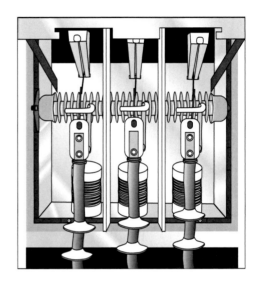

Figure 5-70. Termination of XLPE feeder cable in a switchgear.

Now the terminator and mounting bracket can be attached (bolted) to either a switchgear or a terminal pole. The switchgear has a support channel to which the terminator and mounting bracket can be bolted. See Figure 5-70. The terminal pole has a bracket that can be used as illustrated in the chapter on terminating primary underground cable.

Note: In most cases, the mounting bracket is first attached to the apparatus and then the cable is attached to the bracket.

Terminate XLPE Feeder Cable Using an Elbow

The following is required before starting any terminating job:

- Prepare the work area.

- Visually inspect the kit components.

- Read the manufacturer's instructions and the instructions to familiarize yourself with the elbow.

- Make sure that the proper tools are on hand and that cleanliness is observed throughout the procedure.

To terminate a 13 kV/25 kV copper tape-shielded XLPE feeder cable using an elbow:

1. Phase the cable to be terminated and check the temporary tag to determine where the cable will be connected or mounted.

   Train the cable so that you have sufficient length to reach the termination point. Leave slack if required.

2. Position the cable at the bushing center line and parallel to the apparatus. If there are bends in the top 16 inches of cable, train it until it is straight.

   Cut the outer jacket a distance of 24 inches back from the cable end.

4. Lubricate the inside of the 30MA shield bonding device with the supplied lubricant.

   Slide it onto the cable and push it back past the cut at 24 inches.

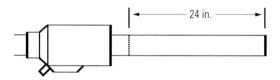

Figure 5-71. Placing the bonding device onto the cable befor attaching the elbow.

5. Remove the cable jacket and any bedding material to a dimension of L + 2-3/4 inches from the cable end. L is dependent on the conductor size and type. There is a table in the manufacturer's instruction that gives the measurement for L.

   Remove the jacket with a straight, smooth and squared cut. Take care not to cut or damage the tape shield (see Figure 5-74).

6. Remove the copper tape shield to a dimension of L + 3/4 inch from the cable end.

   Wrap two turns of adhesive-backed copper tape over the end of the tape shield. Position it so that the edge on the tape shield is L + 1 inch from the end of the cable.

   The tape secures the copper tape shield in place, and it also serves as a marker for future steps in the procedure.

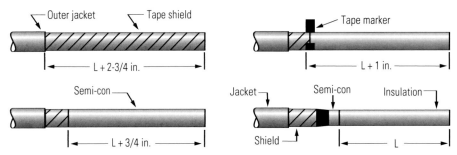

Figure 5-72. Removal of jacket and copper tape shield. Application of copper tape marker and removal of semi-con layer.

7. Remove the semi-conducting shielding layer (semi-con) to a dimension of L. Make a straight, smooth, squared cut with no jagged edges. Take care not to cut or nick the insulation.

8. Measure the length of the cable adapter (supplied in kit). Transfer this measurement to the cable starting from the edge of the tape (on the semi-con) and measuring towards the cable end. Mark the insulation at this point.

   Remove the insulation from this mark to the cable end. Do not nick the conductor. This will ensure that when the cable adapter is installed, the insulation will be flush with the outer end of the adapter.

9. Clean the insulation with an aluminum oxide cloth to remove all traces of the semi-con shield. Solvent-clean the insulation surface. Always wipe from the cable end towards the semi-con.

10. Lubricate (sparingly) the insulation with the supplied lubricant. Lubricate the inside of the cable adapter.

    Slide the adapter, small end first, over the cable with a twisting motion until the end of the adapter is over and flush with the end of the tape marker.

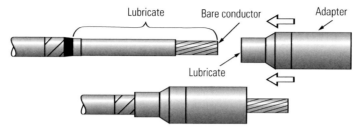

Figure 5-73. Installation of cable adapter.

11. Remove the protective cap from the crimp connector. This connector is supplied in the kit and is sometimes referred to as a spade terminal.

    Wire-brush the aluminum conductor and immediately insert it into the crimp connector. The crimp connector contains an inhibitor to prevent oxidation.

Note: Ensure the conductor is fully inserted into the crimp connector.

12. Position the flat part of the connector so that it is facing the bushing. Refer to the manufacturer's instructions for the correct crimp tool and dies to use. Hold the connector in position as you make the first crimp at the shoulder of the connector. Complete the crimping rotating the tool by 90 degrees after each crimp.

    As a check, measure the distance from the end of the connector to the adapter. This distance should be 6-1/2 to 7-1/4 inches.

    Carefully wipe off any excess inhibitor or compound.

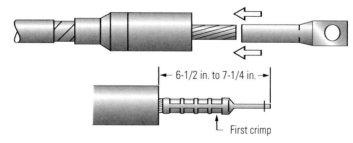

Figure 5-74. Crimping of the connector (spade terminal).

13. Remove the protective cap from the elbow cable entrance. Lubricate the cable adapter (outside) and the inside of the elbow where the cable enters.

14. Slide the cable into the body of the elbow. Push until the cable cannot go any further and the elbow is properly seated.

15. Clean and lubricate both the elbow and the bushing on which it will be installed. Use the lubricant supplied.

16. Push the elbow onto the bushing. Line up the hole in the connector (spade terminal) with the stud on the insulating plug.

17. Clean and lubricate the insulating plug and the opposite end of the elbow. Insert the insulating plug. Hand-tighten the plug. Use a torque wrench to tighten the plug to the proper torque. Refer to the manufacturer's instructions.

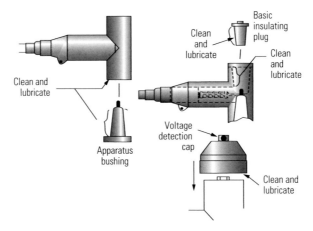

Figure 5-75. Installation of elbow, insulating plug and test point cap.

18. Clean and lubricate the inner surface of the test point cap and place on elbow. Push down hard until the cap snaps in place.

19. During cable preparation, sufficient jacket was removed to expose 1-3/4 inches of copper tape shield behind the elbow cable adapter. This will now be used to make the bonding connection.

    Remove the wooden plug from the corrugated bonding contact. Wrap the contact over the exposed tape shield. Butt the contact against the cut end of the jacket. Ensure that the bonding device lead is facing away from the elbow.

20. Wrap the contact with the rubber sheet supplied Cut the sheet so that it will cover the contact.

    Use clamps to hold the rubber sheet in place. Tighten them so they stay in place sufficiently, but do not over-tighten.

21. Lubricate the tip of the bonding device lead and slide the housing over the contact. Ensure that the lead goes through the small hole in the housing and the housing is properly seated. It should be 1/2 to 3/4 inch away from the taper on the end of the elbow.

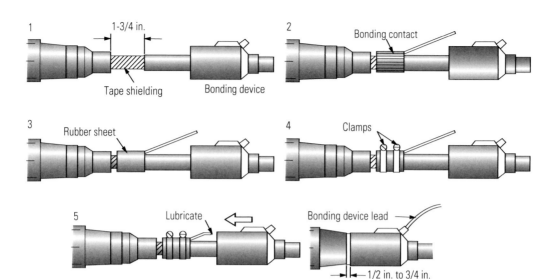

Figure 5-76. Installation of the bonding device.

22. Apply one half-lapped layer of SAP tape from the bottom of the elbow just prior to the juncture between the elbow and the bonding device, down over the bonding device.

23. Apply one half-lapped layer of PVC tape over the SAP tape.

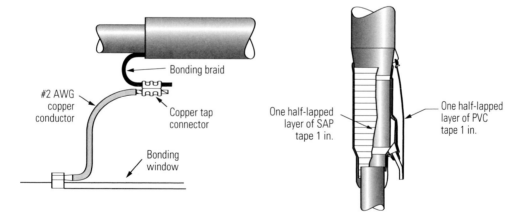

Figure 5-77. Application of SAP and PVC tapes.

This concludes the installation and mounting of the elbow.

Bond the Cable

Bonding together of metallic and semi-conducting components eliminates possible voltage differences between them. Voltage differences may result in damage to equipment and danger to personnel.

Splice:

To bond the splice, use a #2 AWG copper conductor, a copper tap connector and a compression connector.

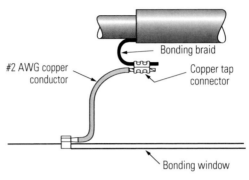

Figure 5-78. Bonding of a splice.

Terminate:

To bond the terminator in a switchgear, use a No. 2 AWG copper conductor, a copper tap connector and a compression connector.

Attach the bonding braid to the No. 2 copper conductor using the copper tap connector, and then use the compression connector to attach the #2 conductor to the ground bus.

To bond the terminator on a pole, follow the same process as for primary underground distribution cables.

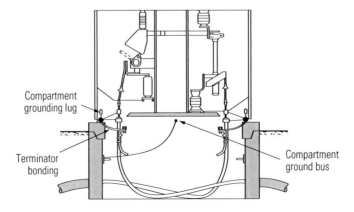

Figure 5-79. Bonding of terminator in a switchgear.

To bond the elbow:

1. Cut a length of No. 14 copper wire to reach from the grounding eye of the elbow to the end of the bonding device lead. This will be used as a bonding wire (drain or bleed wire) for the elbow.

   Attach this bonding wire to the ground eye of the elbow.

2. Cut a length of No. 2 copper conductor to reach from the ground bus to the elbow. This will be used as the bonding conductor.

3. Using a suitable copper tap connector, connect the bonding wire, the bonding device lead and the bonding conductor together.

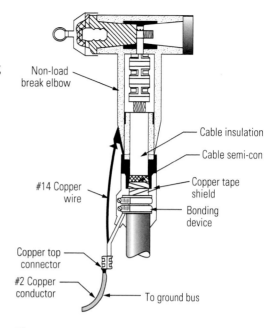

Figure 5-80. Bonding the elbow (cable).

4. Attach the other end of the bonding conductor to the ground bus.

Note: Remember that the temporary tags must now be replaced with permanent tags.

Energize Feeder Cables

After completing the terminating job, the supervisor is notified that the job has been completed and makes arrangements to have the feeder cables energized. The line crew receives the electrical and civil drawings together with a plant alteration work order. The plant alteration is used for updating the person-in-charge and all operating diagrams. The procedures for energizing feeder cables vary greatly and require clear switching orders agreed to between the crew and the person-in-charge.

Splice Primary Cables

Introduction

Although there are different types of splices, the steps involved are very similar. The making of a splice can be divided into cable preparation, connection and reinstallation. This means that the various layers of the two cables being spliced are removed until the conductor is exposed, then the conductors are joined and the layers are rebuilt using various tapes and tubes. When splicing the cable, very precise measurements and dimensions are involved. It is very important that all of the instructions are read before starting the splice. The objective is to build a successful and quality splice.

Remember: No cable is better than the splices that are made in it.

Upon successful completion of this section, you will be able to identify, describe, and perform the various types of underground splices. You will also be able to correctly identify and perform the different bonding procedures.

Note: The splices explained in this section are for a 25 kV, 1/0 XLPE cable with a concentric neutral underground cable. A tape-shielded cable will be explained in the XLPE feeder section. To avoid duplication, only two 12 kV splices have been explained.

Refer to the appropriate manufactures instruction sheet before making any splice.

The topics covered are:

- Tools and materials

- Splice primary underground cable

- Heat shrink

- Cold shrink

- Bond the splice

Tools and Materials

Splicing kits are used when making a splice. The kit used, is dependent on the size and the voltage of the cables being spliced. These kits have specific instructions for the components in them. Before starting, always check the kit to ensure that all the components and instructions are present.

SYSTEM

DRAWINGS

MATERIALS

INSTALLING

SPLICING

FUSING

MAINTENANCE

TROUBLE

JOB SITE

Tools

Tools required to make a primary underground cable splice or termination includes:

- Knives - very sharp; skinning
- Semi-con stripping tools
- Speed stripper
- Needle nosed pliers
- Lineman's pliers
- Cable cutters - small and large banana type
- Crimping tools and dies
- Square cutters for insulation
- Penciling tools
- Probe insert tool
- Propane torch
- Cleaning solvents
- Lint free cloths
- Aluminum oxide cloth (sandpaper texture)
- Lubricants
- Bonding wires
- Bushing insert wrenches
- Multi-screwdriver

There are specific knives and tools used to remove and cut the various layers of cable for splices and terminations:

- Square cutters
- Speed strippers
- Penciling tools
- Probe insert tool
- Propane torch

Insulation stripper

Elbow probe insert tool

Semi-con strippper

Figure 5-81. Typical splicing tools used for an underground cable splice or termination.

Each tool is unique and requires specific operating instructions as per the cable specifications. The manufacturer's instructions will provide specifications of the settings.

Heat Shrink Splice Kit

Within a heat shrink (Raychem style) splice kit you will find various tubes, protection and mastic materials. Mastic is a pliable putty or rubber like material used to seal or fill openings. The heat shrinkable tubings are installed using a torch. The design of each tubing is specific to its application, and the color can be different with each manufacturer. The application of each tube is to reconstruct the appropriate layers of cable.

The tubes and other materials have specific purposes.

Note: Colors refer to the Raychem kit.

- **Stress relief mastic** (SRM) is a yellow material that is used to fill voids, prevent corona discharge and relieve electrical stress by creating a reduced voltage gradient.

- **Red sealant** is a red mastic used to prevent water from travelling past a specific point (a waterstop). It has no electrical properties.

- **Foil** is used to protect parts of the cable during the heating process.

- The **stress control tube** is a piece of black tubing used to relieve electrical stresses.

- The **insulation tube** is a red tubing used to insulate the cable. It is not used on all splices.

- The **dual-layer insulation/shielding tubing** has two purposes: the red inner section acts as insulation while the black outer section replaces the semi-conducting shielding (semi-con) layer and acts as an insulation shield.

- The **jacket replacement tubing** replaces the cable jacket and protects the splice from moisture and mechanical damage.

Although these kits are usually used to do a splice, there may be a time when you will have to build a splice using tapes. Different types of tapes are used at each stage.

They are:

- **Self-amalgamating polyisobutylene tape**, called either SAP tape or SAPT. It is used for reinsulation and corrosion control, and as a filler.

- **Semi-conducting shielding tape**, called semi-con tape. It is used to replace the semi-con layer of the cable.

- **Copper shielding braid**

- **Polyvinyl chloride tape**, called PVC. It is used as a cover tape to protect the other tapes from mechanical damage and builds the jacket.

Primary 13 kV Underground Taped XLPE Cable Splice

Before starting any splicing job:

- Prepare the work area.

- Visually inspect for proper tapes and material.

- Read the manufacturer's instructions to familiarize yourself with the splice.

- Make sure that the proper tools are on hand and that cleanliness is observed throughout the procedure.

Note: Rubber protective gloves must be worn when applying isopropanol and other chemicals.

The steps to follow when doing a non-tension splice on 13 kV **concentric neutral** XLPE underground distribution cable are:

1. Train the cable into the final position and cut, so both ends of the cables butt squarely together.

2. Strip back cable jacket 11 inches, semi-conducting insulation 10-1/2 inches, and cable insulation 1/2 inch + 1/2 of the length of the connector. Pencil insulation back 1-1/2 inches. Fold back and lightly tape the neutral strands on each cable.

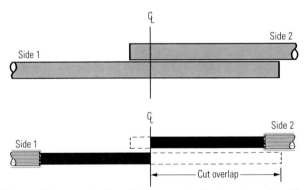

Figure 5-82. Determining centerline, folding neutral strands and cutting cable.

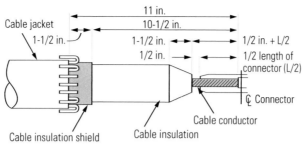

Figure 5-83. Measurements for splice.

3. Clean insulation with aluminum oxide cloth to remove all traces of semi-con shield and wipe with a clean cloth soaked in isopropanol. Rubber gloves must be worn when applying isopropanol. Always wipe from the cable end towards the semi-con. If the wiping is done the other way, the solvent may leach conducting particles from the semi-con and smear them onto the insulation.

Figure 5-84. Install, de-burr, and press the connector.

4. Install, press and de-burr the compression connector.

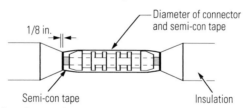

Figure 5-85. Applying the semi-con tape.

5. Apply half-lapped layers of semi-con tape to build up a smooth surface over the connector body. Overlap the tape slightly 1/8 inch onto penciled portion of cable insulation.

6. Measure the diameter of connector and semi-con tape (from step 5) and write it down.

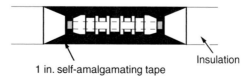

Figure 5-86. Applying the SAP tape.

7. Apply half-lapped layers of 1 inch self-amalgamating (SAP) tape until flush with cable insulation.

8. Apply half-lapped layers of 2-inch self-amalgamating tape over the cable insulation and connector. Edges of SAP tape should be 1/4 inch from cable semi-con cutoff. Buildup the insulation to a thickness of 3/8 inch. The final diameter of the built-up insulation should be the diameter measured in Step 6 plus 2 × 3/8 inch – the build up of insulation thickness. This buildup diameter should be reached within 3 inches of the semi-con cutoff.

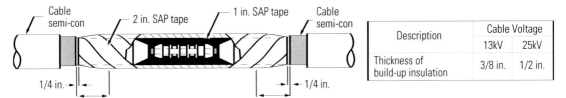

Description	Cable Voltage	
	13kV	25kV
Thickness of build-up insulation	3/8 in.	1/2 in.

Figure 5-87. Building up the insulation.

Example:

If the diameter measured in Step 6 is 7/8 inch, then the diameter over the buildup insulation should be at least 1-5/8 inches {7/8 + (2 × 3/8) = 1-5/8 inches}.

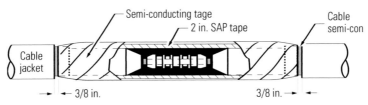

Figure 5-88. Applying semi-con over the SAP tape.

9. Apply the half-lapped layer of semi-con tape over the self-amalgamating tape. Overlap the semi-con tape onto the cable semi-con to within 3/8 inch of the jacket cutback.

10. Apply quarter-lapped layers of shield braid over the semi-con tape and run shield to within 3/8 inch on one end only, such that the braid is connected to the concentric neutral when the water stop is made. End the shield braid 2 inches from the jacket cutback on the other side to ensure that there is no connection between the braid and the concentric neutral. Secure end of the braid with a wrap of PVC tape.

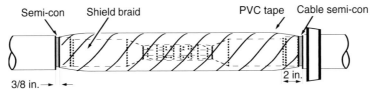

Figure 5-89. Applying the shield braid.

11. Make the waterstop as explained in Waterstop Preparation. See page 214, Step 4.

12. Apply two half-lapped layers of 2-inch SAP tape over the splice. The SAP tape should overlap 3 inches onto the cable jacket.

13. Attach #2 AWG jumper to concentric neutral strands with a copper tap connector. Cover over the tap connector with a mastic pad.

Note: External bonding of the concentric neutral strands is only required on cable runs in excess of 1,000 feet. For shorter runs, no bonding is required.

14. Taper over entire splice with two half-lapped layers of 1-1/2 inch PVC tape.

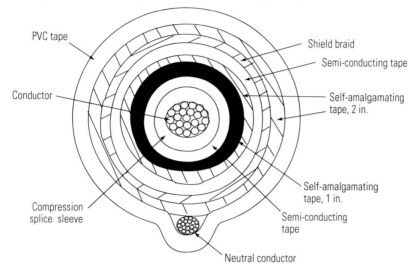

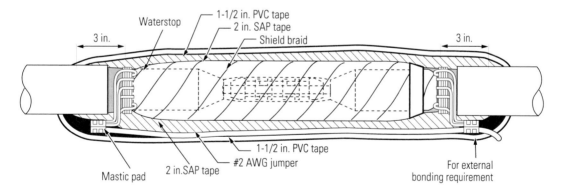

Figure 5-90. Completed sleeve.

15. If cable run is in excess of 1,000 feet, bond splice as per company practices.

SYSTEM

DRAWINGS

MATERIALS

INSTALLING

SPLICING

FUSING

MAINTENANCE

TROUBLE

JOB SITE

Primary 13 kV Underground Heat Shrinkable XLPE Cable Splice

Before starting any splicing job:

- Prepare the work area.

- Visually inspect the kit components.

- Read the manufacturer's instructions to familiarize yourself with the splice.

- Make sure that the proper tools are on hand and that cleanliness is observed throughout the procedure.

Note: Rubber protective gloves must be worn when applying isopropanol and other chemicals.

The steps to follow when using Raychem kit HVS-2511E-J #1-250 kcmil to make a non-tension splice on 13 kV *concentric neutral* XLPE underground cable are:

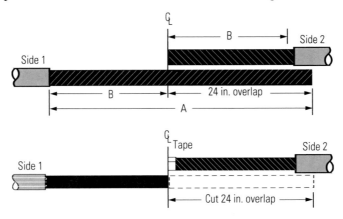

Figure 5-91. Determining centerline, folding neutral strands and cutting cable.

1. Train the cables so that they are in the correct location and position. Overlap the cables by 24 inches and straighten the splice area. The center for the splice will be at the end of Side 2 cable.

2. Remove the jacket (using skinning knife) on Side 1 to dimension A (dimension B plus 24 inches). Remove the jacket on Side 2 to dimension B. These dimensions are dependent on the cable size and the kit being used. Refer to the kit when doing a splice.

3. Fold the neutral strands (wires) back from Side 1, and cut Side 1 at the centerline using a cable cutter.

Table 1

Kit No.	Conductor	A Jacket Cutback/ Neutral Pullback Side 1	B Jacket Cutback/ Neutral Pullback Side 2	C Semi-con Cutback	Connector	D Insulation Cutback
SMOC 1270	500 kcmil, 15 kV	32-1/2 in.	8-1/2 in.	3-3/4 in.	PS 252	1-5/8 in.
SMOC 1271	750 kcmil, 15 kV	32 in.	8 in.	4-1/8 in.	PS 262	2 in.
SMOC 1272	500 kcmil, 25 kV	33-1/2 in.	9-1/2 in.	4-3/4 in.	PS 252	1-5/8 in.
SMOC 1273	750 kcmil, 25 kV	33-7/8 in.	9-7/8 in.	5-1/8 in.	PS 262	2 in.
SMOC 1284	#1, 25 kV	33 in.	9 in.	4-1/2 in.	PS 212	1-1/8 in.
SMOC 1285	500 kcmil, 25 kV	33-1/2 in.	9-1/2 in.	5-1/4 in.	PS 257	2 in.
SMOC 1302	#1/0, 25 kV	32 in.	8 in.	4-1/4 in.	PS 212	1-1/8 in.
SMOC 1260	#2, 25 kV	38 in.	14 in.	5-1/4 in.	PS 202	1 in.

4. Temporarily tape the neutral wire/strand ends to the semi-con layer on Side 2. Slide the heat shrink splice tubings over the cable jacket on Side 2. Then remove the tape and fold the neutral wires back over the jacket.

5. Remove the semi-con on both sides to dimension C. When removing the semi-con layer, make a clean cut with no jagged edges. Do not nick or cut the cable insulation.

6. Select the proper connector for the cable and for connecting the neutral wires/strands. This is dependent on cable type. The connectors are not always in the kit and you may have to obtain from stores.

7. On both sides remove the cable insulation half the connector length plus 1/2 inch to dimension D. Do not nick the conductor. When finished both cable ends should look similar to Figure 5-92.

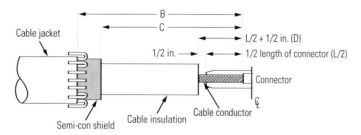

Figure 5-92. Measurements for splice.

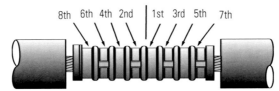

8th 6th 4th 2nd   1st 3rd 5th 7th

Figure 5-93. Connector crimping details.

8. Install the connector by putting the connector on one conductor and then pushing the other conductor into the other end. Push down on the connection until the conductors bottom out (hit the inside part of the connector).

To crimp the connector, consult the manufacturer's instructions to determine the correct dies and tool to use. The MD6 crimp tool is used for most underground cables. With the proper dies installed in the MD6, start crimping at the center of the connector. Move from the center towards the two cable ends in an alternating sequence.

Rotate the crimp tool 90° between each successive crimp to prevent the connector from bowing.

Remove excess connector compound and deburr.

9. Clean the cable insulation with aluminum oxide cloth to remove all traces of semi-con shield. Solvent-clean the insulation surface. Always wipe from the cable end towards the semi-con. If the wiping is done the other way, the solvent may leach conducting particles from the semi-con and smear them onto the insulation.

10. Apply the stress relief mastic (SRM) by removing the release paper from the short, angle-cut piece of SRM. Make three to four tight wraps at each semi-con cutback. This SRM should be tapered to overlap the semi-con and insulation by approximately 1/4 inches.

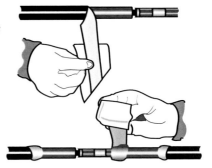

11. To apply SRM around the connector, remove release paper from the side of the long strips of SRM and roll into a convenient size. Applying half-laps, tightly wrap the SRM around the connector and exposed conductor. Fill in all voids.

Figure 5-94. Application of the stress relief mastic.

12. Tightly fill all gaps with the SRM up to the level of the cable insulation. The SRM should overlap onto the cable insulation at least 1/4 inch but not more than 1/2 inch.

13. Snip open the end of the discharge control compound (DCC) ampoule and apply a bead of compound around the circumference of the SRM edge on each side of the connector.

Figure 5-95. Cable showing the completed SRM covering and placement of the discharge control compound.

14. Apply the red sealing mastic by removing the release paper from the mastic and putting two wraps (one directly over the other) one inch back from the semi-con cutback. Do this on both sides.

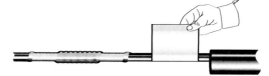

Figure 5-96. Cable showing placement of the protective foil.

15. Apply the protective foil by removing the release backing and wrapping the protective foil sheet around the semi-con layer of the cable. It should be placed right against (butted) the edge of the sealant. Repeat this step on the other side.

Note: The outer tubing will overlap onto the foil when shrunk. Do not remove the foil.

16. Install the dual-layer insulating/ shielding tubing and center it over the splice area. Using a propane torch, begin shrinking at the center of the tubing. Working with a smooth, brushing motion, move around the entire circumference of the tube. The reason for starting at the center and working out is to prevent the trapping of air inside the tubing. Air will cause bubbles and unevenness, resulting in uneven distribution of electrical field lines.

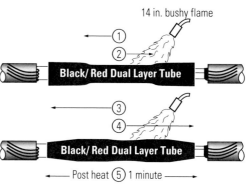

Figure 5-97.

Shrink towards one end and stop about 3 inches short of the end of the tubing. Begin shrinking towards the second end. Stop shrinking 3 inches from the end. Then finish shrinking the first end. Once completed, finish the second end. Then apply heat to the whole tubing for 45 seconds (post-heat). The finished tube should be tight and wrinkle-free.

Note: Adjust the torch as required to provide an overall 12 inch bushy flame. The FH-2629 torch pressure is set at 15 psi and has a blue flame. The FH-2609 torch pressure is set at 5 psi and will have a 3 to 4 inches yellow tip.

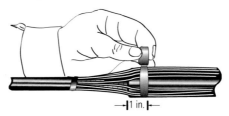

Figure 5-98. Application of grounding spring and joining of neutral strands.

17. To apply the grounding spring, place one wrap of the grounding spring around the dual-layer tubing 1 inch from the end of Side 1. Neatly lay all the neutral strands (evenly spaced) over the grounding spring and across the splice. Continue to wrap the grounding spring until it is completely applied. Bind in place with copper tape or copper shielding braid. These should be in the kit.

18. Twist the neutral strands from both sides of the splice together and join them using a suitable compression connector on Side 2. For larger neutrals, the strands may be divided into two groups. Bind the wires to the splice.

19. Build a waterstop and install a braid that will be used to bond the splice. The braid is a #4 AWG and has a solder block or moisture block at one end.

    Build the waterstop by applying two wraps of sealing mastic around the cable jacket just back from the jacket cutback on the neutral connector side of the splice (Side 2). Lay the braid lengthwise so that the moisture block is positioned over the sealant, and apply two more wraps of sealing mastic over the braid. This ensures that the moisture block is embedded in the mastic.

    Crimp one end of the braid to the neutral strands with a suitable compression connector. The other end of the braid will be used to bond the splice.

20. Clean both cable jackets 6 to 8 inches from the cutback and install the wraparound sealing (rejacketing) sleeve. Remove the release paper and position the sleeve so that the entire splice is covered. Ensure that the end or tail of the braid extends outside the sleeve.

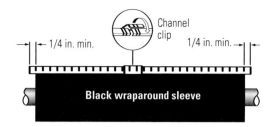

Figure 5-99.

21. Seal the sleeve shut by sliding the channels onto the butted rails of the wraparound sleeve. If two channels are needed, connect the channels with the retention clip. Use pliers to install the clip.

22. Using a propane torch, preheat evenly along both sides of the rails/channel area until this area begins to shrink. Begin shrinking the wraparound sleeve at the center and working towards the ends. Apply heat until the sleeve is fully shrunk and the heat sensitive point is completely converted. Continue heating the rail/channel area for another 5 second per foot. A white line should be visible in the channel gaps indicating sufficient heating.

Note: Heat-sensitive paint will turn black as sleeve shrinks into place.

23. Allow the splice to cool before moving or placing in service.

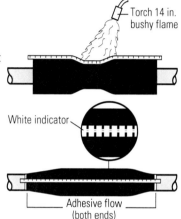

Figure 5-100.

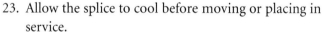

Figure 5-101. Complete non-tension splice of 13 kV concentric neutral XLPE URD/UD cable.

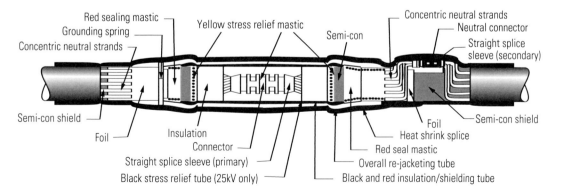

Figure 5-102. Non-tension 13 kV splice with a concentric neutral XLPE underground cable.

Splices and splice kits can vary, so you should always follow the manufacturer's instructions when doing a splice.

Primary 25 kV Underground Taped XLPE Cable Splice

Before starting any splicing job:

- Prepare the work area.

- Visually inspect for proper tapes.

- Read the manufacturer's instructions to familiarize yourself with the splice.

- Make sure that the proper tools are on hand and that cleanliness is observed throughout the procedure.

Note: Rubber protective gloves must be worn when applying isopropanol and other chemicals.

The steps to follow when doing a non-tension splice on 25 kV *concentric neutral* XLPE underground cable are:

1. Train the cable into the final position and cut, so both ends of the cables butt squarely together.

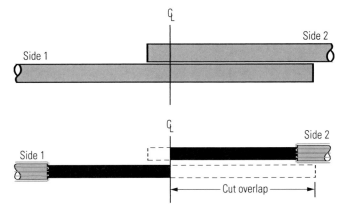

Figure 5-103. Determining centerline, cutting cable and folding neutral strands.

2. Strip back cable jacket 14 inches. Fold back the neutral wires and remove semi-conducting insulation 12-1/2 inches. Remove the cable insulation to a measurement of 1/2 of the length of the connector +1/2 inch . Pencil insulation back 2 inches. Fold back and lightly tape the neutral strands on each cable. When finished both ends of the cable should look like figure 5-104.

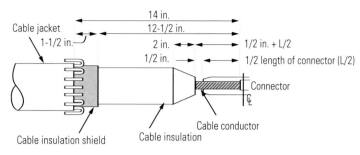

Figure 5-104. Measurements for splice.

3. Clean insulation with aluminum oxide cloth to remove all traces of semi-con shield and wipe with a clean cloth soaked in isopropanol. Always wipe from the cable end towards the semi-con. If the wiping is done the other way, the solvent may leach conducting particles from the semi-con and smear them onto the insulation.

Note: Rubber gloves must be worn when applying isopropanol.

4. Install, press and de-burr the compression connector.

Figure 5-105. Install, de-burr, and press the connector,

5. Apply half-lapped layers of semi-con tape to build up a smooth surface over the connector body. Overlap the tape slightly (1/8 in.) onto penciled portion of cable insulation.

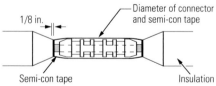

Figure 5-106. Applying the semi-con tape.

6. Measure the diameter of connector and semi-con tape (from Step 5) and write it down.

7. Apply half-lapped layers of 1 inch self-amalgamating (SAP) tape until flush with cable insulation.

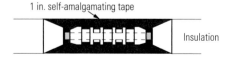

Figure 5-107. Applying the SAP tape.

8. Apply half-lapped layers of 2-inch self-amalgamating tape over the cable insulation and connector. Edges of SAP tape should be 5mm from cable semi-con cutoff. Buildup the insulation to a thickness of 1/2 inch. The final diameter of the built-up insulation should be the diameter measured in Step 6 plus $2 \times 1/2$ inch. This buildup diameter should be reached within 3 inches of the semi-con cutoff.

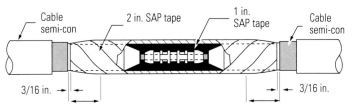

Figure 5-108. Building up the insulation.

Description	Cable Voltage	
	13 kV	25 kV
Thickness of insulation	5/16 in.	1/2 in.

Example:

If the diameter measured in Step 6 is 1 inch, then the diameter over the buildup insulation should be at least 2 inches, (1 inch + 2(1/2 inch)).

9. Apply the half-lapped layer of semi-con tape over the self-amalgamating tape. Overlap the semi-con tape onto the cable semi-con to within 3/8 inch of the jacket cutback.

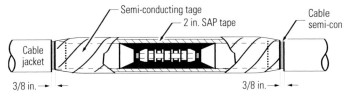

Figure 5-109. Applying semi-con over the SAP tape.

10. Apply quarter-lapped layers of shield braid over the semi-con tape and run shield to within 3/8 inch on one end only, such that the braid is connected to the concentric neutral when the water stop is made. End the shield braid 2 inches from the jacket cutback on the other side to ensure that there is no connection between the braid and the concentric neutral. Secure end of the braid with a wrap of PVC tape.

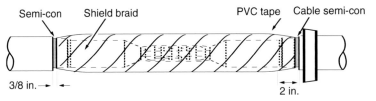

Figure 5-110. Applying the shield braid.

11. Make the waterstop as explained in "Waterstop Preparation."
See page 214, Step 4

12. Apply two half-lapped layers of 2-inch SAP tape over the splice. The SAP tape should overlap 3 inches onto the cable jacket.

13. Attach #2 AWG jumper to concentric neutral strands with a copper tap connector. Cover over the tap connector with a mastic pad.

Note: External bonding of the concentric neutral strands is only required on cable runs in excess of 1000 feet. For shorter runs, not bonding is required.

14. Taper over entire splice with two half-lapped layers of 1-1/2 inch PVC tape.

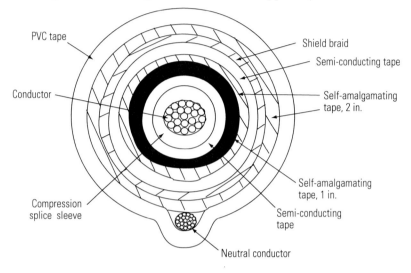

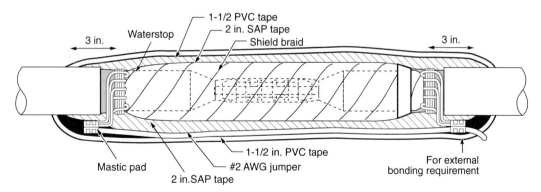

Figure 5-111. Completed sleeve.

15. If cable run is in excess of 1000 feet, bond splice as per company practices.

Primary 25 kV Underground Heat Shrinkable Cable Splice

Before starting any splicing job:

- Prepare the work area.

- Visually inspect the kit components.

- Read the manufacturer's instructions to familiarize yourself with the splice.

- Make sure that the proper tools are on hand and that cleanliness is observed throughout the procedure.

Note: Rubber protective gloves must be worn when applying isopropanol and other chemicals.

The steps to follow when doing a non-tension splice on 25 kV **concentric neutral** XLPE underground cable are:

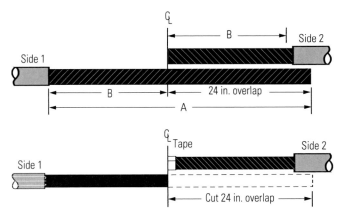

Figure 5-112. Determining centerline, cutting cable and folding neutral strands.

1. Train the cables so that they are in the correct location and position. Overlap the cables by 24 inches and straighten the splice area. The center for the splice will be at the end of Side 2 cable.

2. Remove the jacket (using skinning knife) on Side 1 to dimension A (dimension B plus 24 inches). Remove the jacket on Side 2 to dimension B. These dimensions are dependent on the cable size and the kit being used. Refer to the kit when doing a splice.

3. Fold the neutral strands (wires) back from Side 1, and cut Side 1 at the centerline using a cable cutter.

Table 1						
		A	**B**	**C**		**D**
Kit No.	**Conductor**	**Jacket Cutback/ Neutral Pullback Side 1**	**Jacket Cutback/ Neutral Pullback Side 2**	**Semi-con Cutback**	**Connector**	**Insulation Cutback**
SMOC 1270	500 kcmil, 15 kV	32-1/2 in.	8-1/2 in.	3-3/4 in.	PS 252	1-5/8 in.
SMOC 1271	750 kcmil, 15 kV	32 in.	8 in.	4-1/8 in.	PS 262	2 in.
SMOC 1272	500 kcmil, 25 kV	33-1/2 in.	9-1/2 in.	4-3/4 in.	PS 252	1-5/8 in.
SMOC 1273	750 kcmil, 25 kV	33-7/8 in.	9-7/8 in.	5-1/8 in.	PS 262	2 in.
SMOC 1284	#1, 25 kV	33 in.	9 in.	4-1/2 in.	PS 212	1-1/8 in.
SMOC 1285	500 kcmil, 25 kV	33-1/2 in.	9-1/2 in.	5-1/4 in.	PS 257	2 in.
SMOC 1302	#1/0, 25 kV	32 in.	8 in.	4-1/4 in.	PS 212	1-1/8 in.
SMOC 1260	#2, 25 kV	38 in.	14 in.	5-1/4 in.	PS 202	1 in.

4. Temporarily tape the neutral wire/strand ends to the semi-con layer on Side 2. Slide the heat shrink splice tubings over the cable jacket on Side 2. Then remove the tape and fold the neutral wires back over the jacket.

5. Remove the semi-con on both sides to dimension C. When removing the semi-con layer, make a clean cut with no jagged edges. Do not nick or cut the cable insulation.

6. Select the proper connector for the cable and for connecting the neutral wires/strands. This is dependent on cable type. The connectors are not always in the kit and you may have to obtain from stores.

7. On both sides remove the cable insulation half the connector length plus 1/2 inch to dimension D. Do not nick the conductor. When finished both cable ends should look similar to Figure 5-92.

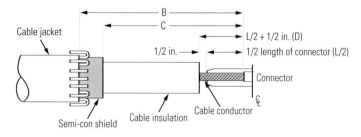

Figure 5-92. Measurements for splice.

8. Install the connector. Do this by putting the connector on one conductor and then pushing the other conductor into the other end. Push down on the connection until the conductors bottom out (hit the inside part of the connector).

To crimp the connector, consult the manufacturer's instructions to determine the correct dies and tool to use. The MD6 crimp tool is used for most underground cables. With the proper dies installed in the MD6, start crimping at the center of the connector. Move from the center towards the two cable ends in an alternating sequence.

Figure 5-114. Connector crimping details.

Rotate the crimp tool 90° between each successive crimp to prevent the connector from bowing.

Remove excess connector compound and deburr.

9. Clean the cable insulation with aluminum oxide cloth to remove all traces of semi-con shield. Solvent-clean the insulation surface. Always wipe from the cable end towards the semi-con. If the wiping is done the other way, the solvent may leach conducting particles from the semi-con and smear them onto the insulation.

10. Apply the stress relief mastic (SRM). Remove the release paper from the short, angle-cut piece of SRM. Make three to four tight wraps at each semi-con cutback. This SRM should be tapered to overlap the semi-con and insulation by approximately 1/4 inch.

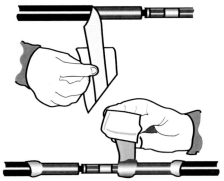

Figure 5-115. Application of the stress relief mastic.

11. To apply SRM around the connector, remove release paper from the side of the long strips of SRM and roll into a convenient size. By applying half-laps, tightly wrap the SRM around the connector and exposed conductor, filling in all voids.

12. Tightly fill all gaps with the SRM up to the level of the cable insulation. The SRM should overlap onto the cable insulation at least 1/4 inch but not more than 1/2 inch.

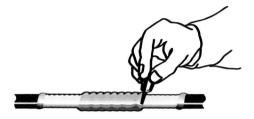

Figure 5-116. Cable showing the completed SRM covering and placement of the discharge control compound.

13. Install and center the stress control tube over the connector. Using a propane torch, begin shrinking the tube at the center. Move around the entire circumference of the tube using a smooth, brushing motion. After the center portion shrinks, work the torch towards one end and then towards the other end.

Note: Adjust the torch as required to provide an overall 12 inch bushy flame. The FH-2629 torch pressure is set at 15 psi and has a blue flame. The FH-2609 torch pressure is set at 5 psi and will have a 3 to 4 inch yellow tip.

Note: Do not point the flame at the cable semi-con layer.

14. Remove the release paper from the sealant strip and put two wraps around the cable on the semi-con. Butt the sealant strip up to the edge of the stress control tube. This is repeated at both ends.

15. Apply the protective foil. By removing the release backing and wrapping the protective foil sheet around the semi-con layer of the cable. It should be placed right against (butted) the edge of the sealant. Repeat this step on the other side.

Note: The outer tubing will overlap onto the foil when shrunk. Do not remove the foil.

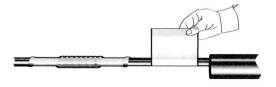

Figure 5-117. Cable showing placement of the protective foil.

16. Install the dual-layer insulating/shielding tubing and center it over the splice area. Using a propane torch, begin shrinking at the center of the tubing. Working with a smooth, brushing motion, move around the entire circumference of the tube. The reason for starting at the center and working out is to prevent the trapping of air inside the tubing. Air will cause bubbles and unevenness, resulting in uneven distribution of electrical field lines.

    Shrink towards one end and stop about 3 inches short of the end of the tubing. Begin shrinking towards the second end. Stop shrinking 3 inches from the end. Then finish shrinking the first end. Once completed, finish the second end. Then apply heat to the whole tubing for 45 seconds (post-heat). The finished tube should be tight and wrinkle-free.

17. To apply the grounding spring. Place one wrap of the grounding spring around the dual-layer tubing 1 inch from the end of Side 1. Neatly lay all the neutral strands (evenly spaced) over the grounding spring and across the splice. Continue to wrap the grounding spring until it is completely applied. Bind in place with copper tape or copper shielding braid. These should be in the kit.

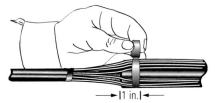

Figure 5-118. Application of grounding spring and joining of neutral strands.

18. Twist the neutral strands from both sides of the splice together and join them using a suitable compression connector on Side 2. For larger neutrals, the strands may be divided into two groups. Bind the wires to the splice.

19. Build a waterstop and install a braid that will be used to bond the splice. The braid is a #4 AWG and has a solder block or moisture block at one end.

    Build the waterstop by applying two wraps of sealing mastic around the cable jacket just back from the jacket cutback on the neutral connector side of the splice (Side 2). Lay the braid lengthwise so that the moisture block is positioned over the sealant, and apply two more wraps of sealing mastic over the braid. This ensures that the moisture block is embedded in the mastic.

    Crimp one end of the braid to the neutral strands with a suitable compression connector. The other end of the braid will be used to bond the splice.

20. Clean both cable jackets 6 to 8 inches from the cutback and install the wraparound sealing (rejacketing) sleeve. Remove the release paper and position the sleeve so that the entire splice is covered. Ensure that the end or tail of the braid extends outside the sleeve.

Figure 5-119.

21. Seal the sleeve shut by sliding the channels onto the butted rails of the wraparound sleeve. If two channels are needed, connect the channels with the retention clip. Use pliers to install the clip.

22. Using a propane torch, preheat evenly along both sides of the rails/channel area until this area begins to shrink. Begin shrinking the wraparound sleeve at the center and working towards the ends. Apply heat until the sleeve is fully shrunk and the heat-sensitive point is completely converted. Continue heating the rail/channel area for another 5 second per foot. A white line should be visible in the channel gaps indicating sufficient heating.

Note: Heat-sensitive paint will turn black as sleeve shrinks into place.

23. Allow the splice to cool before moving or placing in service.

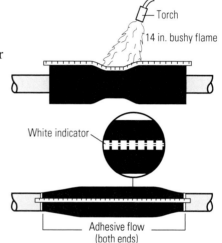

Figure 5-120.

Figure 5-121. Complete non-tension splice of 13 kV concentric neutral XLPE underground cable.

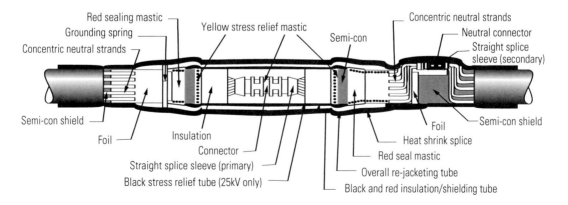

Figure 5-122. Non-tension 13 kV splice with a concentric neutral XLPE underground cable.

Splices and splice kits can vary, so you should always follow the manufacturer's instructions when doing a splice.

Primary 25 kV 3M Quick Splice Inline Splicing Kit (Kit 5420)

Before starting any splicing job:

- Prepare the work area.

- Check for proper kit (number and type).

- Visually inspect the kit components.

- Read the manufacturer's instructions to familiarize yourself with the splice.

- Make sure that the proper tools are on hand and that cleanliness is observed throughout the procedure.

Note: Rubber protective gloves must be worn when applying isopropanol and other chemicals.

Note: The splice that is explained in detail is a non-tension splice on 25 kV, 1/0 *concentric neutral* XLPE underground cable. Refer to the 3M instruction sheet for other voltages and conductor sizes.

Extruded Neutral

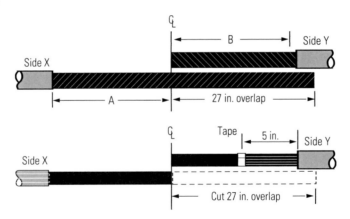

Figure 5-123. Determining centerline, folding neutral strands and cutting cable.

1. Train the cables so that they are in the correct location and position. Overlap the cables by 27 inch and straighten the splice area. The center for the splice will be at the end of Side Y cable.

2. Remove the jacket (using skinning knife) on Side X to (dimension A) 17 inches plus 27 inches. Remove the jacket on Side Y to (dimension B) 10 inches. These dimensions are dependent on the cable size and the kit being used. Refer to the kit when doing a splice.

3. Gently fold the neutral wires back over the cable jacket. Avoid making sharp bends.

4. Remove the semi-con 5-1/8 inch on each cable.

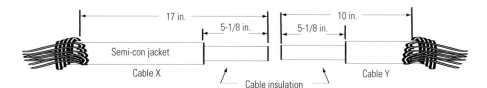

Figure 5-124. Measuring and cutting the cable.

5. Remove the insulation 1-5/8 inches on each cable and bevel the insulation 1/8 inch.

Note: A special 3M "CI" series connector is necessary for use in all quick splices. Connector CI-1/0-A will be used for this splice.

6. Clean the cable insulation with aluminum oxide cloth to remove all traces of semi-con shield. Solvent-clean the insulation surface. Always wipe from the cable end towards the semi-con. If the wiping is done the other way, the solvent may leach conducting particles from the semi-con and smear them onto the insulation.

7. In order to facilitate the splice installation, wrap a small amount of vinyl tape around the edge of the jacket on cable X to form a ramp (this tape will be removed later).

8. Lubricate the both cables with silicone grease and slide an end cap onto each cable. Clean and re-lubricate the insulation of cable X.

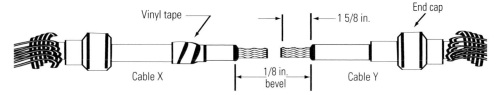

Figure 5-125. Installing end caps.

9. Install the splice body and 3M cold shrink splice jacket onto cable X.

Figure 5-126. Installing the splice body.

Note: If jacketed concentric neutral, install cold shrink tube at this time.

SYSTEM

DRAWINGS

MATERIALS

INSTALLING

SPLICING

FUSING

MAINTENANCE

TROUBLE

JOB SITE

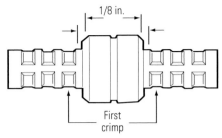

Figure 5-127. Special "CI" series connector.

10. Install the connector and crimp (2) with the BG die of the MD6. Refer to the connector crimping table for other dies.

11. Re-clean and lubricate the exposed insulation. Center the splice body over the connector.

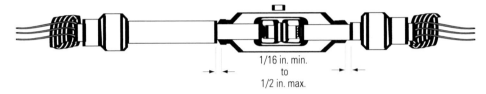

Figure 5-128. Center splice body and seat end caps.

12. Apply silicone grease over the exposed insulation.

13. Two locking grooves exist on the splice body Firmly seat one end cap against the splice body and twist onto the splice body.

Note: You should feel two snaps as the end caps are positioned against the splice body.

14. Check for proper spacing between the splice body and jacket of the other cable.

15. Firmly seat the other end cap against the splice body.

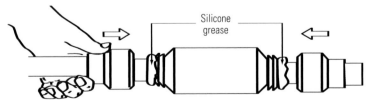

Figure 5-129. Install end cap.

16. Position concentric neutral wires back over cable and splice. Attach one strand from each cable to its respective grounding eye, returning it back to the neutral wire bundle.

17. Join neural wires using an appropriate connector(s). A low profile inline compression connector is recommended.

SYSTEM | DRAWINGS | MATERIALS | INSTALLING | **SPLICING** | FUSING | MAINTENANCE | TROUBLE | JOB SITE

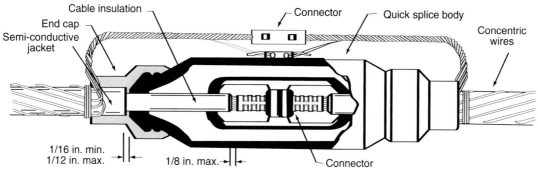

Figure 5-130. Join concentric neutrals over splice body.

Jacketed Concentric Neutral

The splicing procedures for the jacketed concentric neutral are the same as the extruded neutral, except, the cold shrink jacketing tube must be installed before pressing the sleeve.

18. On each side of the cable jacket opening, apply 3 wraps of rubber mastic) 1/4 inch from the end. Apply the mastic side towards the cable jacket.

Figure 5-131 Applying the rubber mastic seal.

19. Center the accessory splice jacket over the splice and exposed neutral wires. Hold the leading core end outside the tube as the assembly is moved into position.

Note: Center the rubber tube over the jacket opening, not the inner supporting core.

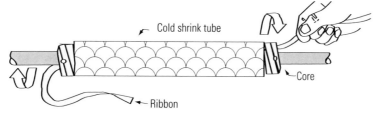

Figure 5-132. Cold shrink jacketing tube.

20. From each end of the tube assembly, remove the inner supporting core. Remove the cores by unwinding the ribbon in a counter-clockwise direction.

Tip: As the core is being unwound, an occasional tug on the ribbon may aid in its removal.

SPLICING

Primary 25 kV 3M Quick Splice II
Molded Rubber Cable Repair Splicing Kit (Kit 5451R)

Before starting any splicing job:

- Prepare the work area.

- Check for proper kit (number and type).

- Visually inspect the kit components.

- Read the manufacturer's instructions and the instructions to familiarize yourself with the splice.

- Make sure that the proper tools are on hand and that cleanliness is observed throughout the procedure.

Note: Rubber protective gloves must be worn when applying isopropanol and other chemicals.

Note: The splice that is explained in detail is a non-tension splice on 25 kV, 1/0 *concentric neutral* XLPE underground cable. Refer to the 3M instruction sheet for other voltages and conductor sizes.

1. Cut out damaged section of cable, but do not exceed 6 inches. Check to make certain that the cable insulation diameter is between 0.870 and 1.055 inches.

2. Measure 15 inches from the end of cable and remove the outer jacket on cable X. Carefully fold the neutral wires back over the cable.

3. Measure 7 inches from end of the cable and remove the outer jacket on cable Y. Carefully fold the neutral wires back over the cable.

4. Measure 4-3/4 inches from the end of the cable and remove the semi-con layer from the insulation.

5. Measure 1-1/2 inches and remove the insulation. Do not nick the conductor. Pencil the insulation 1/8 inch.

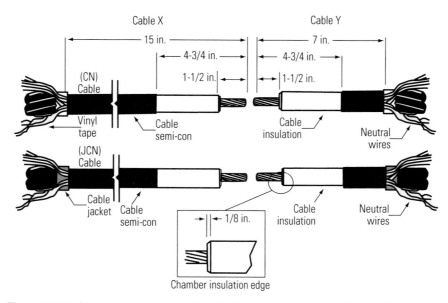

Figure 5-133. Measuring and removing the jacket, semi-con, and insulation for concentric neutral (top) and jacketted concentric neutral (bottom).

6. Clean the cables. Clean the insulation with aluminum oxide cloth to remove all traces of semi-con shield. Solvent-clean the insulation surface. Always wipe from the cable end towards the semi-con. If the wiping is done the other way, the solvent may leach conducting particles from the semi-con and smear them onto the insulation.

7. Slide the cold shrink splice jacket tube onto the cable. The cold shrink assembly is designed with two supporting cores. Make sure a core end is extended from each end of the assembly. Hold the leading core end outside the assembly when positioning onto cable.

Note: For cables with an external ground lead, refer to the 3M instruction sheet.

8. Install the 3M CIR connector onto cable X only and crimp with the MD6 (BG die).

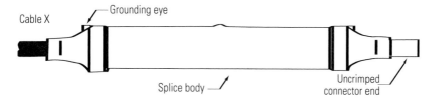

Figure 5-134. Installing the body splice on the cable.

9. Remove excess inhibitor from the connector and file off any sharp flashings.

10. Lubricate the connector, cable X insulation and both ends of splice bore with the silicone grease provided.

11. Slide the splice body onto connector and cable X until uncrimped connector end is exposed. For easier installation, the splice body may be rotated while being installed.

12. Slide accessory splice jacketing components onto the cable.

13. Connect exposed connector end to cable Y and crimp with the MD6 (BG die).

14. Remove excess inhibitor from the connector and file off any sharp flashings

15. Place a tape marker on cable Y semi-con insulation, 1/2 inch from end of cable semi-con.

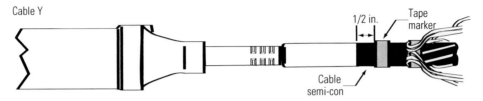

Figure 5-135. Install the cable and press, install the marker tape.

16. Lubricate exposed connector and cable Y insulation with silicone grease.

17. Center splice body over connector, so leading edge aligns with marker tape. Remove the marker tape.

Figure 5-136. Centering the splice body and aligning it with the tape.

18. Position concentric neutral wires back over cable and splice. Attach one strand from each cable to its respective grounding eye, returning it back to the neutral wire bundle.

19. Join neutral wires using an appropriate connector(s). A low profile inline compression connector is recommended.

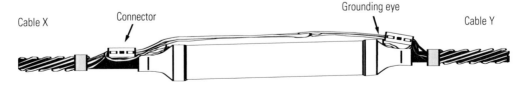

Figure 5-137. Joining the ground over the splice body.

20. On each side of the cable jacket opening, apply 3 wraps of rubber mastic, 1/4 inch from the end. Apply the mastic side towards the cable jacket.

Figure 5-138. Applying the rubber mastic seal.

21. Center the accessory splice jacket over the splice and exposed neutral wires. Hold the leading core end outside the tube as the assembly is moved into position.

Note: Center the rubber tube over the jacket opening, not the inner supporting core.

22. From each end of the tube assembly, remove the inner supporting core. Remove the cores by unwinding the ribbon in a counter-clockwise direction.

Tip: As the core is being unwound, an occasional tug on the ribbon may aid in its removal.

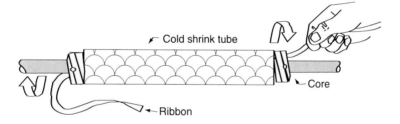

Figure 5-139. Cold shrink jacketing tube.

SYSTEM | DRAWINGS | MATERIALS | INSTALLING | SPLICING | FUSING | MAINTENANCE | TROUBLE | JOB SITE

MBSM Cable Rejacketing, Sleeve Outer Jacket Sheath Repair

Before starting any splicing job:

- Prepare the work area

- Check for proper kit (number and type)

- Visually inspect the kit components

- Read the manufacturer's instructions to familiarize yourself with the splice.

- Make sure that the proper tools are on hand and that cleanliness is observed throughout the procedure.

Note: Rubber protective gloves must be worn when applying isopropanol and other chemicals.

1. Determine the minimum length of MBSM required to cover the damaged jacket.

    Cut length of MBSM = damage + dimension A

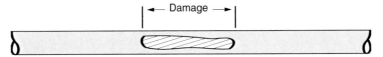

Figure 5-140. Measure the damaged cable.

2. Lay the MBSM on a flat surface and measure the required length. Using a straight edge or square, mark along the line to be cut. Cut line must be square as possible to the rails.

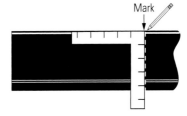

Figure 5-141. Mark the MBSM.

3. Cut the MBSM with a sharp knife or tin snips. The cut must be smooth with no jagged edges. When using a knife, support the MBSM on a flat surface and use a square or straight edge.

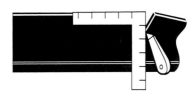

Figure 5-142. Cutting the MBSM.

4. For a neater installation, trim the overlap as shown.

5. Cut the channel 1/2 inch longer than the MBSM. Remove sharp corners and burrs. If more than one channel is required, lay the channels end to end before cutting.

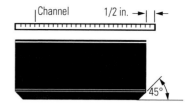

Figure 5-143. Cutting the channel and cropping the MBSM.

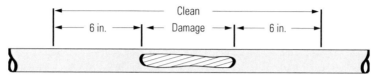

Figure 5-144. Cleaning the cable.

6. Using an approved solvent (isoproponal), clean and degrease the damaged area and the cable on either side of the damage. Remove any sharp points from the damaged area to be covered with MBSM.

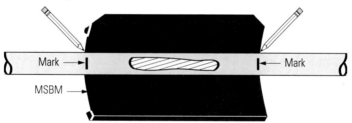

Figure 5-145. Centering the sleeve and marking the cable.

7. Center the sleeve over the damaged area and mark the cable.

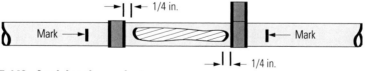

Figure 5-146. Applying the sealant.

8. Apply one complete wrap of sealant 1/4 inch from the edge of the damaged jacket. This will be inside the previously made centering marks.

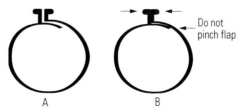

Figure 5-147. Position the sleeve over the damaged conductor.

SYSTEM | DRAWINGS | MATERIALS | INSTALLING | **SPLICING** | FUSING | MAINTENANCE | TROUBLE | JOB SITE

9. Remove the plastic protective wrapper from the wraparound sleeve before installing. Center the sleeve between the cable marks and butt the two top rails together. Do not pinch the flap where the two ends connect.

Figure 5-148. Installation of one channel.

10. If only one channel in required: Butt the rails together and slide the channel over the rails. Center the sleeve between the two marks.

Channels must extend beyond the edge of the sleeve.

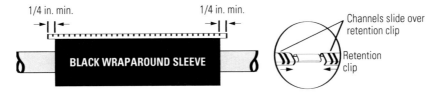

Figure 5-149. Heating and shrinking the sleeve.

11. If two channels are required: slide the metal retention clip onto the butted rails. Connect the two channels with the short channel retention clip. Use pliers to install the clip.

12. Using a propane torch, preheat evenly along both sides of the rails/channel area until this area begins to shrink. Begin shrinking the wraparound sleeve at the center and working towards the ends. Apply heat until the sleeve is fully shrunk and the heat-sensitive point is completely converted. Continue heating the rail/channel area for another 5 second per foot. A white line should be visible in the channel gaps indicating sufficient heating.

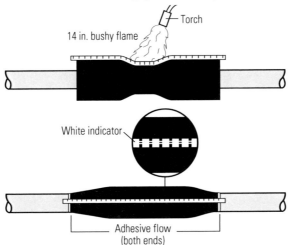

Figure 5-150.

Bond the Splice(s)

Bonding together of metallic and semi-conducting components eliminates possible voltage differences between them. Voltage differences cause damage to equipment and danger to personnel.

Bonding of the splice is required only if the splice is in a manhole. The bonding is completed by bonding all the splices together using a No. 2 copper conductor and compression tap connectors.

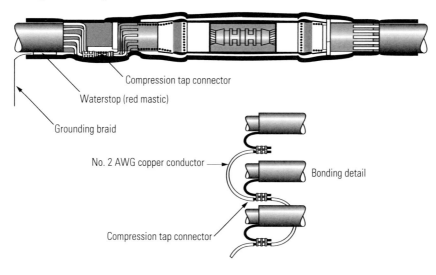

Figure 5-151. Manhole splice and bonding details.

The connectors are used to attach the grounding braid to the copper conductor. Once all the splices are bonded together, the last piece of the copper conductor is attached to the bonding window of the manhole using another compression connector.

Terminate Primary Cables

Introduction

Terminating cable can be defined as installing a device on the end of a cable that allows it to be connected to the equipment in the system. Although there are different types of terminating devices, the steps involved in installing them are very similar. The installation of a terminating device can be divided into cable preparation, termination and reconstruction procedures. All outdoor terminations must perform four functions. They must provide a stress relief at the end of the terminated shield, protect against tracking or burning on the exposed surface of the termination, keep moisture out of the cable, and protect against flashover. The use of a stress cone is the most common method of reducing the stresses at the end of the shield. The factory molded kits are designed to fit a range of underground cables and comes complete with a stress cones that is pre-molded also designed to fit a range of cable insulation diameters.

Upon successful completion of this section, you will be able to identify, describe and perform the various type of underground terminations. You will also be able to describe and perform the bonding procedures required for each type of termination (elbow and terminator) and the mounting procedures.

Note: The terminations explained in this section are for a 25 kV, 1/0 XLPE cable with a concentric neutral underground cable. Termination for a tape shielded cable is explained in the XLPE feeder section.

Note: Refer to the appropriate manufacturer's instruction sheet before making any splice.

Terminations must perform four functions:

- Provide stress relief at the end of the terminated shield

- Protect against tracking or burning on the exposed surface of the termination

- Keep moisture out of the cable

- Protect against flashover

At one time, stress cones were used to reduce the stresses at the end of the shield. Now the termination components/devices have stress relief or cones built into them so that the premolded or tape-made stress cone is not required.

As with splices, there are concise measurements and instructions that must be followed. Read all instructions before starting a termination. The objective is to complete a successful and quality termination.

The topics covered are:

- Tools and materials

- Terminate primary underground cable using a heat shrinkable terminator

- Mount the terminator

- Bond the terminator

- Terminate primary underground cable using an elbow

- Mount the elbow

- Bond the cable (elbow)

- Energize the cable

Tools and Materials

Terminating kits are used when doing a termination. The kit used depends on the size and voltage of the cable as well as where the cable is going to be connected (transformer, junction box, switchgear, pole). These kits have specific instructions for the components in them. You should always check the kit to ensure that all the components and instructions are present.

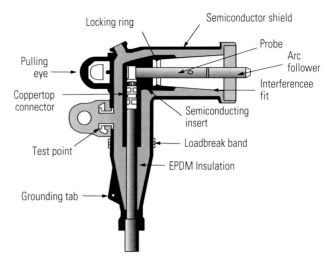

Figure 5-152. Terminating device (loadbreak elbow).

The tools used to do a primary underground cable termination are the same as those used to do a primary underground cable splice. Refer to the section "Splice Primary Underground Cable" for this information.

For the most part, the various tubes and mastic materials used in doing a splice are also used in terminating a cable. The main difference is that the jacket replacement tubing is not needed since a terminating device is installed. The terminating devices can be premolded, heat shrinkable, cold shrinkable or hand-taped.

Terminators consist of a body (insulation tubing) and skirts. The skirts serve two purposes:

- To protect the terminated cable end from rain.

- To increase the tracking distance (distance that the electricity has to jump or travel to reach ground).

Terminators are mounted in an upright (vertical) position in switchgear, on terminal poles or in customer's indoor vaults.

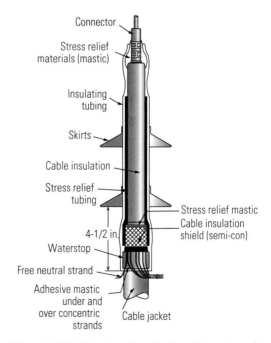

Figure 5-153. Terminating device - in/out door (terminator).

Loadbreak elbows are connected to transformers or junction bars. When installing an elbow, you would most likely use the tapes mentioned in the splicing chapter. The tapes regularly used are:

• Self-amalgamating polyisobutylene tape (SAP)

• Polyvinyl chloride tape (PVC)

• Semi-conducting shielding tape (semi-con)

Terminate Primary Underground Cable Using a Heat Shrinkable Terminator

Before starting any terminating job:

- Prepare the work area.

- Visually inspect the kit components.

- Read the manufacturer's instructions and the instructions to familiarize yourself with the termination.

- Be sure the proper tools are on hand and that cleanliness is observed throughout the procedure.

To terminate a 13 kV/25 kV concentric neutral XLPE underground cable using a heat shrinkable terminator:

1. Phase the cable to be terminated and check the temporary tag to determine where the cable will be connected or mounted.

   Train the cable so that you have sufficient length to reach the termination point. Leave slack if required.

2. Remove the jacket and separator tape to a dimension of 11 inches plus L from the cable end. L is the strip length required for the connector. Each connector has to be measured to determine what L equals. Remember to allow 1/4 inch for expansion when crimping the connector.

3. Bend the concentric neutral strands (wires) back along the jacket.

4. Remove the semi-conducting shielding layer (semi-con) to a dimension of 9 inches plus L + 1/4 inch from the cable end. Make a clean cut with no jagged edges. Do not cut into cable insulation.

5. Remove the insulation to L dimension + 1/4 inch. Do not nick the conductor.

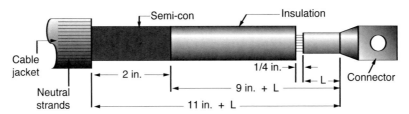

Figure 5-154. Cable preparation dimensions for concentric neutral XLPE cable.

6. Install the connector. It may be a compression connector or a lug connector. This depends on where the terminator is going to be installed, for example, mounted on a bracket (compression connector) or bolted to the equipment (lug connector). Wire brush the conductor and immediately push it into the connector until the conductor firmly butts against the end of the connector. This eliminates any potential oxidation.

The connector is installed by crimping it onto the cable end. You will have to consult the manufacturer's instructions to determine the correct dies and tool to use. When using the Burndy MD6 crimping tool, install the correct dies in the MD6 and start crimping at the top of the connector and move towards the cable. Rotate the crimp tool 90° between each successive crimp to prevent the connector from bowing.

Deburr the connector. Remove excess inhibitor and metal filings from the assembly.

7. Clean the cable insulation to remove any residual carbon particles on the insulation by wiping with a solvent-soaked, lint-free cloth. Use aluminum oxide cloth to remove any semi-con traces. Wipe from connector to ground end (cable jacket).

8. Lift the neutral strands away from the cable jacket. Solvent wipe the jacket for 2 inches below the jacket cutback.

Using light tension, wrap two layers of sealant mastic around the jacket just below the cutback under the neutral strands.

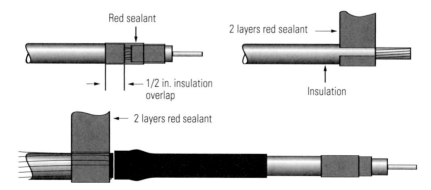

Figure 5-155. Using sealant and neutral strands to build a waterstop.

Fold the concentric neutral strands back over the jacket and press them into the sealant. Wrap two more layers of sealant over the neutral strands. Ensure that the strands are totally embedded in the sealant. This area will act as a waterstop.

9. To apply the angle-cut piece of stress relief material/mastic (SRM). Remove the release paper and place the point of the SRM at the edge of the semi-con cutback (with the angle pointing away from the cutback).

Pull the SRM to half its original width while wrapping it around the cable. Apply two or three wraps and ensure that there are no spaces or edges. The semi-con must taper towards the insulation. This will assist in controlling electrical stress at that point. The SRM must overlap the insulation and semi-con by 1/8 to 1/4 inch. Since the kit usually contains more SRM than required, only use what is required and leave the rest.

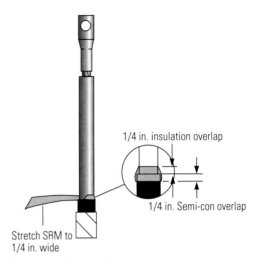
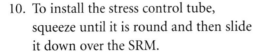

Figure 5-156. Application of the stress relief material (mastic).

10. To install the stress control tube, squeeze until it is round and then slide it down over the SRM.

Position it so that it overlaps the semi-con by 1-1/2 inches. Begin shrinking the tube at the ground end. Move the torch with a smooth brushing motion around the circumference of the tube from the ground end to the top of the tube.

11. Inspect the surface to ensure that the tube is evenly shrunk and conforms to the cable under it. To correct flat spots, reheat the tube.

12. Solvent-clean the connector barrel. Then, using light tension, wrap the sealant onto the connector barrel. Use the sealant to build up the diameter of the connector to that of the insulation. Overlap the sealant onto the insulation by 1 inch.

13. Install the insulating tubing (HVTM) by positioning it so that it covers the sealant on the jacket. Shrink it into place starting at the ground end.

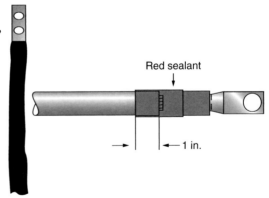

Figure 5-157. Application of sealant on connector barrel and installed insulating tubing (HVTM).

Apply extra heat at the ground and connector ends to soften the sealant. Also heat the bare portion of the connector for 10 seconds. This will help to soften the sealant.

Inspect the surface to ensure that there are no flat spots and that the tube has been evenly shrunk. The entire tube should be wrinkle-free with the profile or image of the inner components clearly defined. If flat spots exist, correct them by reheating the tube.

If the HVTM surface has been burned or blistered, after the tubing has cooled clean it off with a solvent wipe.

In the case of a lug connector, if the tubing extends onto the flat area (contact area) of the connector, remove that excess by ring-cutting once the tubing has cooled (hot tubing will split). It must not interfere with good contact being made between the lug and other equipment.

14. Install the skirts by positioning the first skirt at 4-1/2 inch from the bottom of the red tube. Use pliers to hold the edge of the skirt to keep it in place and straight. Shrink it into place by brushing the flame tip around the outside of the skirt collar. Only the collar will shrink. If a second skirt is needed, position it approximately 4-1/2 inch above the first skirt and shrink it into place.

Note: One skirt for 13 kV two skirts for 25 kV.

This completes the installation of the heat shrinkable terminator. Now the terminated cable must be mounted and bonded.

Before doing the mounting and bonding, form a tail with the concentric neutral strands. Leave one free neutral strand. The tail will be used for the bonding process and the free neutral will be used in the mounting process.

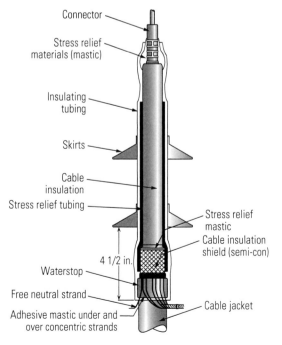

Figure 5-158. Complete heat shrinkable terminator assembly.

3M Quick Term II Silicone Rubber Termination (with high-K stress relief)

Before starting any terminating:

- Prepare the work area.

- Visually inspect the kit components.

- Read the manufacturer's instructions and the instructions in to familiarize yourself with the termination.

- Be sure the proper tools are on hand and that cleanliness is observed throughout the procedure.

To terminate a 13 kV/25 kV concentric neutral XLPE underground cable using a cold-shrinkable terminator:

1. Phase the cable to be terminated and check the temporary tag to determine where the cable will be connected or mounted.

   Train the cable so that you have sufficient length to reach the termination point. Leave slack if required.

2. Remove the jacket and separator tape to a dimension of 10-1/2 inches plus L from the cable end. L is the strip length required for the connector. Each connector has to be measured to determine what L equals. Remember to allow 1/4 inch for connector growth during compression (crimping).

3. Remove the semi-conducting shielding layer (semi-con) to a dimension of 9 inches plus L + 1/4 inch from the cable end. Make a clean cut with no jagged edges. Do not cut into cable insulation.

4. Remove the insulation to L dimension + 1/4 inch. Do not nick the conductor.

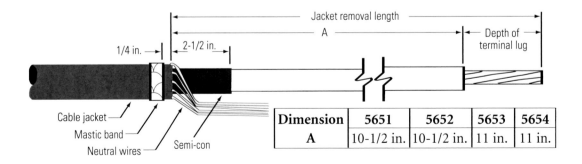

Dimension	5651	5652	5653	5654
A	10-1/2 in.	10-1/2 in.	11 in.	11 in.

Figure 5-159. Measuring and removal of the jacket, semi-con, and insulation.

5. Tie down concentric neutral with bonding wire 5/8 inch above jacket cutback. Select the mastic strip from the kit and remove the white release liners. Using high tension, wrap a band of mastic around the cable jacket 1/4 inch from the cut edge. Cut off the excess mastic strip.

6. Bend the concentric neutral strands (wires) back over the applied sealing mastic and compress neutral wires into the mastic. Apply sealing mastic over bent back concentric neutrals and secure to the cable jacket 2-1/2 inch below jacket cut edge using vinyl tape or binding wire.

Note: Do not extend vinyl tape wrapping more than 1/4 inch beyond mastic strip.

7. Place a marker tape 4 inch back from the semi-con leading edge.

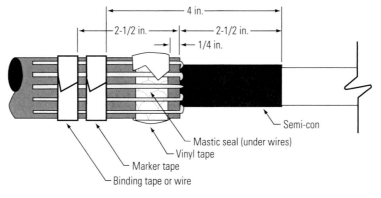

Figure 5-160. Prepare concentric neutral.

Note: The 3M Quick Term II are designed to fit over the Scotchlok and 3M copper and aluminum lugs. If other lugs will not fit through the core of the terminator, clean the insulation and slide the terminator onto the cable before installing the lug. Do ***not*** remove the core at this time.

8. Position the connector/lug and crimp with the BG die MD6. Remove excess inhibitor and burrs from the connector/lug.

Figure 5-161. Installing the connector lug.

9. Clean the cable insulation to remove any residual carbon particles on the insulation by wiping with a solvent-soaked, lint-free cloth. Use aluminum oxide cloth to remove any semi-con traces. Wipe from connector to ground end (cable jacket).

10. Cover the edge of the semi-con insulation shield with a liberal coating of silicone grease. (With the 3M Quick Term II Kit, the silicone grease does not serve as a lubricant, but is used to fill the step in the semi-con cutoff).

Note: If a 3M designed stem connector is not used, a track resistant moisture seal must be made between the termination insulator and the connector/lug using gray Scotch Rubber Electrical Tape (contained in the kit). After removing the two clear release liners, wrap a band of silicone tape around the base of the terminal lug.

Note: If barrel diameter is equal to or greater than the cable primary insulation, the tape should not exceed 2 layers.

If barrel diameter is smaller than the cable primary insulation, use one full tape strip to form the tape band.

Silicone grease   Gray silicone tape

Figure 5-162. Complete installation of the connector lug.

13. Slide the termination body onto the cable and remove the core. Starting with the loose end, pull while unwinding in a counter-clockwise. Make sure the termination body (not the core) is butted up to the edge of the marker tape.

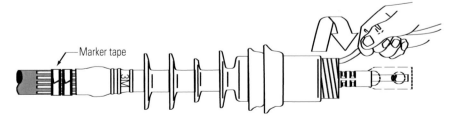

Marker tape

Figure 5-163. Installing the terminator.

Note: Once the termination insulator has made contact over the mastic seal area, there is no need to continue supporting the assemble. Do not push or pull on the termination assembly while removing the core material.

14. With the termination installed, complete the lug area moisture seal using gray by Scotch No. 70 silicone rubber electrical tape. Overlap the termination insulator by approximately 1 inch and extend the tape wrapping over the non-crimped region of the lug/connector barrel.

15. Remove the previously installed marker tape.

16. Collect concentric neutral wires together and connect to system ground according to company practices.

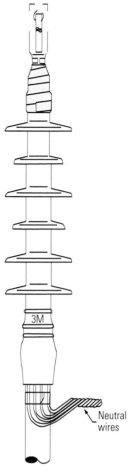

Neutral wires

Figure 5-164. Completed termination.

Elastimold Single-Piece Outdoor Terminator

Before starting any terminating job:

- Prepare the work area.

- Visually inspect the kit components.

- Read the manufacturer's instructions to familiarize yourself with the termination.

- Be sure the proper tools are on hand and that cleanliness is observed throughout the procedure.

To terminate a 13 kV/25 kV concentric neutral XLPE underground cable using a heat shrinkable terminator:

1. Phase the cable to be terminated and check the temporary tag to determine where the cable will be connected or mounted.

    Train the cable so that you have sufficient length to reach the termination point. Leave slack if required.

2. Remove the jacket and separator tape to a dimension of 15 inch from the end. Using the material supplied, fold the concentric neutral back and make a water stop. Twist the loose concentric wires together to form a ground lead.

3. Measure the cable 1-7/8 inches from the end and carefully remove (do not nick the conductor) the insulation.

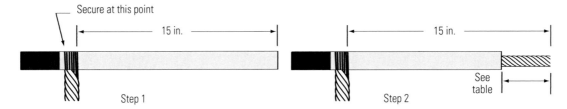

Conductor Contact Style	Conductor Size	Remove Insulation
![-4 (Universal Rod)] -4 (Universal Rod)	No. 6 thru 1/0 Str. Contact 00500180 to 00500220, 00501230, 00501240	1-7/8 in.
	No. 1 thru 4/0 Str. Contact 00500230 to 00500270	3-3/4 in.

Figure 5-165. Measuring and removing the jacket.

4. Remove the semi-con for a distance of 6 inches from the end of the cut insulation. Bevel the edge of the insulation 1/4 inch.

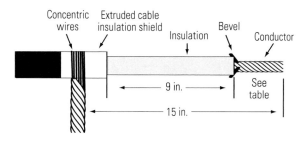

Figure 5-166. Removing the semi-con and insulation.

5. Clean the cable insulation to remove any residual carbon particles on the insulation by wiping with a solvent-soaked, lint-free cloth. Use aluminum oxide cloth to remove any semi-con traces. Wipe from connector to ground end (cable jacket).

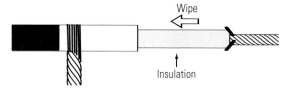

Failure to remove all conductive residue from cable insulation will be cause for failure

Figure 5-167. Clean and mark cable (note the wiping arrow).

6. Mark the cable with vinyl tape 1 inch from the end of the cut insulation. To prevent the cable conductor form damaging the inside of the terminator, wrap a piece of tape around the leading edge of the conductor.

Note: Damage to the inner surface of the terminator could result in premature failure.

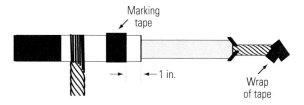

Figure 5-168. Clean and mark cable (note the wiping arrow).

7. Apply lubricant (supplied) or Elastimold approved lubricant sparingly to the cable insulation and to the inside base surface of the terminator.

Note: Do not substitute other lubricants, as this may be harmful the terminator or cable.

8. Using a spiral motion, slide the terminator housing down the cable until the base of the terminator housing lines up with the tape on the cable. The top of the terminator should be flush with the end of the cable insulation.

9. Check the distance from the top of the terminator housing to the end of the conductor. Do not proceed if the measurement is incorrect. Recheck the previous steps.

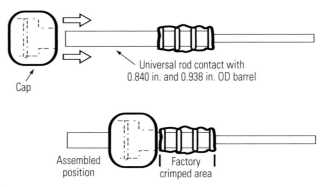

10. Apply lubricant (supplied) or Elastimold approved lubricant to the inside of the rubber cap and outside of the conductor contact.

Figure 5-169. Installing the rubber cap on the conductor.

11. Slide the rubber cap onto the conductor contact starting from the bottom, making sure that the small inside diameter of the cap goes on first.

12. Remove the tape from the conductor and brush the conductor with inhibitor. Place the bare wire over the conductor and immediately slide the contact on the conductor. Clean the excess inhibitor from around the top of the terminator. Slide the rubber cap down on the contact so it is fully seated and the grove in the bottom of the cap snaps into place over the matching ring on the top of the terminator housing.

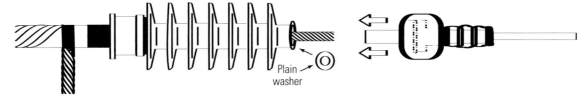

Figure 5-170. Installing the conductor contact on the conductor.

13. Start the first crimp at the upper (top) crimp mark on the contact, crimping towards the terminator and rotating each successive crimp 90°. When crimping, the contact should be held tightly and pushed down towards the plain washer. Check position of the terminator cap to be sure that the cap did not move during the crimping of the connector. If necessary, re-position.

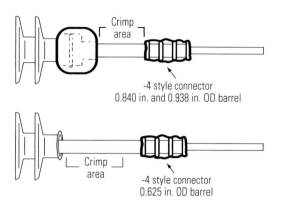

Figure 5-171. Crimping the connector.

14. If the terminator is not bracketed, place the grounding clamp around the terminal base. It is to be located directly under the shoulder and above the projecting rib. Remove the marking tape and wipe off any grease on the cable. Insert a separate copper wire from the terminator ground lug to the ground lead.

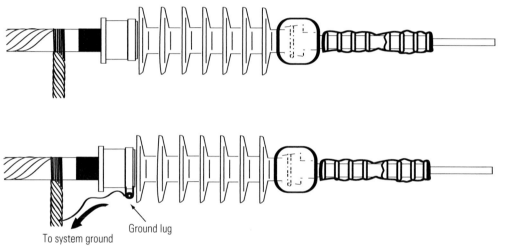

Figure 5-172. Installing the ground wire to the terminator.

SYSTEM | DRAWINGS | MATERIALS | INSTALLING | SPLICING | FUSING | MAINTENANCE | TROUBLE | JOB SITE

Mount the Terminator

Once the terminator has been installed on the cable end it must be mounted. It can be mounted in a switchgear or on a terminal pole.

To mount the terminator, a bracket attached to it. To install the bracket:

1. Attach the mounting bracket to the terminator by tightening the upper clamp around the bottom of the insulation tubing. Do not over-tighten. Tighten the lower clamp firmly over the cable jacket.

2. Attach the free neutral strand to the mounting bracket via the grounding lug. See Figure 5-141 for the complete mounting assembly.

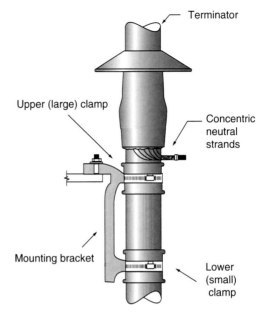

Figure 5-173. Mounting bracket attachment for heat shrinkable terminator.

Now the terminator and mounting bracket can be attached (bolted) to either a support bracket under the fuse side of a switchgear, or to a bracket on the terminal pole. Figure 5-142 shows it mounted or attached to a terminal pole.

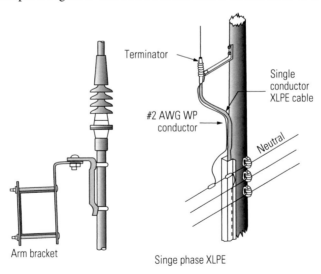

Figure 5-174. Termination of primary underground cable on a pole.

Bond the Cable

Bonding together of metallic and semi-conducting components eliminates possible voltage differences that may result in damage to equipment and danger to personnel.

The cable must be bonded to the ground bus in the switchgear or to the neutral wire on a pole.

To bond the cable in a switchgear, use a copper tap connector, a No. 2 copper conductor and a C-type compression connector. Attach the tail formed with the neutral strands to a No. 2 copper conductor using a copper tap connector. Then attach the other end of the conductor to the ground bus in the switchgear using the C-type compression connector.

To bond the cable on a pole, use a copper tap connector, a #2 copper conductor and a compression connector. Attach the tail formed with the neutral strands to a No. 2 copper conductor using a copper tap connector. Wrap the conductor around the cable and run it down to the neutral wire. Attach the conductor to the neutral wire using a compression connector.

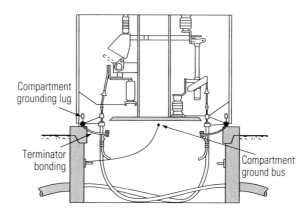

Figure 5-175. Bonding of terminator in a switchgear.

If lightning arresters are used, they must also be bonded to the terminator with a piece of No. 2 copper conductor.

Note: Remember that the temporary tags must now be replaced with permanent tags. Refer to the section Install underground Cable for information on permanent tags.

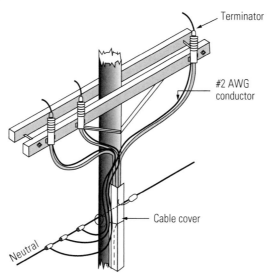

Figure 5-176. Terminator bonded on a pole.

Terminate Primary Underground Cable Using an Elbow

Before starting any terminating job do the following:

- Prepare the work area.

- Visually inspect the kit components.

- Read the manufacturer's instructions to familiarize yourself with the termination.

- Be sure the proper tools are on hand and that cleanliness is observed throughout the procedure.

Note: The termination (elbow) explained in this section are for a 25 kV, 1/0 XLPE cable with a concentric neutral underground cable. A tape-shielded cable will be explained in the XLPE feeder section.

Refer to the appropriate manufactures instruction sheet before making any splice.

To do a termination on a concentric neutral cable using an elbow:

1. Train the cable so that there is sufficient length to reach the termination point. Leave slack, by shoving down into duct, so cable is slack to reach stand off position.

2. Position the cable at the bushing centerline and parallel to the apparatus. If there are bends in the top 16 inches of cable, train it until it is straight.

   Cut the cable square at the centerline of the bushing. (To a maximum of 1" below center of bushing).

3. Measuring from the cable end, remove 9 inches of cable jacket.

4. Build a waterstop. The purpose of the waterstop is to prevent water from migrating along the concentric neutral strands (wires) or from the concentric neutral ground connection. To prepare a waterstop:

   - Tie down concentric neutral strands approximately 1/2 inch above the jacket cutback with a No. 14 AWG copper wire. The No. 14 AWG copper wire is referred to as a tie wire.

   - Cut a 3/8 inch strip out of a mastic pad. Stretch the mastic strip until the plastic backing comes off, and apply it so that it covers the neutral strands between the tie wire and the jacket cutback. Ensure that the mastic fills the gaps between the strands (force it into the gaps). This will result in an effective waterstop.

   - Fold back the concentric neutral strands.

- Cut a strip 3/4 inch wide from the mastic pad and use it to cover the exposed neutral strands and the first mastic layer.

- Force the mastic of this second layer between the strands by binding down the pad with another tie wire. The waterstop is now complete.

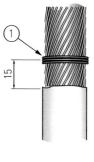

15

① Step 1 - Tie down concentric neutral strands 5/8 in. above jacket cutback

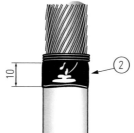

10

② Step 2 - Take 3/8 in. wide strip cut from mastic pad and cover over neutral strands between the wire and jacket cutback Force mastic into gap between strands. The mastic pad must be placed with the mastic on the inside (vinyl side out).

③ Step 3 - Fold back concentric neutral strands.

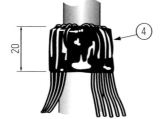

20

④ Step 4 - Take 3/4 in. wide strip cut from mastic pad and cover over exposed neutral strands and first mastic pad (vinyl side out).

⑤ Step 5 - Force second mastic pad between strands by binding down pad with tie wire.

Figure 5-177. Steps involved in building a waterstop.

5. Form a tail with the concentric neutral strands. Leave one strand of the concentric neutral unbundled. This strand will be used to bond the elbow to the cable (bleed or drain wire). The tail will be used for bonding.

6. Remove the semi-con to a point 6-7/8 inches from the end of the connector. Do not nick the insulation. Make a clean cut with no jagged edges.

7. Since the connectors will vary in size, measure the inside of the connector. Remove this amount of insulation (usually between 1 and 2 inches) from the cable end. It is advisable to leave 1/4 inch for expansion when crimping the connector. Do not nick the conductor.

8. The installation of the elbow is easier if the edge of the insulation is chamfered or slightly beveled. Chamfer for approximately 1/16 inch to 1/8 inch at a 45° angle.

9. Wire brush the conductor and immediately push it into the compression connector. The conductor must butt against the end of the connector. Rotate the connector until it is positioned with a flat side facing the bushing and install probe before pressing to ensure correct alignment.

SYSTEM | DRAWINGS | MATERIALS | INSTALLING | **SPLICING** | FUSING | MAINTENANCE | TROUBLE | JOB SITE

10. Consult the table for the crimp tool and the dies required. Using the correct tool and die, begin to crimp the connector starting at the end of the connector and moving towards the insulation.

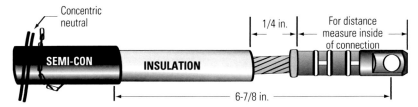

Figure 5-178. Dimensions for removal of semi-con and insulation.

Crimp in the sequence indicated without overlapping crimps or having a partial crimp on the end of the connector. (Each connector is marked with the the number of crimps required.) Rotate crimp tool 90° between each successive crimp.

Smooth any sharp edges on the surface of the crimped connector. This can be done with the aluminum oxide cloth, or a sharp file. Use a lint-free cloth to remove any metal filings and excess inhibitor (Penatrox) squeezed from the connector.

11. Clean the cable insulation with the aluminum oxide cloth to remove all traces of the semi-con and foreign material, then wipe with a clean cloth soaked in isopropanol. The cable insulation must be cleaned before and during the installation of the elbow.

12. Lubricate the exposed cable insulation and the mouth of the elbow (where the cable will go) using silicone grease or the grease that comes with the elbow.

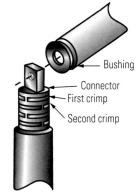

Figure 5-179. The connector crimped and aligned with the bushing.

Slowly push and twist the elbow onto the cable until the connector reaches the top of the inside of the elbow.

Clean off excess lubricant with a lint-free cloth. Make sure that no lubricant enters the threaded part of the connector, as this will prevent a good contact between the elbow probe and connector and may cause overheating.

13. Orient the elbow so that the elbow probe (sometimes called the contact probe) can be screwed into the hole of the connector.

Insert the elbow probe into the connector and finger-tighten to avoid crossthreading. Complete the tightening with the probe wrench.

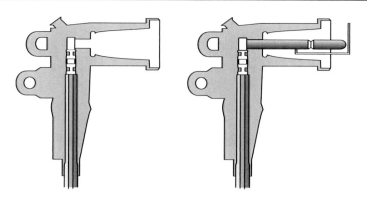

Figure 5-180. Installation of the elbow and the elbow probe (contact probe).

14. Attach a bonding wire to the tail formed with the concentric neutrals. Measure a length of No. 2 copper conductor (bonding wire) long enough to be connected to the ground bus and to allow the elbow to be moved from the bushing to a parking stand. Use a copper tap connector to attach the bonding wire to the tail.

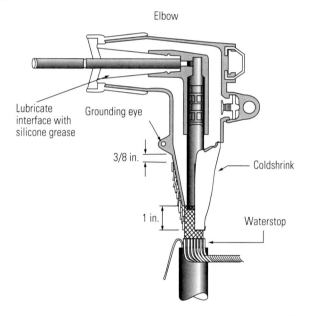

Figure 5-181. Arrangement of the elbow, the connectors and the SAP and PVC tape or a coldshrink.

15. Apply a half-lapped layer of self-amalgamating (SAP) tape over the elbow, cable jacket and tap connector.

16. Apply a half-lapped layer of PVC tape over the SAP tape.

Note: Self-amalgamating tape and PVC tape only required in below-surface installations.

Note: A 6 inch long piece of heat shrink or cold shrink tube can be used in place of the PVC and SAP tape.

17. Connect the free neutral strand (bleed or drain wire) to the grounding eye on the elbow by putting it through the eye and twisting it.

Note: To ensure the elbow does not "pop off" the bushing while energized, seat the elbow on the bushing firmly until the elbow clicks into position.

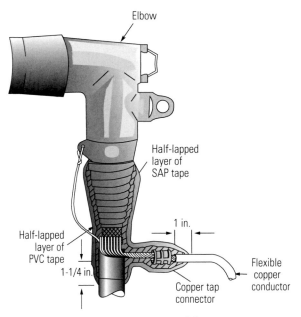

Figure 5-182. Completed elbow connector assembly.

Terminate Primary Underground Cable Using an Elbow (3M Cold Shrink)

Before starting any terminating job:

- Prepare the work area.

- Visually inspect the kit components.

- Read the manufacturer's instructions to familiarize yourself with the termination.

- Be sure the proper tools are on hand and that cleanliness is observed throughout the procedure.

To do a termination on a concentric neutral cable using an elbow:

1. Train the cable so that there is sufficient length to reach the termination point. Leave slack as required.

2. Position the cable at the bushing centerline and parallel to the apparatus. If there are bends in the top 16 inches of cable, train it until it is straight. Cut the cable square at the centerline of the bushing.

3. Measuring from the cable end, remove 9 inches of cable jacket.

4. Build a waterstop. The purpose of the waterstop is to prevent water from migrating along the concentric neutral strands (wires) or from the concentric neutral ground connection.

5. When using 3M cold shrink tube in place of SAP and PVC tape, install tube on cable. To build a waterstop:

   - Tie down concentric neutral strands approximately 1/2 inch above the jacket cutback with a No. 14 AWG copper wire. The No. 14 AWG copper wire is referred to as a tie wire.

   - Using a mastic pad strip from coldshrink kit, stretch the mastic strip until the plastic backing comes off, and apply it so that it covers the neutral strands between the tie wire and the jacket cutback. Ensure that the mastic fills the gaps between the strands (force it into the gaps). This will result in an effective waterstop.

   - Fold back the concentric neutral strands.

   - Cut a strip 3/4 inch wide from the mastic pad and use it to cover the exposed neutral strands and the first mastic layer.

   - Force the mastic of this second layer between the strands by binding down the pad with another tie wire. The waterstop is now complete.

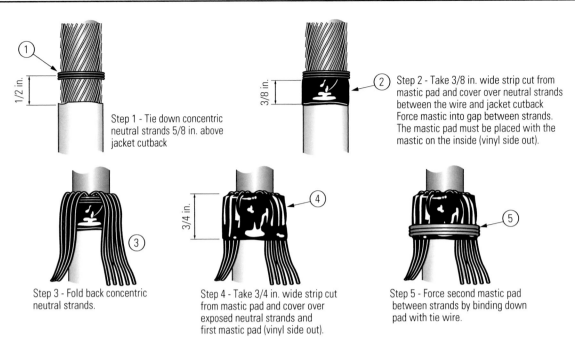

Step 1 - Tie down concentric neutral strands 5/8 in. above jacket cutback

Step 2 - Take 3/8 in. wide strip cut from mastic pad and cover over neutral strands between the wire and jacket cutback Force mastic into gap between strands. The mastic pad must be placed with the mastic on the inside (vinyl side out).

Step 3 - Fold back concentric neutral strands.

Step 4 - Take 3/4 in. wide strip cut from mastic pad and cover over exposed neutral strands and first mastic pad (vinyl side out).

Step 5 - Force second mastic pad between strands by binding down pad with tie wire.

Figure 5-183. Steps involved in building a waterstop.

5. Form a tail with the concentric neutral strands. Leave one strand of the concentric neutral unbundled. This strand will be used to bond the elbow to the cable (bleed or drain wire). The tail will be used for bonding.

6. Remove the semi-con to a point 6-7/8 inches from the end of the connector. Do not nick the insulation. Make a clean cut with no jagged edges.

7. Since the connectors will vary in size, measure the inside of the connector. Remove this amount of insulation (usually between 1 and 2 inches from the cable end. It is advisable to leave 1/4 inch for expansion when crimping the connector. Do not nick the conductor.

8. The installation of the elbow is easier if the edge of the insulation is chamfered or slightly beveled. Chamfer for approximately 1/16 to 1/8 inch at a 45° angle.

9. Wire brush the conductor and immediately push it into the compression connector. The conductor must butt against the end of the connector. Rotate the connector until it is positioned with a flat side facing the bushing.

10. Consult the table for the crimp tools and dies needed. Using the correct tool and die, begin to crimp the connector starting at the end of the connector and moving towards the insulation. Should install probe prior to crimping.

   Crimp in the sequence indicated without overlapping crimps or having a partial crimp on the end of the connector. (Each connector has on it an indication of the number of crimps required.) Rotate crimp tool 90° between each successive crimp.

Smooth any sharp edges on the surface of the crimped connector. This can be done with the aluminum oxide cloth, or a sharp file. Use a lint-free cloth to remove any metal filings or excess inhibitor (Penatrox) squeezed from the connector.

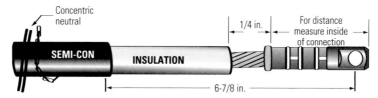

Figure 5-184. Dimensions for removal of semi-con and insulation.

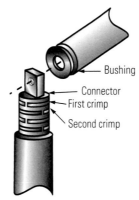

Figure 5-185. The connector crimped and aligned with the bushing.

11. Slide the 3M Cold Shrink Cable Accessory Sealing Tube onto the cable. The tube end with the loose core end should go on first, away from the connector.

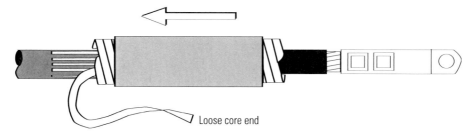

Figure 5-186. Installing the cold shrink.

Note: The 3M Cold Shrink Sealing Tube or self-amalgamating tape and PVC tape are only required in below-surface installations.

12. Clean the cable insulation with the aluminum oxide cloth to remove all traces of the semi-con and foreign material, then wipe with a clean cloth soaked in isopropanol. The cable insulation must be cleaned before and during the installation of the elbow.

13. Lubricate the exposed cable insulation and the mouth of the elbow (where the cable will go) using silicone grease or the grease that comes with the elbow.

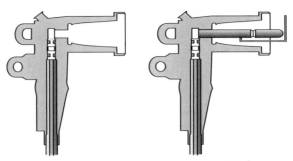

Figure 5-187. Installation of the elbow and the elbow probe (contact probe).

Slowly push and twist the elbow onto the cable until the connector reaches the top of the inside of the elbow.

Clean off excess lubricant with a lint-free cloth. Make sure that no lubricant enters the threaded part of the connector, as this will prevent a good contact between the elbow probe and connector and may cause overheating.

14. Orient the elbow so that the elbow probe (sometimes called the contact probe) can be screwed into the hole of the connector.

    Insert the elbow probe into the connector and finger-tighten to avoid crossthreading. Complete the tightening with the probe wrench.

15. Attach a bonding wire to the tail formed with the concentric neutrals. Measure a length of No. 2 copper conductor (bonding wire) long enough to be connected to the ground bus and to allow the elbow to be moved from the bushing to a parking stand. Use a copper tap connector to attach the bonding wire to the tail.

16. If surface irregularities exist in the seal area of the molded elbow, wrap a mastic strip around the end of the elbow. Over wrap the mastic with two lapped layers of vinyl tape.

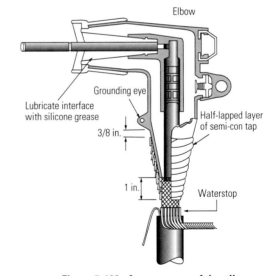

Figure 5-188. Arrangement of the elbow and the connectors.

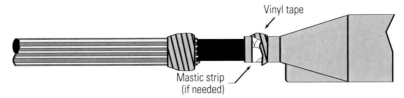

Figure 5-189. If irregularities exist, install mastic.

17. Position the Cold shrink tube over the seal area and remove the core by unwinding the loose core end counter-clockwise.

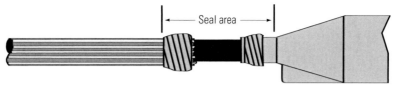

Figure 5-190. Position cold shrink over the seal area.

18. Connect the free neutral strand (bleed or drain wire) to the grounding eye on the elbow by putting it through the eye and twisting it.

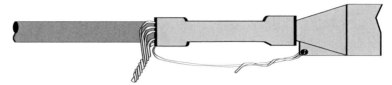

Figure 5-191. Connect the concentric neutral.

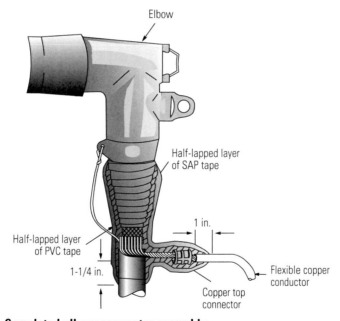

Figure 5-192. Completed elbow connector assembly.

Note: To ensure the elbow does not "pop off" the bushing while energized, seat the elbow on the bushing firmly until the elbow clicks into position.

Next the terminated cable must be mounted and bonded.

SYSTEM | DRAWINGS | MATERIALS | INSTALLING | SPLICING | FUSING | MAINTENANCE | TROUBLE | JOB SITE

Mount the Elbow

The completed elbow can now be inserted onto the bushing. Clean the elbow and the bushing so that no dirt or foreign material interferes with the contact surface. Lubricate the contact surfaces of the bushing and the elbow with the silicone grease supplied in the kit. This will help to eliminate sticking and will make the installation easier to accomplish.

Note: Clean the elbow, or bushing insert, should be cleaned with an approved cable cleaner.

To mount the elbow:

1. The area must be clear of obstructions or contaminants that would interfere with operation of the elbow connector.

2. Position tip of probe into the end of the loadbreak bushing.

Note: Some types of elbows require burping by means of an insulated tube being inserted between the mouth of the elbow and the insert.

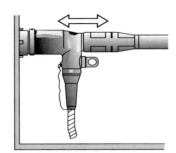

Figure 4-193. Elbow being mounted to a bushing using a shotgun.

3. Grasp elbow firmly with shotgun.

4. Slowly insert elbow onto bushing until a slight bump is felt.

5. Maintaining a firm grasp on the shotgun, thrust the elbow the rest of the way onto the bushing until a click is heard.

6. Push again on the elbow using the shotgun, and then pull gently to make sure that it is secure.

Bond the Cable (Elbow)

Bonding together of metallic and semi-conducting components eliminates possible voltage differences that may cause damage to equipment and danger to personnel.

The elbow is bonded via a No. 2 copper conductor to the ground bus in either a transformer or a junction box. The conductor has already been attached to the concentric neutral strands during the installation process. To do the bonding, use a compression connector in junction boxes and a compression lug connector in transformers. In junction boxes, crimp the bonding wire to the ground bus. In transformers, crimp the lug connector on the end of the bonding wire and bolt the lug to the ground bus.

Note: Remember that the temporary tags must now be replaced with permanent tags.

Energizing the Cable

Once the terminators and elbows have been mounted and bonded, the next step is to connect to the apparatus so that the cable (circuit) can be energized.

At the switchgear, the lug connector of the terminator is bolted to the bus (metal plate) of the fuse.

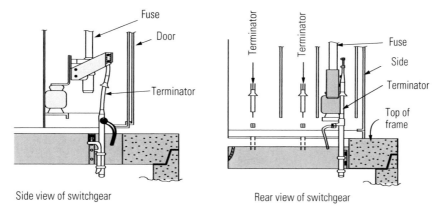

Figure 5-194. Terminator connected to fuse side of the switchgear.

On poles, the terminators are connected to the cutouts using suitable connectors and lengths of No. 2 AWG copper conductor. To energize at the terminal pole, a live line tool is used to close the fused cutout. For more information on cutouts and energizing at terminator poles, refer to the section Perform Underground Switching.

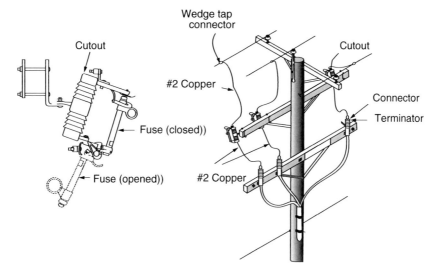

Figure 5-195. Cutout and fuse (left). Terminators connected to cutouts on a terminal pole.

Splice and Terminate Secondary Cables

Introduction

The principles for splicing and terminating secondary underground cables are the same for primary underground cables, and the procedures are far less complex. The reason for this is that secondary underground cables generally consist of conductor strands and insulation only (sometimes there is an outer jacket). They also only operate at 110 to 600 volts.

An underground service can be provided in two different ways:

- By a "dip" service from the overhead secondaries via underground ducts.

- By a straight underground service connection from the underground distribution system.

"Point of delivery" is the location at which the power company's service line makes electrical connection to the customer's wires. This location can be the meter, the customer's wiring, or the customer's switch – whichever comes first.

"Service connection" is that portion of the power company's distribution facilities extending from the point of delivery back to the first attachment point on the power company's distribution system.

Dip Service

In a dip service, the wires run down the pole from the overhead powerlines, protected by fiberglass cable covers and a guard section. At the base of the pole, the conductors run through a pilaster and into the underground duct to the customer. The customer is responsible for the installation of all civil work, which includes the guard section, pilaster, duct, and trenches.

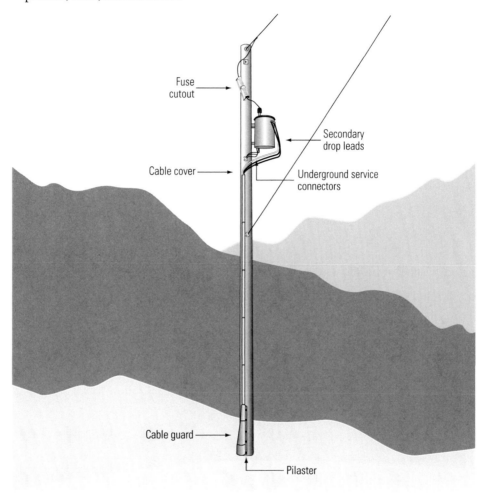

Fuse cutout

Secondary drop leads

Cable cover

Underground service connectors

Cable guard

Pilaster

Figure 5-196. Dip service.

SYSTEM

DRAWINGS | MATERIALS

INSTALLING

SPLICING

FUSING

MAINTENANCE

TROUBLE

JOB SITE

Underground Secondary Service

Introduction

In a underground service, the service wires run through underground ducts from a service box or low profile transformer (LPT). The utility is responsible for the ownership and maintenance of the service from the service box or LPT to the point of delivery, as well as any duct up to the customers property line. The customer is responsible for installing and maintaining any duct on their own property.

When underground lines are provided to a residential subdivision, the developer runs a section of duct into each property to be serviced and snubbed off 3 feet from the lot line.

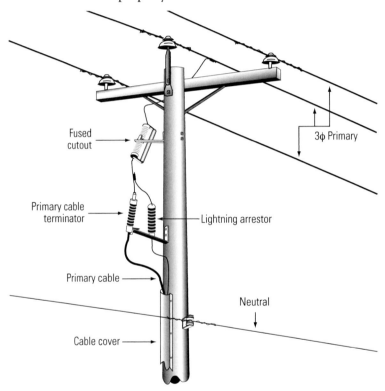

Fused cutout

3φ Primary

Primary cable terminator

Lightning arrestor

Primary cable

Neutral

Cable cover

Figure 5-197.

The topics covered are:

- Tools and materials

- Splice secondary underground cable

- Terminate secondary underground cable

- Bonding and grounding

- Energize the secondaries

Tools and Materials

Splicing and terminating of secondary underground cables do not require the use of special kits. The procedures are very simple since when dealing with secondaries you only have to work with conductor strands and insulation (and sometimes an outer jacket).

The equipment and materials needed to do a secondary underground cable splice or termination is:

- Sharp knife and a skinning knife

- Installation stripper

- Cable cutters

- Crimp tool and dies

- Approved cleaning solvent and a clean, lint-free cloth

- Connectors or terminators

- Bonding and grounding wires

- Tapes

Splice Secondary Underground Cable

The following is required before starting any splicing job:

- Prepare the work area.

- Visually inspect all the equipment and materials. Ensure that you have everything you need to complete the job.

- Maintain cleanliness throughout the procedure.

Splice secondary (triplex) underground cable:

1. Train the cables so that they are in the correct location and position.

2. Prepare the cable ends by cutting the ends so that they are square to each other. Select an appropriate connector and measure it to determine how much insulation to remove. Remember to allow an additional 1/4 inch on each end of the connector for growth during crimping.

   Use a skinning knife to strip off the required amount of insulation. Do not nick the conductor. Chamfer the insulation at a 45° angle for 1/4 inch. If connector does not contain inhibitor, the conductor must brushed with

SYSTEM

DRAWINGS

MATERIALS

INSTALLING

SPLICING

FUSING

MAINTENANCE

TROUBLE

JOB SITE

inhibitor before installing the connector. Wire-brush the conductor strands and immediately insert into the connector. If any time is going to elapse before the connector is installed, paint the strands with an electrical inhibitor.

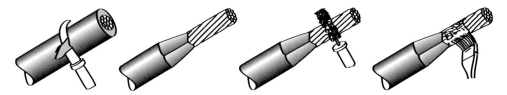

Figure 5-198. Secondary underground cable preparation.

3. Install the connector. Bend both cable ends up and push or tap the connector into one cable end. Insert the second cable end and push down until the splice is straight and the second cable end hits the end of the connector.

   Crimp the connector using a Burndy MD6 crimping tool (or Y35 for larger conductors) and the appropriate dies. Rotate the tool 90° after each crimp. Start crimping at the center and move towards the two ends in an alternating sequence.

4. Clean the connector and cable before starting the taping process. Use a lint-free cloth and approved solvent.

5. Determine the diameter of the connector and apply half-lapped layers of 1 inch self-amalgamating tape around the connector. Build the tape up to the diameter of the connector plus 3/8 inch.

   At a distance of 2 inches plus the length of the connector, start to taper the tape towards the insulation (slope). Stop the tapering at a distance of 3-1/2 inches plus the length of the connector).

6. Cover the self-amalgamating tape with two half-lapped layers of 3/4 inch PVC tape.

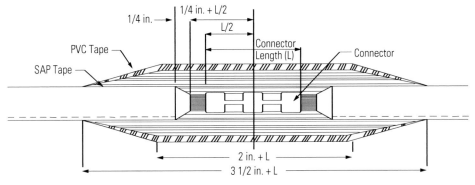

Figure 5-199. Completed secondary cable splice.

Terminate Secondary Underground Cable

Secondary underground cables feed from a transformer to a customer. For connection to a transformer, a terminator is installed on the end of the cable. For connection to a customer, the insulation is stripped off and the bared end of the cable is inserted into a customer's fuse box and held in place by the pressure of a screw.

In some cases, secondary cables are pulled into service boxes and connected to busbars. These service boxes are used to split up or divide the load. Service boxes are installed (by the civil contractor) at various locations to enable several customers to be serviced from one source (a transformer). Figure 5-168 shows one source conductor coming in and being connected to a busbar from which two customers are serviced (customer conductors). Before starting any terminating job, the service boxes (if present) must be prepared.

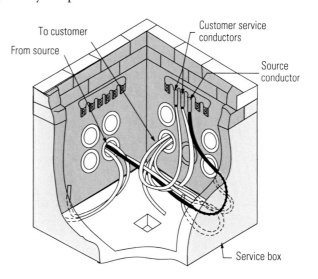

Figure 5-200. Set-up of service box and busbars. For clarity, only one source conductor and two customers' conductors are shown. The source conductor has been darkened.

Prepare Service Box

Before the secondary underground cables can be terminated, the busbars must be installed in the service box. These busbars are also referred to as squids or multi-connectors.

To install the busbars, drill two holes for each busbar to be installed on the concrete walls close to the top of the service box. Insert a anchor (using a hammer) into each drilled hole. The inside of each anchor is threaded so that it can accept a bolt (of the appropriate size). Now insert bolts into the anchors and place the busbar on the protruding end of the bolts so that they support the busbar. This completes the installation of the busbar. The service box is now prepared for secondary cables to be terminated and connected.

Other requirements that must be completed before the cable can be terminated are:

• Prepare the work area.

• Visually inspect all equipment and materials. Ensure that you have everything you need to complete the job.

• Maintain cleanliness throughout the procedure.

To terminate a secondary underground cable for connection to a transformer:

1. Identify and position the cable. Do this by phasing the cable and checking the temporary tag to determine where the cable will be connected.

   Train the cable so that it reaches its termination position. Leave slack, as required. Cut the cable.

2. To prepare the cable end, select the appropriate lug connector (this depends on the type of transformer and the cable size) and measure the connector to determine how much insulation must be removed from the cable. Allow an additional 1/4 inch for growth of the connector during crimping.

   Remove the insulation by doing a ring cut (this results in a straight edge all around the cable). Do not nick the conductor. Slice the insulation from the ring cut to the cable end and remove the insulation. Wire-brush the conductor strands and immediately install the connector. If connector does not contain inhibitor, the conductor must brushed with inhibitor before installing the connector.

3. Install the lug connector by pushing it onto the conductor and positioning it so the flat area and the holes are facing the secondary terminal on the transformer.

   Crimp the connector in place using an MD6 or Y35 crimping tool and the appropriate dies. Rotate the tool 90° after each crimp. Start crimping at the top of the connector body and move towards the cable. Wipe any excess inhibitor off the cable.

4. Connect the terminated cable to the appropriate secondary terminal on the transformer. When bolting it in place, make sure Belleville washers are installed to maintain constant pressure on the lug.

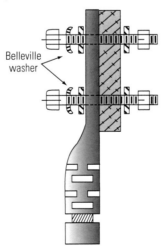

Belleville washer

Figure 5-201. Secondary, terminated with a lug connector, bolted to a terminal on the transformer.

To terminate a secondary cable (using a slotted compression lug) for connection to a busbar in a service box:

1. Identify and position the cable. Do this by phasing the cable and checking the temporary tag to determine where the cable will be connected.

   Then train the cable so that it reaches its termination position. Leave slack, as required. Cut the cable. Train cable in such a way as to avoid criss-crossing within the service box.

2. Cut the universal rubber sleeve so that it will fit snugly on the cable. Grease the cable and slip on the universal sleeve.

3. To prepare the cable end, select the appropriate lug connector (this depends on the type of busbar and the cable size) and measure the connector body to determine how much insulation must be removed from the cable. Allow an additional 1/4 inch for growth of the connector during crimping.

   Using a skinning knife, remove the required amount of insulation. Do not nick the conductor. Chamfer the insulation at a 45° angle for 1/4 inch. Wire-brush the conductor strands and immediately install the connector. If connector does not contain inhibitor, the conductor must brushed with inhibitor before installing the connector.

4. Install the slotted lug connector by pushing it onto the conductor and positioning it so the slots are lined up to the busbar.

   Crimp the connector in place using an MD6 or Y35 crimping tool and the appropriate dies. Rotate the tool 90° after each crimp. Start crimping at the top of the connector body and move towards the cable. Wipe off any excess inhibitor.

5. Bolt the terminated cable in place on the busbar.

6. Lubricate the busbar so that the universal sleeve can be pushed onto the busbar.

   Squeeze the rubber sleeve so as to remove all air once the sleeve is on the busbar. This termination is now complete.

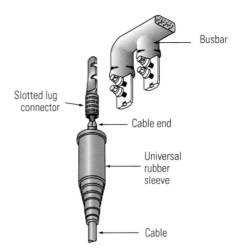

Figure 5-202. Slotted lug connector going on the end of the secondary cable. Bus bar ready for installation of the terminated secondary.

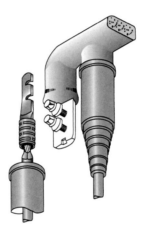

Figure 5-203. Busbar with one secondary installed and another secondary getting prepared for installation.

Bonding and Grounding

In the case of secondary splices, bonding is not required.

When terminating secondary underground cables in transformers, the neutral bushing must be bonded. There is usually a copper strap installed by the manufacturer that is connected to the neutral for this purpose.

When connecting secondary underground cables in a service box, the ground must be connected to one of the busbars. Using a grounding connector, connect a piece of 1/0 copper from the ground to the service box busbar. A universal rubber sleeve is used to cover the grounding connector and mastic material is used to cover the crimp connection.

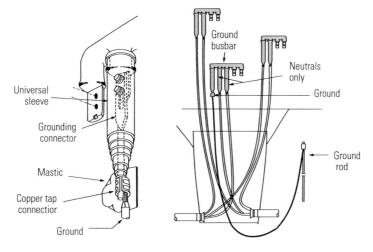

Figure 5-204. Attachment of ground wire to a bus bar. Grounded bus bar used only for neutrals.

Note: Remember that the temporary tags must now be replaced with permanent tags.

Energize the Secondaries

In some cases, installations or extensions of secondaries or services require handling secondaries that are energized. There are basically three possible situations, and basic work practices and safety procedures must be followed.

The three situations are:

- Secondary extensions from service box.

- Service boxes to main meter base or switch of customer.

- Low profile transformer (LPT) or dead front transformer (DFT) service or secondary extension.

Before starting, the following tools are required:

- Voltmeter

- Ratchet wrenches

- Brushes

- Inhibitors (Penetrox)

- Magnetic blanket buttons

- Magnetic rubber blankets

- Secondary (Salisbury) covers

- Safety glasses

- Secondary rubber gloves

- Box end wrenches

The basic work practices that must be observed are:

1. Always check the voltages to confirm what is energized and know what fault currents are available.

2. Always use appropriate safety cover-up and insulation.

3. Always connect neutrals first on and last off.

4. Never get in series with connections.

5. If possible, do not pick up load on the secondaries.

6. *Caution:* Check for backfeeds!

Energizing a Secondary Extension from a Service Box to Service

- Use rubber gloves, safety glasses and rubber blankets to insulate yourself from ground potential.

- Check voltages from phase to phase and from phase to ground.

- Confirm that the extension is isolated and covered.

- Connect grounds first.

- Handle the phases one at a time.

- Bare secondary squid covers.

- Make connection by handling insulation of conductors.

- Cover up and fold into box, making sure that there are no sharp bends are nicks.

- Repeat for last phase.

- Replace service box lid.

Energizing a Secondary Extension from a Service Box to Meter Base or Main Switch

- Check voltages in meter base or main switch for backfeed hazards.

- Prepare base or main switch terminations and check whether main switches are locked open or meter is removed.

- Use the same energization practices as described for energizing a secondary extension from a service box to service.

- Take socket checks or notify customers that the switch is live.

Note: A utility decal could be used on the main switch panel to confirm that ducts are sealed properly.

Energizing a Low Profile Transformer or Deadfront Transformer

- Use appropriate safety glasses, rubber gloves and blankets or covers.

- Check phase-to-phase and phase-to-ground voltages.

- Apply protective blankets to the rear of the transformer secondary terminal's tank to insulate it from accidental contact.

- Cover all other secondaries to be worked on nearby with blankets or approved covers.

- Attach and secure grounds, making sure not to get in series.

- Uncover secondary leg to be energized, and cover grounds completely.

- After brushing and applying inhibitor, install bolts through spades or terminals start nuts and lock washers to hand tight.

- Tighten nuts and bolts using covered box end wrenches, making sure not to contact other parts of the transformer or your body.

- Repeat procedure for other leg.

Bonding and Grounding at Padmounted Enclosures

General

All metallic and semi-conducting components in a padmounted enclosure must be bonded together and grounded.

The ground electrode consists of a bare metallic conductor surrounding the enclosure (called a counterpoise) and 2 ground rods. The placement of the counterpoise and rods varies with the type of enclosure used. The counterpoise and rods are normally made of galvanized steel, but in high corrosion areas, may be copper/copperclad steel.

Bonding

Bonding together of metallic and semiconding components eliminates possible voltage difference between them. Voltage differences can result in damage to equipment and danger to personnel, as well as cause radio interference.

Ground Electrode

The primary function of the counterpoise is to reduce the touch potential under fault conditions to a safe level by setting up an equi-potential zone around the enclosure. It also reduces the step potential. The dimensions of the counterpoise and the number of ground rods were chosen so that the potential difference between the enclosure and the earth immediately surrounding the enclosure is at a safe level for a majority of conditions and sequence of events. The ground rods further reduce the step and touch potential in the vicinity of the enclosure to an acceptable level during a fault and also reduces the seasonal variation in resistance. Placement of the ground rods is selected to ensure maximum protection for the journeyman operating the equipment.

SYSTEM | DRAWINGS | MATERIALS | INSTALLING | SPLICING | FUSING | MAINTENANCE | TROUBLE | JOB SITE

Connection Between the Ground Bus and Counterpoise

The general method of connecting a steel counterpoise to a grounding conductor or rod is with a U-bolt ground connector. For connecting a copper counterpoise, a compression tap connector is used.

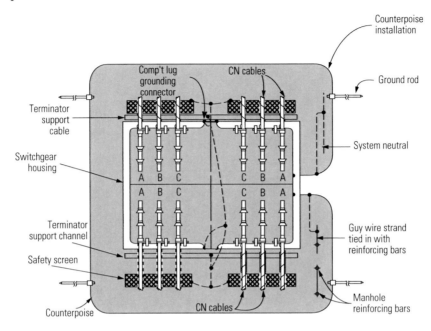

Figure 5-205. Grounding diagram (schematic) for cables.

Size of Bonding and Grounding Conductors and Ground Busses

All bonding conductors (except between the neutrals of concentric neutral cables) and ground busses in primary installations must be #2 AWG copper except those for semi-conducting components which must be a minimum of #14 AWG copper. Ground busses may, for mechanical support reasons be increased in size or made of bar stock. The grounding conductor between the H_0X_0 and the ground bus on all transformers should be sized according to the available secondary fault level of the transformer.

The bonding conductor between the neutrals of concentric neutral cables must be sized to adequately handle the expected current in the neutral of the cables.

The bonding conductor on the neutral of all cables terminated with elbows must be the flexible type so as to not impede operation on the elbow.

CHAPTER 5 – Splice, Terminate Cables

SYSTEM

DRAWINGS

MATERIALS

INSTALLING

SPLICING

FUSING

MAINTENANCE

TROUBLE

JOB SITE

Bonding and Grounding - Job Checklist

The following job checklist contains the most common components in padmounted enclosures that require bonding and grounding:

(a) All separable insulated connectors (elbows, plugs, caps, inserts, etc.).

(b) All neutrals (primary, secondary, and service).

(c) H_0X_0 terminal of transformer.

(d) Enclosure itself.

(e) Any subcomponents of the enclosure (removable roof and panels, doors, removable compartments etc.).

Bonding and Grounding at Subsurface Structures

General

All metallic and semi-conducting components is a subsurface structure must be bonded together and grounded.

The ground electrode consists of a single ground rod driven 1 foot below finished grade. The placement of the ground rod varies with the subsurface structure type. The ground rod is normally made of galvanized steel, but in high corrosion areas may be copper clad steel.

Bonding

Bonding together of metallic and semiconding components eliminates possible voltage difference between them. Voltage differences can result in damage to equipment, danger to personnel and a possible cause of radio interference.

Ground Electrode

The function of the ground rod is to reduce the step potential and fault conditions to a safe level.

Note: Touch potentials are not a problem on subsurface structures as these are not a metal enclosure. Any exposed metal covers or grating are isolated from the ground bus through design. The placement of the ground rod is selected to ensure maximum protection for the lineworker operating the equipment.

Connection Between Ground Bus and Counterpoise

The general method of connecting a ground conductor to a ground bus is with a compression tap connector for wire ground busses or a one-hole compression lug for flat bar ground busses.

Size of Bonding and Grounding Conductors and Ground Busses

All bonding conductors (except between the neutrals of concentric neutral cables), conductors and ground busses in primary installations must be #2 AWG copper except those for semi-conducting components which must be a minimum of #14 AWG copper. Ground busses may, for mechanical support reasons be increased in size or made of bar stock. The grounding conductor between the H_0X_0 and the ground bus on all transformers should be sized according to the available secondary fault level of the transformer.

The bonding conductor between the neutrals of concentric neutral cables must be sized to adequately handle the expected current in the neutral of the cables.

The bonding conductor on the neutral of all cables terminated with elbows must be the flexible type so as to not impede operation on the elbow.

Bonding and Grounding - Job Checklist

The following job checklist contains the most common components in padmounted enclosures that require bonding and grounding:

(a) All separable insulated connectors (elbows, plugs, caps, inserts, etc.).

(b) All neutrals (primary, secondary, and service).

(c) H_0X_0 terminals of transformer.

(d) All metallic mounting hardware.

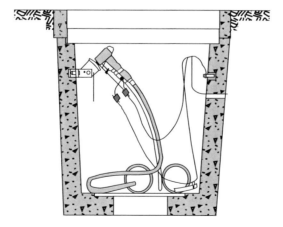

Figure 5-206. Diagram of bonding and grounding.

SYSTEM

DRAWINGS

MATERIALS

INSTALLING

SPLICING

FUSING

MAINTENANCE

TROUBLE

JOB SITE

CHAPTER

FUSING

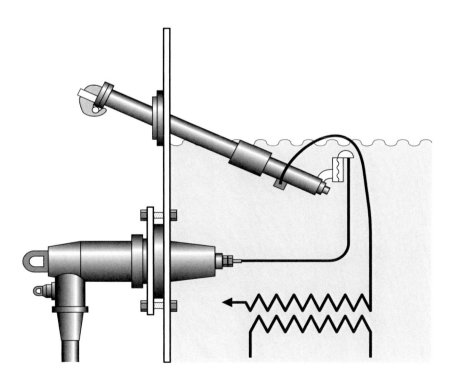

SYSTEM

DRAWINGS

MATERIALS

INSTALLING

SPLICING

FUSING

MAINTENANCE

TROUBLE

JOB SITE

Fusing Deadfront Transformers

Introduction

The fuses in deadfront transformers protect the transformer in the event of a secondary fault and serve to isolate the transformer from the distribution system if a transformer fault occurs.

The majority of the single phase deadfront transformers are protected by a series combination of a replaceable expulsion fuse and a backup current limiting fuse. The expulsion fuse is designed to protect against overloads and faults on the secondary side. The current limiting fuse protects against short circuits on the primary winding and limits the energy that is dissipated in the transformer tank. The current limiting fuse is mounted inside the transformer tank and is not replaceable in the field, although, there are a few single phase transformers that are protected by current limiting fuses mounted in dry-well canisters that can be replaced on the field.

Also, there are some older types of low profile transformers (LPTs) in service that are only protected by a replaceable expulsion fuse. In high fault level areas, current limiting fuses have been installed at cable terminal poles to protect a string of transformers.

Two types of three-phase padmounts are purchased, one for use on loop feed circuits and the other for radial circuits. Single-phase LPTs are suitable to be used in either circuits.

Three-phase deadfront transformers are protected with either canister mounted current limiting fuses or the expulsion/current limiting fuse combinations. Transformers for loop feed application also have internal gang operated loadbreak switches, interlocked with fuses to prevent accidental fuse withdrawal while energized.

Upon successful completion of this section, you will be able to describe and identify the three types of dead front transformer and the two types of fuses currently used.

MATERIALS

INSTALLING

SPLICING

FUSING

MAINTENANCE

TROUBLE

JOB SITE

Overview of Deadfront Transformers

The term "deadfront transformer" means that the primary connections in the operating compartment are insulated and the outside of the connections are maintained at ground potential. The sealed tank holds the transformer, primary bus, fuses, and switch. The internal bus can be energized from either primary bushing and the transformer is tapped off this internal bus. The transformer fuse is connected between the internal primary bus and the transformer, therefore, when an internal fuse blows the primary bus inside the transformer is still energized. Only the transformer primary coil has been interrupted.

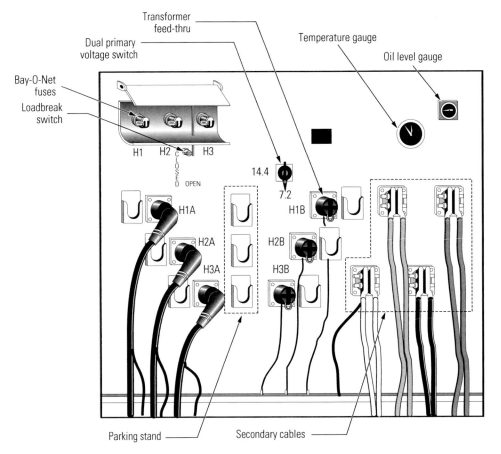

Figure 6-1. Deadfront transformer components.

Fuse Types

Deadfront transformer may be equipped with either the Bay-O-Net or NX current limiting fuse. Although the manufacturer says Bay-O-Net fuses can break load, it is not the practice of some utilities to break load with any padmounted transformer fuses, and new transformers have a decal, "Do Not De-energize with Fuse." You must first de-energize the transformer by standing off the elbows or by opening the primary switch.

Bay-O-Net Fuses

The oil-immersed Bay-O-Net fuse assembly is used in most LPTs and some padmounts. The Bay-O-Net's dual sensing link is a single element fuse sensitive to both current and oil temperature. The link is used to sense secondary faults, excessive load current, and transformer faults. It will also limit long time transformer overheating due to overloads and environment temperatures. Most Bay-O-Net fuses are connected in series with an isolation link that melts if it is exposed to fault currents in excess of the Bay-O-Net fuse rating. The isolation link has no interruption rating and is used only to prevent fault current beyond the Bay-O-Net's fault handling capacity.

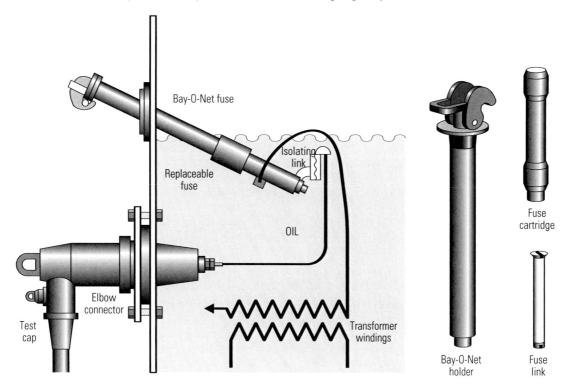

Figure 6-2. Bay-O-Net fuse holder.

Figure 6-3. Bay-O-Net fuse.

To Remove Bay-O-Net Fuses

- De-energize transformer by standing off the elbow or opening the gang-operated loadbreak switch.

- Attach universal hot line tool, or hook stick to fuse handle eye. Stand to one side. Unlock handle.

- Push down and rotate handle 90° in the tube. During this procedure internal tank pressure escapes and inside and outside pressures are equalized. Also the 90° rotation of the fuse holder breaks any adhesion between the seal gasket and the outer tube assembly. If pressure is not released, use the pressure relief valve to release the tank pressure.

- Pull out the fuse holder approximately three inches and wait a few seconds for the oil to drain into the tank. The inner fuse holder assembly can now be removed without dripping excess oil. The total length of the inner fuse holder assembly, including fuse element cartridge, is 14 inches.

- Wipe any oil from the holder before removing fuse cartridge and fuse link element. Unscrew the fuse cartridge, remove end plug, and inspect fuse link element. Each link is clearly marked with a series number. A 358C indicates current sensing type and 358C indicates dual sensing type. If not legible on the blown fuse, refer to stencil on transformer cover or other specifications. Remove fuse link (element) from cartridge by forcing from plug end.

Note: If Teflon tube is not melted, it is necessary to straighten the tulip tip (serrated end).

- Inspect cartridge bore to make sure it is clean.

- Insert new fuse link (element) into cartridge from either end.

- Be sure the formed end ferrule of the fuse element is secured in place between the fuse cartridge and the holder and tightened before the end plug is inserted.

- Tighten the end plug to expand the scalloped end ferrule and complete reassembly of the Bay-O-Net inner fuse cartridge holder assembly ready for refusing.

Note: Do not use a wrench on the brass ferrules of the cartridge, but a wrench may be used on end plug.

To Install Bay-O-Net Fuses

- Attach the handle eye of the inner fuse holder assembly to the hot stick.

- Place fuse holder into the Bay-O-Net outer tube assembly.

- When the inner fuse holder assembly is inserted as far as possible, push down and rotate the locking handle, hooking it over the shoulder of the outer tube assembly. When handle is in locked position, *make sure* the stainless steel cover washer is seated against the shoulder of the outer tube assembly. If this is not done, the electrical contacts on the fuse holder will not line up with the matching contacts in the canister and arcing will develop.

- Energize transformer by replacing the elbow or closing the gang-operated loadbreak switch.

NX Current Limiting Fuses (Dry-Well Canister)

The NX current limiting fuse is housed in a dry-well canister. Most three-phase padmounted distribution transformers are protected by this type of fusing.

There are a number of problems which are unique to padmounted distribution transformers protected by the NX current limiting fuse in a dry-well canister.

Problems may be evident as soon as a transformer door is opened (e.g. oil running from the fuse canister or fuse ejected from the canister). Both of these problems indicate that a transformer change out will be required.

Other problems defects are evident when the fuse is removed from the canister.

Defects to look for are:

1. Discoloration or burning of the fuse outer shell.

2. Corrosion or arcing damage to the electrical contacts.

3. Contamination or signs of tracking on the wall of the canister.

4. Oil on the fuse.

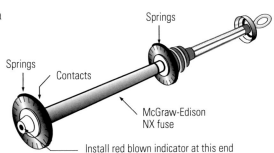

Figure 6-4. NX current limiting fuse.

Causes of Defects

One cause of defects stems from the operating characteristics of current limiting fuses – the fuse "hangs up" during certain high impedance faults which may occur on the secondary system. During high impedance faults of this type, the fuse link heats up, but not to a temperature that causes it to melt. These faults can exist for long periods of time (hours). During this time, the silicone sand around the fuse element becomes very hot and causes gases to form and leak out the end of the fuse. The fiberglass fuse shell may also discolor or even burn through and allow silicone sand and combustion by-products to escape through. During such an event, the fuse, the fuse holder, and the dry-well canister become contaminated and/or damaged.

Another cause is improper seating of the fuse assembly inside the canister. This results in a poor connection between fuse and canister contacts, causing arcing, and ultimately a hole burned into the canister. Oil then leaks through the hole into the canister and may run from the canister into the transformer's operating cubicle. Also, the NX Fuse inside the canister may absorb some of the oil which will affect its operation. Poor seating may be a result of incorrect installation of the fuse by operating personnel or by transformer vibration.

Fault Finding and Inspection

Whenever an electrical fault is suspected, remove the fuse assembly and:

1. Check the condition of the fuse and fuse holder.

   - Normally, when a fuse operates, it will remain intact with no visible damage to it. A red indicator located on the top end of the fuse will dislodge when the fuse is blown. Some fuses may be assembled with the indicator located under the top insulator assembly. To check the indicator, loosen the set screws on the insulator assembly and remove it from the fuse.

   - Look for signs of burning, minor discoloration (browning) of the fiberglass fuse shell or extensive charring. Where signs of burning are found, it is likely that burning by-products have been released from the fuse and deposited in the dry-well canister. Carefully check the canister, as it may need replacing.

   - Look for arcing or corrosion damage on both contacts of the fuse assembly. Damage to either contact indicates similar damage to the corresponding canister contact(s) and will usually require that the canister be replaced.

2. Check for oil on the fuse and in the canister:

   - If there is oil on the fuse or inside the canister, the canister has been damaged in some way and must be replaced.

3. Check the condition of the canister (use a flashlight). A dry-well canister should be inspected each time the fuse is removed. *Never poke* anything into the canister unless you are sure it is dead (de-energized) and grounded.

   - Check fuse to ensure fuse springs are intact.

   - Check the canister to ensure it is dry and clean.

   - Where there has been excessive temperatures inside the fuse, gases and other contaminants will likely have been released into the canister and the canister may have some damage. A damaged canister must be replaced.

Fuse Replacement

Loosen set screws on the insulator assembly, remove shield from fuse ferrule, replace blown fuse and reassemble. Fuses with blowout indicators must always be assembled with indicator end in the contact assembly (inner end) to allow gasses to expel past the blown indicator when the fuse blows.

Note: When inserting a fuse assembly into a dry-well canister, push the assembly all the way into the canister so that the part of the fuse assembly which caps the opening of the canister is seated flush with the canister flange. If this is not done, the electrical contacts on the fuse holder will not line up with the mating contacts in the canister and arcing will develop leading to some or all of the foregoing problems.

Fusing Livefront Transformers

Introduction

Livefront transformer kiosks were installed during the original development of underground distribution systems. They are basically overhead style transformers inside a metal enclosure. Originally the primary cables were terminated with stress cones only and connected directly to the transformer bushing. For livefront transformer kiosks with no switchgear, switching is done with the terminal pole cutouts.

Most livefront transformer kiosks were constructed with S&C padmounted fuse units and disconnect blades (see Figure 5.5). The fuse unit has a colored cap that melts or changes color when the fuse blows. When the fuse blows, the complete fuse unit must be replaced. Later, they were equipped with S&C SM-4 type fuse links and holders. Both types are still in service in many areas, although conversion programs are steadily replacing them with deadfront transformers (DFTs). The majority of the SM-4 fuse holders can be operated and isolated with the use of a loadbuster tool.

Upon successful completion of this section, you will be able to describe and identify the various types of fuses and disconnect switches found in livefront transformer kiosks and describe the procedure and safety hazards involved in isolating and changing fuses in these kiosks.

Caution: There are some livefront transformers that look identical to deadfront transformers from the outside. ***Do not*** mistake these for deadfront transformers.

Fire-orange target appears in this "blown" indicator window
when fuse has operated (visible through translucent holders)

Figure 6-5. S&C SM-4.

Livefront Fusing and Switching

Livefront switches must be operated a proper loadbuster tool, except those designed by the manufacturer to have load breaking capability, for example S&C PMH Model.

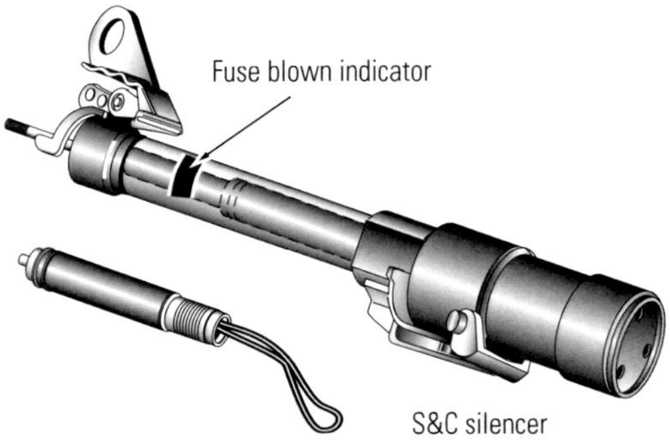

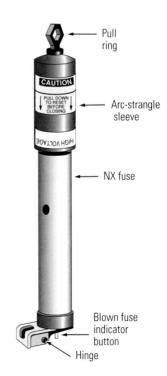

Figure 6-6. PMH fuse holder and SM4 fuse link.

S&C Fused Disconnect Switches

The switching unit may be single pole, a three pole cluster, or a four pole cluster with a combination of fused and solid blades. The S&C fused disconnect blade is a fused unit that must be replaced when the fuse link blows. Fuse unit ratings range from 6k to 65k.

S&C Type SM-4 Replaceable Fuse Links

The S&C type SM-4 fuse holder incorporates a replaceable fuse link. When the fuse blows, a fluorescent red indicator seen through the translucent casing, moves up to the "Blown" window. The holder must be removed from the unit, disassembled and a new SM-4 fuse link installed. Since there are two different size of fuse holders, check and install the correct fuse (15 or 25 kV).

McGraw-Edison Hinge Style Arc-Strangler Fuse

The NX Type unit combines a current limiting fuse with loadbreak/make capabilities. These units were originally intended to provide both protection and loadbreak switching for the transformer, but are not to be used as such on most power systems.

If the NX fuse is blown, a button will be exposed on the bottom of the hinge assembly. Normally this button is flush with the hinge assembly.

Before replacing the switch blade back into the lower contact hinge, the loadbreak sleeve must be recocked by pulling it down on the NX fuse body. Once closed, the arc strangler sleeve pops up against the switch contacts and is ready for the next loadbreak operation.

Figure 6-7. Arc strangler NX type fuse.

Figure 5.8 shows the McGraw-Edison arc strangler fuse which does not have current limiting capabilities, but is operated the same as the NX type.

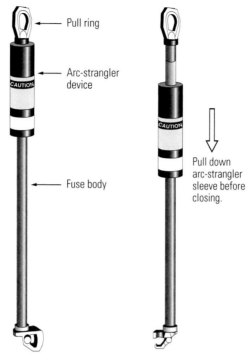

Figure 6-8. McGraw-Edison arc strangler fuse.

Note: The McGraw-Edison hinge style arc strangler fuses (NX or regular) are not used to break loads. The cable must be de-energized before operating the fuse.

Fusing Mark II Switchgear

Introduction

The purpose of padmounted switchgear is to sectionalize or reroute power within a main feeder cable system in residential or commercial areas.

The term Mark II (or MK II) is commonly used to refer to all S&C padmounted switchgear units. These units are the three-phase, livefront, padmounted switching kiosks used on many underground distribution systems. The MK II contains a combination of gang-operated switches and fuses. There are two types of Mark II switchgear: the older, Mark II models with non-loadbreak fuses, and the newer PMH Models with loadbreak fuses (incorporating a Uni-Rupter assembly).

Upon successful completion of this section, you will be able to describe and operate the MK II switchgear.

Mark II Architecture

Mark II switchgear can be outfitted with combination of switches and fuses in a cabinet divided into four separate compartments. The switches are operated with the cabinet doors closed by operating the handle mounted on the outside of the unit.

Generally, the switches are on the line side (incoming) feed and the fuses, on the other side, allow power to be tapped from the switchgear to feed transformers and customer switchgear. Alternatively, there may be one incoming feed in one switch compartment, with two or three outgoing feeds in fuse compartments. The switches are uniquely identified by switch numbers.

Before operating, make sure you have the correct compartment. Visually confirm which compartment is Normally Open (NO). Visually check the status of switches after operating them.

Mark II and PMH, PMS Models

S&C metal enclosed, manually operated switchgear incorporates interrupter switches and power fuses. It is designed to handle all three-phase live switching duties, including full load and associated transformer's magnetizing and cable charging current, plus fault closing operation. Various combinations of switches and fuses are offered in circuit configurations to fit most requirements in a high voltage underground distribution system.

The majority of the switchgear units installed by many utilities are the Mark II model, while later units are the PMH and PMS models. They all feature external handle operated mini-rupters for three pole switching of source circuits or a combination of mini-rupters and power fuses. The fuses provide single pole switching and protection.

A few of the older model PMC-SF models may still be found. They contain single pole stick operated switches and fuses and require a S&C Loadbuster tool to interrupt load current.

The PMH and PMS line of switchgear have been redesigned to eliminate the need for the S&C Loadbuster tool when opening the fuses. An interrupting device called Uni-Rupter, is incorporated into the fuse holder, which, during fuse opening, will interrupt the load. A live line P2 stick is required for operating the fuses.

Note: Opening the fuses in the Mark II switchgear must still be done with the aid of a Loadbuster.

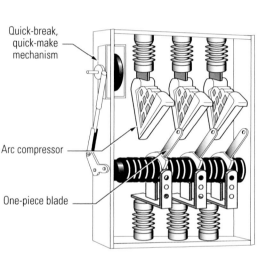

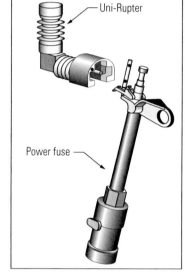

S&C Mini-Rupter switch — Power fuse with Uni-Rupter

Figure 6-9. S&C Mini-Rupter switch.

Ratings

Mark II and PMH Models		
	7.2/12.4 kV System	14.4/25 kV System
Nominal Voltage	14.4 kV	25 kV
Maximum Design Voltage	17 kV	27 kV
Basic Insulation Level (BIL)	95 kV	125 kV
Continuous	600A	600A
Short Circuit (RMS)	12.5kA	12.5kA
Fault Closing (First Time)	20kA	20kA
Fault Closing (Second Time)	13KA	13kA
Load Splitting	600A	600A
Load Dropping	600A	400A

Power fuses are the S&C SM and SML type fuses, 200 amperes maximum size.

Overhead Current Limiting Fuses

Introduction

Current limiting fuses are installed on the terminal pole and in series with the fused cutout. The fuses are installed in particularly sensitive areas to protect the cable or apparatus and for public protection. They will operate only upon sustained primary faults and not on transient or secondary faults.

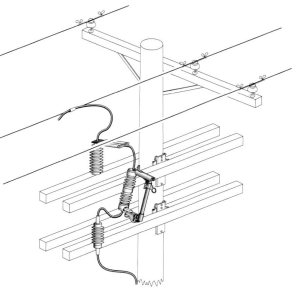

Figure 6-10. Overhead switching.

Has the Fuse Blown

Depending on the fault magnitude of the fault current, the current limiting fuse may blow and not the expulsion fuse. The following methods can be used to determine if the current limiting fuse has blown:

Method 1

1. The preferred method is to use phasing tools and check to ground on each side of the current limiting fuse. If there is appropriate voltage to ground on the source side and no or strange voltage on the load side, then the fuse is blown.

Method 2

1. Establish a safety permit to enable you to check the current limiting fuse for continuity.

2. Check the current limiting fuse with a low voltage continuity tester.

3. If the test does not show continuity, the fuse must be replaced.

Note: If the fuse is blown, there could be a primary fault that must be repaired before re-energizing is attempted.

Method 3

1. Buzz each side of the current limiting fuse. If you don't get the same amount of arc on both sides of it, the fuse has most likely blown. Another method is to check for potential at an elbow test point on the suspected faulted cable.

2. Repeat for all three phases. With the appropriate safety permit in place and safety grounds applied, replace the faulted current limiting fuse.

Current Limiting Fuses as Tools

Portable, modified current limiting fuses can be used for additional protection when re-energizing transformers from a cutout after a fault has caused the cutout to open. Some utilities use the McGraw-Edison NX Fault Guard Tool and the modified NX fuse.

Check Fuses

Introduction

Fuses are used in circuits to protect equipment from fault currents and can be used as isolation points. The fuse does its job by opening the circuit before high current, (caused by short circuits) can cause any damage to equipment etc.

A fuse has to do three things:

*   It has to know, or sense, when a short circuit exists.

*   It has to open the circuit before any damage is done.

*   It has to have no effect on the circuit during normal operation.

The maximum current (rating) that a fuse can carry is usually marked on the fuse.

Fuses are checked before a new piece of equipment is put in service and when a fuse is suspect and requires verification that it is OK.

Upon successful completion of this section, you will be able to describe, analyze and check fuses for continuity.

The topics covered are:

*   Equipment and materials

*   Check fuses

Equipment and Materials

If the continuity of the fuse must be checked, a continuity set is used. The continuity set consists of a buzzer and a phasing lead. The phasing lead is plugged into the buzzer and the two clips of the lead are connected to the fuse (one on each end).

A hot stick and Grappler (fuse-holding device) are required to remove the old fuse and holder from the cut-out, transformer, or switchgear.

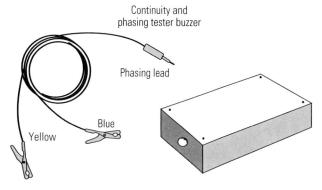

Figure 6-11. Continuity set used to check fuses.

Check Fuses

Fuses can be checked visually or by using a continuity set (buzzer and phasing lead).

Some fuses may have a built-in indicator to show when they are blown or have a fluorescent fire-orange target in the translucent holder that moves to the blown indicator window when the fuse operates (blows). This permits a positive visual check of the fuse's condition without removing it from its holder. The target fluoresces when illuminated.

Fire-orange target appears in this "blown" indicator window
when fuse has operated (visible through translucent holders)

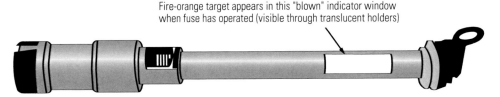

Figure 6-12. Fuse showing indicator area.

To check the fuse in a switchgear you would have to:

- Open the doors of the switchgear. Refer to Chapter 7, Underground Switching, and the manufacturer's instructions for information.

- Using a hot stick, hook into the fuse ring holder eye.

Note: If switchgear is designed for a loadbuster tool, it **must** be used to open the fuse

- Pull the fuse vigorously through its full travel without hesitation at any point.

- Remove the hot stick from the fuse pull ring and attach a grappler to the stick. Use this grappler to lift out the fuse from its mounting (the target cannot be seen while the fuse is in its mounting).

- Inspect the fuse. If it is in good condition, return it to its holder. If it is not in good condition replace it with a good fuse.

- Close the fuse using the procedures explained in Chapter 7, Underground Switching, and in the manufacturer's instructions.

Besides the visual check to see if the fuse is in good condition, you can also check fuses using a continuity set.

To check a fuse using a continuity set, remove the fuse from the switchgear:

- Plug the phasing lead into the continuity box (buzzer).

- Touch the two clips of the phasing lead together. If the buzzer is operating, it will buzz. If it does not buzz, change the battery in the buzzer or get another buzzer.

- To test whether the fuse allows a circuit to flow through it, touch the ends of the fuse with the phasing lead clips.

Figure 6-13. Checking fuse with a continuity set.

- If the fuse is good, the buzzer will buzz.

CHAPTER

SYSTEM MAINTENANCE

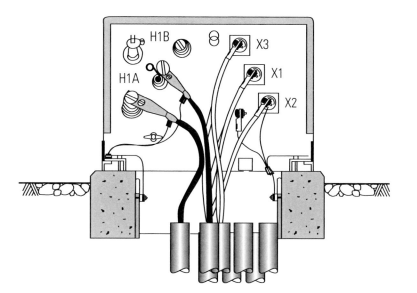

Test For Potential

Introduction

Before working on any cable or apparatus it must be checked for potential. If there is no potential the cable or apparatus is confirmed as being de-energized.

Potential Indicators

The following potential indicators are used on underground systems:

- Salisbury AC Voltage Detector, Underground Model

- Modiwark Voltage Detector, Underground Model

- Hastings Phase-Tell Model 6702 when equipped for underground potential testing

- Safety Line Voltage Detector Phasing Tester Model 8128024H6

- Chance Multi-Range Voltage Detector Model T403-3228 or C403-0979 when equipped for underground Potential testing.

Follow the manufacturer's operating instructions.

Modiwark

The most commonly used equipment to check for potential is the Modiwark. It is designed to detect the presence of an alternating electrical field. The Modiwark has a switch for different voltages and a sensitivity dial. It can be used in conjunction with a hot stick. To check for potential using the Modiwark:

- Check the Modiwark against a known live source. The live source should be at least 120 volts AC. The Modiwark should make a continuous noise when put close to the live source. If it does not, the Modiwark is not working.

- Adjust the Modiwark to the underground setting. Select the voltage (if the voltage feature is present).

- With the aid of a hotstick, place the sensing end of the Modiwark (large round end) close to the cable capacitive test point (observe Limits of Approach).

- A continuous tone indicates the presence potential and indicates the cable or apparatus is energized.

Figure 7-1. Modiwark.

The absence of sound confirms that the cable or apparatus is de-energized.

Cable Phasing Meter

The following are operating instructions for the Cable Phase Meter (Model CPM-2). Although the meter in your area may be of different manufacture, other operating procedures and principle will be similar. Refer to the manufacturer's instructions for the meter in your area.

Warning: This instrument is designed to be connected to the potential test points on the elbows. The instrument must not be connected directly to the high voltage conductors. Always use rubber gloves or liveline tool method when connecting probes or handling the instrument when connected.

General Description

The cable phasing meter is an electronic instrument designed to:

- Measure cable voltage

- Determine phase rotation

- Phase-out cables

Operating Procedures

The instrument operates on two 9-volt alkaline batteries and its performance depends on the condition of these batteries. The batteries must be checked before using the meter. The instrument must not be exposed to the cold weather for prolonged periods of time as this may cause the batteries to freeze and the instrument to be inoperative.

Steps To Measure Cable Voltage and Phase Out Cables (use Class 1 rubber gloves)

1. Turn the instrument on using the toggle switch.

2. Test condition of batteries by depressing the test buttons. New batteries will read about 9 on the meter. Batteries should be replaced when reading drops to 6.

3. Connect instrument to a good ground.

4. Select proper range – 15 kV or 30 kV.

5. Set function switch to P.V. (Phasing Voltmeter)

   • The instrument will indicate the phase-to-ground voltage of the cable, when either probe is connected to each cable's potential test point and the other lead to ground.

   • The instrument will indicate the phase-to-phase voltage of the cables, when the probes are connected to the cable's potential test points.

   • If the instrument reads zero when the second probe is connected to the potential test point of the second cable, then this cable's voltage matches the voltage of the first cable, and the two cables are in phase.

   • If the instrument reads the phase-to-phase voltage when the second probe is connected to the potential test point of the second cable, then the two cables are out of phase.

Note: Due to inequalities in the capacitance of the potential test points, a small residual reading, rather than a zero, may be obtained.

A.B. Chance Voltage Detectors

Chance multi-range voltage detectors are available to check for potential on UD. These units are designed to read line-to-ground voltage and can also be used to test capacitance points on elbows.

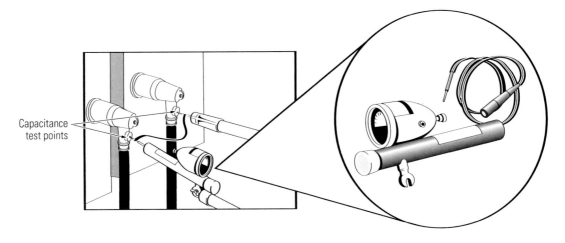

Capacitance
test points

Figure 7-2. A.B. Chance voltage detector.

A.B. Chance Phasing Testers						
Voltage Rating	**Resistance (megohms)**			**Amps**		**Cable Volts**
	Basic Tool	Extension (each)	Total	Phase to phase Meter (ma)	Line to Ground (ma)*	Maximum Line to ground
16kV	12.24	----	12.24	1.307	1.509	4.62kV
48kV	12.24	12.24	36.72	1.307	1.509	13.80kV
80kV	12.24	24.48	61.20	1.307	1.509	23.09kV
120kV	98.00	----	98.00	1.224	1.414	34.64kV
120kV	122.00	----	122.00	1.230	1.420	43.30kV

* Amps (line to ground) assumes the lead insulation loses its insulative value and allows the lead to contact the ground.

Loadbreak Elbows

Introduction

Underground switching often requires breaking load in switchgear, transformers, or junction boxes. In dead front transformers and in junction boxes, this task is accomplished by pulling energized loadbreak elbows, which act as terminators, connectors, and switches.

Upon successful completion of this section, you will be able to demonstrate elbow pulling and standing off of cable, as well as list possible hazards and the required personal protective equipment.

Personal Protection

You are responsible for wearing the required personal protective equipment when pulling elbows (or performing any underground switching). This equipment includes:

- Approved fire retardant clothing

- Eye protection

- Hard hat

- Safety footwear

- Hearing protection is recommended

Operation to Break Load

As the pin contact is withdrawn, arcing occurs between it and the socket contact, causing the surrounding air to ionize. This reduces the air's insulating value and allows the arc to stretch out. When enough distance exists between the contacts, the arc is extinguished. It will not restrike if the atmosphere surrounding the contact gap is de-ionized. This de-ionization (re-establishing of the insulating value of air) is accomplished by the generation of a carefully controlled quantity of gas resulting from the evaporation of snuffer and follower material. The close fit between the follower and sniffer and small primary chamber confined these gases producing localized pressure which helps in extinguishing the arc.

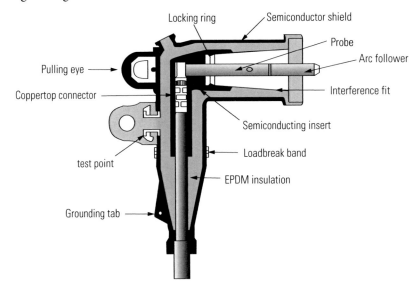

Figure 7-3. Components of a loadbreak elbow.

Loadmake/Fault Close

As the pin contact moves towards the socket, pressure is formed from an arc strike that generates gas. The gas pressure is largely due to the materials used and to the amount and of current flow. This would be greater during a fault close operation than a loadmake operation.

Ideally, there should be no gas generated during a fault close operation. The best alternative is to minimize the amount of gas produced, or to minimize the pre-strike distance.

The contact gap design is critical to pre-strike distances as it provides an uncontaminated area between the pin and socket. The configuration of the snuffer in this area and the distance to the outer conductive tube are also critical to a successful operation. All of these dimensions have been carefully calculated, studied and verified by laboratory tests.

Carbon contaminated snuffer and follower surfaces, also contribute to a longer pre-strike. By selecting the proper materials, the by-products created by arcing on these surfaces are not carbonaceous and contamination is minimized.

Since the gas produced must be dissipated, it is critical that they are minimized by careful selection and location of the arc quenching burring loadbreak, but if the arc is excessive, trouble could result in load making.

The small amount of gases produced can flow from the primary chamber into the secondary chamber through the annular valve. Gases in the secondary chamber leak back into the primary chamber through the control leakage valve until the pressure in the two chambers is equal and stabilized.

Since the pre-strike and gas volume have been minimized, the closure speed becomes far less critical. When closing, speeds of approximately 40 in./sec. are quite adequate.

The important part of the elbow operation is to reduce the time of making or breaking contact. As explained earlier, the material from the loadbreak assembly is actually spent during the operation. Therefore, the quicker the operation, the less arcing and resulting contamination.

Loadbreak elbows are used to terminate primary cables and provide a connection that can be used to break current up to 200 amps. A white ring around the elbow body identifies it as a loadbreak elbow.

Note: Loadbreak elbows are identified by the double white band.

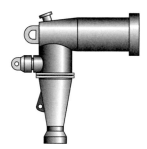

Figure 7-4. Loadbreak elbow.

Equipment

Before the loadbreak elbow is pulled, an insulated standoff insulator or feed-thru must be installed to park the elbow. The standoff is mounted on the U-shaped mounting bracket with a shotgun. The bleeder wire is connected to the system neutral to bleed off any static charge.

Insulated standoffs are used to park elbows to allow for Normally Opens and/or provide for isolation points.

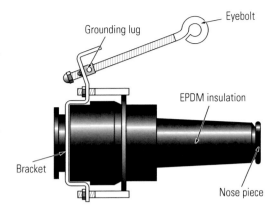

Figure 7-5. Insulated standoff.

A feed-thru tool can be used to provide a temporary bypass, i.e. the changeout of an LPT. However, each job requires specific procedures.

Feed-thrus can be used to:

- Provide a temporary bypass

- Test for full line potential

- Isolate a cable

- Phasing

- Provide a grounding interface

Feed-thrus are mounted on the transformer case or junction rack similar to an insulated standoff. This allows the current to flow from the feed elbow to the load elbow without an electrical connection to a transformer.

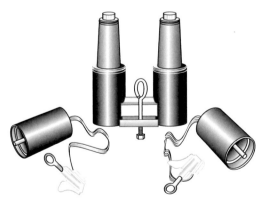

Figure 7-6. Feed-thru tools.

Procedures

General Steps in Loadbreak Elbow Operation

1. Clean away any loose debris that may have fallen onto the operating interface.

2. Ensure it is a loadbreak type.

3. Check cable identification using the one-line diagram.

4. Check condition of the elbow and bleed wire.

5. Install an insulated stand-off on the parking stand and connect bleeder wire.

6. Attach the elbow pulling tool to the elbow.

7. Pull elbow with the elbow puller in line with the elbow. A force applied out of line can break off the probe.

8. Install the elbow onto the insulated stand-off.

9. Install insulating cap on exposed module.

Installing Elbows

1. Attach elbow puller to elbow.

2. While standing off to one side, align probe and push the elbow into the insert bushing.

3. Make the connection with one swift motion.

4. Visually check to ensure the elbow is fully seated.

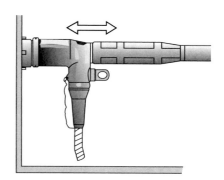

Figure 7-7. Installing elbows.

Approved Tools

There are many elbow pulling tools; however, the recommended pulling tool is the ratchet type.

Note: The eye on the shotgun is not designed for heavy pulls. This could damage the metal on fiberglass components of the shotgun, setting up other hazards when using the shotgun.

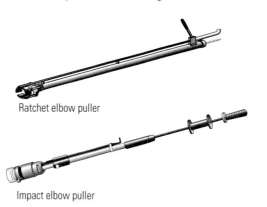

Ratchet elbow puller

Impact elbow puller

Figure 7-8. Elbow pullers.

SYSTEM

DRAWINGS

MATERIALS

INSTALLING

SPLICING

FUSING

MAINTENANCE

TROUBLE

JOB SITE

Safety Hazards

Watch out for the following indicators of a possible hazard:

- The elbow is hard to pull (use ratchet pulling tool to break seal).

- Insufficient cable to allow mobility of the elbow to the standoff.

- Contamination tracking on the elbow.

- Obstructions or contaminants that could interfere with the operation of the elbow.

- Elbow coming close to a grounded plane.

- Limits of approach.

- Listen for buzzing noise.

- Burnt off bleeder wires.

- Congested operating room around the apparatus to be switches (i.e. shrubs, debris, etc.)

- Identify problem elbows (i.e. a series of RTEs).

- Encapsulated cable.

CHAPTER 7 – System Maintenance

SYSTEM

DRAWINGS

MATERIALS

INSTALLING

SPLICING

FUSING

MAINTENANCE

TROUBLE

JOB SITE

Underground Switching

Introduction

Whenever possible underground systems are designed to include multiple feeds providing an alternate source for the primary portion of the system. When multiple feeds exist, the system is referred to as a loop system.

Depending on the size and layout of the underground system, any number of feeds into the system can exist. However, each transformer has only one feed at any given time because of strategically placed Normally Open points located throughout the loop system. These alternate feeds are created to limit outages when repairs are required to damaged equipment or provide flexibility for managing system load.

One of the essentials for the safe operation and maintenance of the system, is an up-to-date one-line diagram. Each source and Normally Open point on a loop primary must be shown. The Normally Open point is marked NO.

Switching is performed to open or close a circuit or to change the direction of the power flow through a circuit.

Switching can be performed at the following points:

- Terminal poles
- Switchgears (MK II)
- Transformers
- Junction boxes

The method used to accomplish the switching depends on where the switching is being performed and why it is being performed.

The topics are:

- Switching at terminal pole
- Switching at switchgear (MK II)
- Switching at transformer
- Switching in junction box

Standard Looped Primary

Normally Open points provide separation between:

(a) different phases of the same system (circuit)

(b) different source points (but same phase) of same system

(c) a combination of (a) and (b) above

(d) different circuits

In a loop system, Normally Open points are established by placing one of the cables on an insulated stand-off bushing in transformers or switching units. To perform "in-loop switching," phasing is always required across the Normally Open point except in dedicated switchgear. Once correct phasing has been established the Normal Open point can be closed and a new Normally Open point established at a pre-determined location.

Approved phasing tools are used to perform phasing checks at Normally Open points.

Note: To avoid tying two different circuits through the underground system it is recommended the overhead circuits be tied first.

Switching at Terminal Pole

Cutouts provide a high voltage mounting for the fuse element used to protect the distribution system or the equipment connected to it. In closed position, these fuses connect the circuit and allow power to flow through. To do switching at a terminal pole, the fuses may be opened or closed.

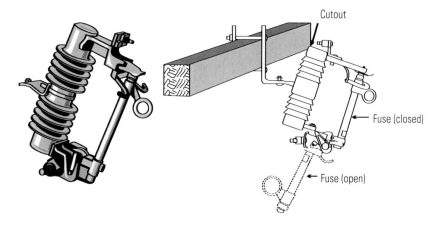

Figure 7-9. Fuse and cutout.

To open the fuse cutouts, a hot stick equipped with a loadbuster tool must be used.

A P2 hot stick is used to close the fuse and energize the terminal pole.

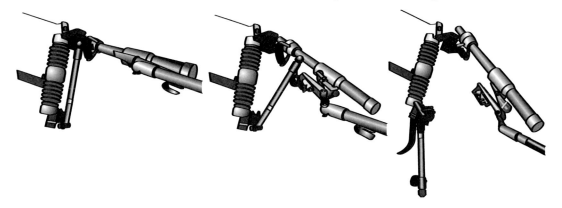

Figure 7-10. Using a loadbuster to open a fuse on a pole.

Switching at Switchgear (MK II)

The MK II switchgear is designed for high voltage underground distribution in residential and commercial areas. It can consist of various combinations of switches and fuses for sectionalizing and/or protection of cable. It is also used for switching and protection of transformers. There are two types of MK II switchgear, the older MK II with non-loadbreak fuses and the newer PMH models with load break fuses incorporating a Uni-Rupter assembly.

There are usually four compartments in the MK II switchgear, two house switches and two house fuses or a combination of each. The switch compartments are usually on one side and the fuse compartments are on the other side.

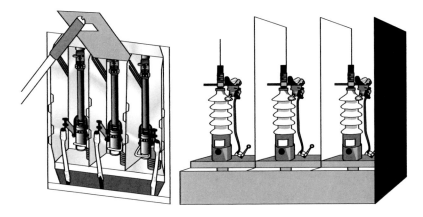

Figure 7-11. Switch and fuse compartment are located in one switchgear.

Switching can be done using the switches, the fuses or both. What is used depends on the switching situation and what is to be accomplished.

MK II Operating Procedures

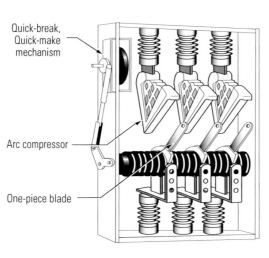

S&C Mini-Rupter switch

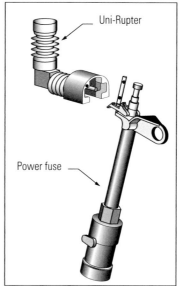

Power fuse with Uni-Rupter

Figure 7-12. S&C Mini-rupter switch.

Operation of mini-rupter switches in S&C padmounted gear is easily accomplished as follows:

- Open switch compartment and visually inspect.

- Remove the padlock from the operating handle access cover associated with the switch to be operated. Move the handle access cover to the open position.

- Remove the operating handle from its storage position and slide it onto the mini-rupter switch operating shaft. Note that a target located below the switch operating shaft indicates the position – opened or closed – of the mini-rupter switch, and the arrows indicate the turning direction required to open or close the switch.

- Rubber gloves must be worn (Class 1 minimum).

- Rotate the operating handle to the opened or closed position as desired.

- Observe the target to determine that the switch has been operated to the intended position.

- Remove the operating handle and return it to the storage position. Close the operating handle access cover and replace the padlock.

- Visually check switch blades are in the desired position (open or close).

Fuse Operation in Mark II

Replacement of fused in these units is normally a routine task; however, two qualified workers are required to replace these fuses for the following reasons:

- Public safety near a worksite is the worker's responsibility. Therefore, the worker must control the movement of people near energized equipment and, while doing this, may interrupt the worker's concentrations of the task at hand.

- Handling the weight of an S&C fuse (approx. 8-1/2 lbs.) on the end of a live line tool.

- In some cases, both the bottom and the top of the switch remain energized, and any inadvertent movement from ground position could quickly move a person into an extremely dangerous position.

- S&C padmounted gear is constructed to provide segregation of circuits. It is extremely important that certain precautions be observed in handling fuses or in performing any maintenance or repair work within the enclosure.

Fuse Replacement

In Mark II switchgears, a loadbuster tool must be used when opening fuses to interrupt load currents, magnetizing and charging currents.

- Open the door of the fuse compartment to be changed.

Warning: Always assume that both terminals of any power fuse are energized unless proved otherwise by test or by visual evidence that both terminals are grounded.

- Remove the dual purpose front barrier to gain access to the fuse. Use a universal pole at least 6 feet long. Keep the barrier dry and clean.

- Use loadbuster to open the fuse holder, make sure the loadbuster is reset.

- Reach across in front of the power fuse with the loadbuster and hook the anchor located at the top of the fuse.

Note: Only one attachment hook is provided.

- Maneuver the loadbuster so that its outer tube clears the interphase barrier, and pass the pull ring hook through the pull ring of the power fuse. The loadbuster pull ring will deflect and lock onto the pull ring of the fuse. The loadbuster is now connected across the upper contact of the power fuse.

- To open the circuit, operate the loadbuster with a firm, steady pull until it is extended to its maximum length. Avoid jerking and hesitation. The resetting latch will keep it open.

- To detach the loadbuster after circuit interruption, roll the tool upward by turning the pole. This will deflect the pull ring hook from the pull ring of the fuse unit or holder. Then, disengage the anchor from the attachment hook and withdraw the tool.

- Reset loadbuster for the next operation.

Caution: A disconnecting fuse in its full open position constitutes visual evidence of an open circuit from the jaw side. This does not necessarily mean that the hinge side is de-energized.

- Wearing rubber gloves, grasp the dual purpose front barrier at the lower end and, taking care to stay clear of the power fuse, start the barrier toward its "slide-in" position. Release the barrier and allow it to slide into place between the upper (jaw) contact and the hinge end contact of the fuse mounting. If necessary, nudge the barrier into place using the universal pole. During this operation, stay clear of the power fuse, since an open visual gap does not necessarily mean that either end or both ends of the power fuse are de-energized.

- Remove the fuse holder, using the large clamp on the universal pole.

- Refuse with a new refill unit.

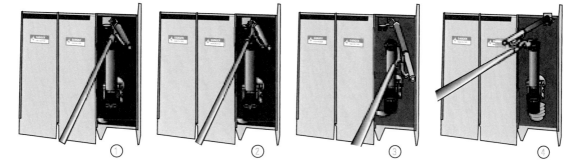

Figure 7-13. Sequence showing how to open a fuse in a switchgear.

- Replace the holder in its hinge, using the large clamp.

- Remove the dual-purpose front barrier from its "slide-in" position, using the universal pole.

- Using the universal pole, reclose the fuse holder.

- Grasp the dual purpose front barrier at its lower end and position the barrier so that the holes near the upper end are engaged by the barrier support hooks. Release the barrier to allow it to drop into its normal suspended position. If necessary, nudge the barrier into position using the universal pole.

- Close and padlock the door of the affected fuse compartment.

Caution: If fuse holders are removed from the mountings, they should be stored in a clean, dry location. Do not store fuse holders inside the enclosure.

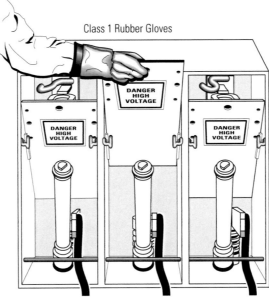

Figure 7-14. Mark II barrier installed.

Fuse Operation in PMH, PMS Models

- In the PMH and PMS models, the fuses can be opened with an insulated hook stick, as current interruption is accomplished with the built-in Uni-Rupters. At the end of the moving contact opening stroke, after the arc has been extinguished, the external current carrying contacts part and the Uni-Rupter automatically self resets for the next opening operation.

- Procedure for removal of these fuse holders are the same as the fuse operation in Marks IIs.

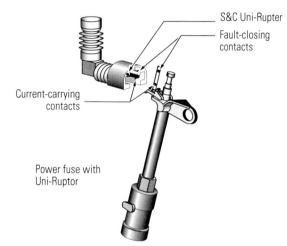

Current-carrying contacts

S&C Uni-Rupter

Fault-closing contacts

Power fuse with Uni-Ruptor

Figure 7-15. S&C Uni-rupter.

Maintenance

Mechanical maintenance is seldom required for S&C padmounted gear. However, cleaning and inspection of mini-rupter, uni-rupter switches, fuses and bus support insulators should be performed periodically, at intervals based on environmental conditions. Also, occasional operation of mini-rupter switches is recommended.

Dual purpose front barriers, furnished for all compartments, must be inserted into the open gaps of the mini-rupter switch or power fuses, to provide physical isolation for additional security, in the event that it is necessary to work on the cables connected to that mini-rupter switch or power fuse.

Take particular care, to be sure that the compartment doors are securely padlocked, with a lock in each hasp, and that the switch operating handle access covers are securely padlocked before leaving or have the gear attended by a qualified person.

Barrier Use for Safety Isolation Points

Isolation points at all padmount switchgear that are included in a safety permit must have barriers installed between the switch contact points for the duration of the safety permit.

Livefront Kiosk Switching

Livefront transformer kiosks were installed during the original development of underground systems. They are basically an overhead transformer inside a metal kiosk. Most livefront transformer kiosk were constructed with S&C padmounted fuse units and disconnect blades.

Operating Switches

- Use the required personal safety protection equipment.

- **Portable barriers**

    - When operating switches in close proximity to cubicle sides, the use of portable protective barriers is required to prevent flash over.

- **Limits of Approach**

    - All switching on underground livefront transformers is considered live line work, although no Live Line Permit is needed. Appropriate work practices must be applied.

- **Breaking load**

    - Use the correct model of S&C Loadbuster for underground switching, Model 5300R3-E, which is equipped with an extended insulating hood. After operating and resetting the loadbuster, check for proper resetting by extending the tool about three inches by hand – you should feel an increasing spring resistance throughout this travel. For operating and maintenance instructions see The S&C Loadbuster – Instructions for Operation and Maintenance #811-505.

Note: Most utilities require *two* qualified workers when performing on livefront kiosk switching.

Switching at Transformer

The fuses in transformers are used to transfer the power from the primary cables to the secondaries, not for switching. The elbows are used for switching in transformers. An elbow puller must be used to break the seal and move the elbows from the bushing wells to the parking stands.

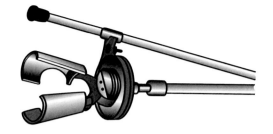

Figure 7-16. Elbow puller.

After the seal has been broken, a shotgun may be used to move the elbow from the bushing to the parking stand. A shotgun with the elbow pulling tool may be used in certain circumstances.

If switching is being done in order to repair a cable, a feed-thru is used. Install the feed-thru, then mount the elbow on it. The cable can now be grounded with a grounding elbow before being work begins.

Switching in Junction Boxes

The elbows are used in the same way as for transformers.

Caution: 40 in. × 40 in. junction boxes are currently not used in most new installations because these units are congested and leave very little room for maneuvering an elbow to an insulated standoff. The standoffs are close to the walls of the junction box and, therefore, set ups a possibility of a flashover while maneuvering the elbow to the standoff position.

Whenever possible, switching in these units should be avoided. If switching is required, work methods must be determined to minimize the hazards while performing the switching task.

Switching Procedures

Switching procedures are followed when performing these tasks:

- Replace a transformer

- Install cable in MK II switchgear

In general, switching procedures involves the following steps:

- Obtain the one-line diagram for the circuit. It is with a work order, or it can be found in the first apparatus from the terminal pole.

- Check the one-line diagram to determine switching points for the circuit. Work with the person in charge, to determine the switching sequence.

- The person in charge (PIC) usually directs the switching procedure. The journeyman/woman, while checking each switching step on the one-line diagram, follows the PIC's directions.

- De-energize the section via switching. This process is also referred to as isolating the section.

- After the switching procedures are completed, obtain the appropriate safety protection guarantee.

- Test for potential using a Modiwark, and buzz (if possible). Apply safety grounding before making any hand contact.

- Once the job is completed, do the following post-job tasks:

  - Remove diodes (if applicable)

  - Remove grounds.

  - Return safety permits.

  - Switch and re-energize.

> **Caution:** The procedures described from here to the end of this chapter are used by many utilities, but might not apply to you. Always follow your own company's switching procedures and safe work practices.

Switching to Replace a Transformer

This example will explain the switching sequence required to replace a transformer. The section involved contains two terminal poles and five transformers, with one Normally Open (NO). Transformer K104 must be replaced. The Normally Open is at transformer K102.

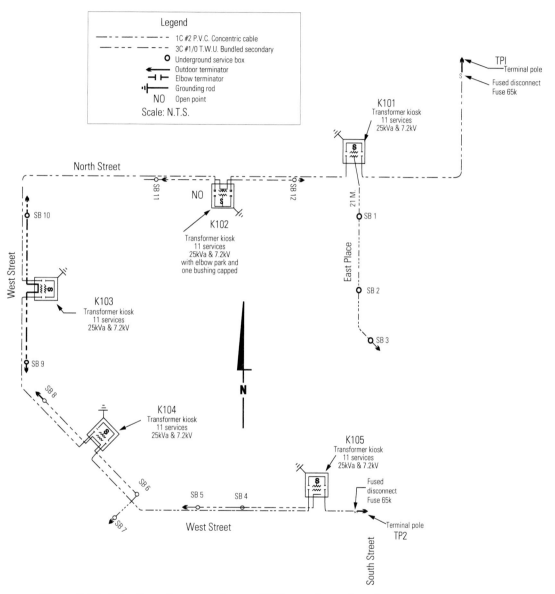

Figure 7-17. Situation where transformer K104 must be replaced.

To replace transformer K104:

- Obtain the correct one-line diagram print. If one-line diagram is not with the work order, one should be available in transformer K101 or K105.

- Ensure that communications are in place with the PIC and that the switching procedure is clear. Switching is done under the direction of the PIC.

- Go to transformer K103 and stand-off the cable to transformer K104. This is accomplished by checking the cable tag and removing the elbow for that cable and putting it on the parking stand. This will de-energize transformer K103.

- Install an insulating cap on the exposed bushing and hang a Clearance tag on the elbow.

- Check K103 to ensure it is de-energized, if not, cable ID must be performed.

- Go to the normally open (NO) at transformer K102. Remove the insulating cap from the energized bushing. Remove the elbow from the stand-off and install it on the energized bushing. This will energize the cable and, therefore, transformer K103.

- Go to transformer K105 and stand-off the cable to transformer K104. This is done by removing the elbow for that cable (check ID) and putting it on the parking stand. This will de-energize transformer K104.

- Install an insulating cap on the exposed bushing and hang a Clearance tag on the elbow.

Alternate Method

- At transformer K102, using a phasing tool, ensure the the phasing is correct. Move the elbow (cable from transformer K103 situated on the parking stand) to the transformer bushing. This will close the normal open point.

- Go to transformer K103 and stand-off the cable to transformer K104. This is accomplished by checking the cable tag and removing the elbow for that cable and putting it on a feed-thru. Install a Clearance Tag on the elbow.

- Go to transformer K105 and stand-off the cable to transformer K104. This is accomplished by checking the cable tag and removing the elbow for that cable and putting it on a feed-thru. Install a Clearance Tag on the elbow.

- At transformer K104, remove the elbows from the transformer bushings and install on feed-thrus.

Transformer K104 is now de-energized (isolated) and the cables to K105 and K103 are also de-energized. Obtain the appropriate safety protection guarantee, then test to confirm there is no potential and install safety grounding. Work on transformer K104 can now be performed.

When the work has been completed, all safety grounds are removed and the PIC is notified. The PIC once again directs the switching procedure. To restore service, the switching procedure is as follows:

- Return the safety protection guarantee.

- Go to transformer K105. Remove the Clearance tag. Remove the insulating cap from the bushing. Remove the elbow from the stand-off and install it on the bushing. This will energize transformer K104 and the cable going to transformer K103.

- Go to the normally open (NO) at transformer K102. Remove the elbow feeding the cable going to transformer K103 and install it on the stand-off. Install an insulating cap on the bushing.

  This will de-energize transformer K103 and the cable going to K103. This situation is now back to the way it was.

- Go to transformer K103. Remove the clearance or Test and Work tag. Remove the insulating cap from the bushing. Remove the elbow from the stand off and install it on the bushing. This will energize transformer K103 and the cable feeding the elbow on the stand-off at the normally open (NO) in transformer K102.

- The switching procedure is now complete.

Switching in a MK II Padmount Switchgear

In this example, the MK II padmount switchgear is energized and a cable must be pulled and terminated under the switchgear. Due to Limits of Approach, there is not enough clearance to do the work with the switchgear energized, and it will have to be de-energized. To simplify the description of the switching required, there are two feeds (A & B) and one fused output (C).

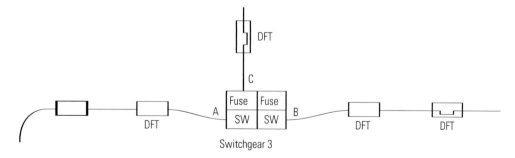

Figure 7-18. Switchgear 3 to be de-energized.

To de-energize or isolate the MK II switchgear (3):

- Locate the correct one-line diagram print and determine the closest switching point for each of the cables (A, B, C). Remember to keep as many customers energized as possible.

- Ensure that communications are in place with the PIC and that the switching procedure is clear. Switching is done under the direction of the PIC.

- Go to the switching point for cable A that is closest to the switchgear to be de-energized and open the switch for cable A. This may involve several steps since you want to keep as many customers energized as possible while working on switchgear (3).

  This will de-energize cable A feeding into switchgear (3). Install a Clearance tag on cable A at this location.

- Go to the switching point for cable B that is closest to switch gear 3 and open the switch for cable B. This may involve several steps.

  This will de-energize cable B feeding into switchgear (3). Install a Clearance tag on cable B at this location.

- Go to the switching point for cable C that is closest to switchgear (3) and de-energize cable C at that end. Since cable C is a lateral or tap off switchgear (3), it probably feeds into a transformer. To de-energize cable C at that end would involve standing off an elbow. Install a Clearance tag on cable C at this location.

- Obtain the appropriate safety protection guarantee for the job to be done at switchgear (3).

- Test for potential and buzz switchgear 3.

- Apply safety grounding.

Work in switchgear 3 can now be performed.

This procedure was very simply explained. On the job, this sort of switching procedure could take several hours to do. It would involve changing loads, tying circuits and keeping as many customers a possible in service.

When the work has been completed, all safety grounds are removed and the safety protection guarantee is returned to the PIC. The PIC will then direct the switching sequence required to restart service.

Paralleling and By-Pass Operations

Introduction

Paralleling is tying two systems together that have equal potential. This can be done only if they have the same voltage and the circuits are in phase. Paralleling is done to keep as many customers energized as possible. By-passing allows a transformer to be isolated and removed with only a short power outage to the customers not serviced by the transformer.

To replace a faulty transformer, paralleling and by-passing is required to keep as many customers in service as possible.

The topics covered are:

- Paralleling

- Paralleling situation

- Switching procedure for paralleling

- By-passing and isolating

- By-passing situation

- Switching procedure for by-passing

Paralleling

Paralleling is done when an open point is closed and is established at a different location.

An example of paralleling.

Note: Paralleling must only be done on dedicated switchgear and junction box, unless the cables are indicated to be in phase. Cables not marked in phase, must be phased in before closing, or another open point is established.

Rule: On underground circuits, open before you close.

Switching Procedures for Paralleling Situation

The work order states transformer K304 is leaking oil and must be taken out of service and replaced with a new one.

The one-line diagram that shows the circuit involved and shows that transformer K304 is situated within a loop-fed circuit. There are two underground feeds from terminal poles, TP1 and TP2. Both are fed from the same phase of a three-phase overhead circuit. The diagram also shows that the open point in the loop is at transformer K305 (designated by NO).

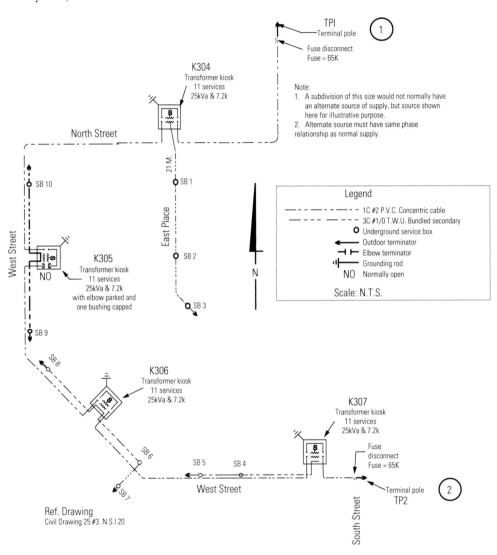

Figure 7-19. One-line diagram of circuit containing transformer K304, which must be de-energized and replaced.

In order to de-energize transformer K304 and replace it, the two feeds at transformer K305 must be paralleled and the open point must be moved to the other side. In Figure 7-19, the open point in K305 must be moved to the K304 side in the kiosk. By moving the open point to the other side, transformer K304 will no longer energize transformer K305. After this is completed, only K304 will be energized from the terminal pole, TP1. The last step in de-energizing K304 would be to isolate the cable at TP1. Once this is done, K304 will be de-energized and can be replaced.

Before starting the job, confirm the following:

• TP1 and TP2 are fed off the same phase of the overhead line.

• The open point is at K305. The cable tagged to transformer K306 is on a stand-off bushing.

• The cable tags at K304 and K305 confirm the one-line diagram.

To carry out the job described:

1. At transformer K305, set up the cable phasing meter and ensure that the meter is working. Refer to the section Perform Tests.

2. Using a Gripall shotgun remove the test caps from the elbows tagged to transformers K304 and K306.

3. Using the cable phasing meters, phase in the cables between K304 and K306. The phase meter should give a near-zero reading if the two cables are in phase with each other. This confirms the one-line diagram.

4. Replace the test caps with the hot stick.

5. Remove the insulating cap from H1B with the hot stick.

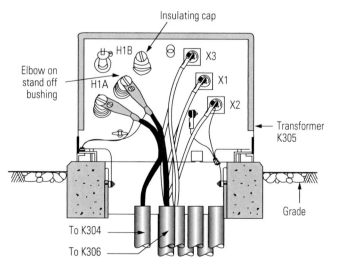

Figure 7-20. Transformer K305 before any switching has been done.

6. Move K306 elbow to the exposed H1B bushing insert and install it. Make sure it is firmly seated. The two feeds, K304 and K306 are now tied together and are in parallel.

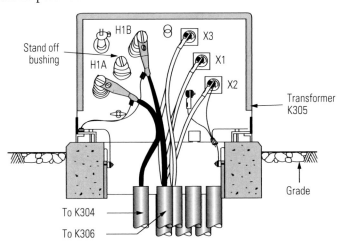

Figure 7-21. The cables are now in parallel. Both feeds are together and the loop is closed.

7. Using a hot stick, move K304 elbow from H1A and install it on the stand-off bushing. Make sure it is firmly seated. Install the insulating cap on the H1A bushing. The open point (NO) has now been moved to the other side.

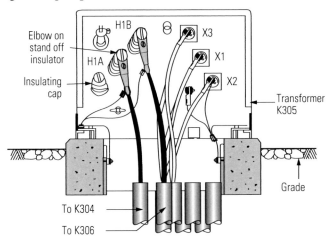

Figure 7-22. Transformer K305 after the switching has been completed. The open point has been moved to the other side.

The parallel procedure is now complete. The open point (NO) has been moved to the other side of K305 without any outages. The one-line diagram shows the new Normal Open point.

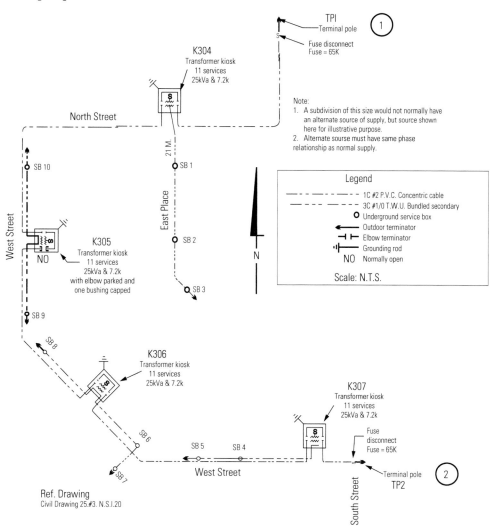

Figure 7-23. One-line diagram illustrated in Figure 7-19, but open point (NO) has been moved to other side of K305.

To complete the job, the cable has to be isolated at the terminal pole, TP1. Using a hotstick and loadbuster, open the fuse and de-energize the cable going to transformer K304. Once the cable has been isolated, the primary terminator should be tagged with a safety protection guarantee and safety grounded.

Removal Procedure

The procedure is as follows:

- With the transformer isolated, check for potential on the primary and secondary cables. Feedback from external sources is always possible.

- After ensuring that there is no potential, isolate the secondaries and short them together.

- Now the transformer is de-energized and grounded. The secondaries are disconnected from the transformer.

- The ground connector to the transformer body is the last connection removed.

- Remove the transformer securing bolts and replace the transformer.

When removing equipment, ensure that the neutrals, perimeter ground and bonding wires remain bonded to a common point and a temporary ground is connected from the ground to the equipment. When the equipment is lifted above and clear of the feed-thru, remove the ground. Do the opposite when installing the new transformer. This will keep your equipotential zone intact.

Installation Procedure

When the new transformer is securely in place, connect the ground, neutrals, secondaries and primary cable (elbow). Energize the transformer and return the circuit (Normally Open point) back to its original configuration. Return the circuit back to the normally Open position in which it started.

Switching Procedure for By-Passing and Isolating

By-Passing and Isolating

A by-pass is used when the feed needs to continue through the system to keep other transformers or junction boxes (customers) energized. By-passing allows a transformer to be isolated and removed without a long outage to other customers. To do this you must use a feed-thru that allows the feed to continue past the problem transformer so that other apparatus in the system can be energized.

By-Passing Situation

In the example below, the work order states that transformer K305 is leaking oil and must be taken out of service and replaced with a new one. Since the customers must not experience a long outage transformer K305 will be replaced using the by-pass method. The decision is to by-pass K305.

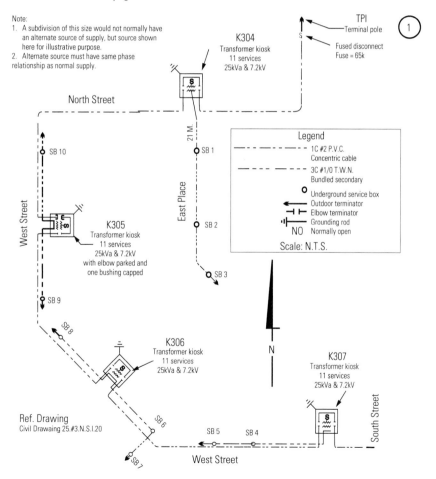

Figure 7-24. One-line diagram of circuit containing transformer K304, which must be de-energized and replaced.

The one-line diagram shows the circuit as a radial circuit feed from TP1 and contains three transformers, K305, K306, and K307.

In order to replace transformer K305 without causing a long power outage to other customers, a feed-thru by-pass at transformer K305 must be installed and the transformer must be isolated. The feed-thru will allow the customers of transformers K306 and K307 to remain energized while transformer K305 is being replaced.

Before starting this job, confirm the following:

- The cable is energized at TP1.

- The cable tags confirm the one-line diagram.

Procedure for By-Passing

In the situation explained, there are two methods to by-pass transformer K305:

1. De-energize TP1 and install a feed-thru at transformer K305.

2. Isolate the cables at transformer K305 from transformer K304 and K306. Install a feed-thru at transformer K305 and re-energize the isolated cables.

De-energize TP1 and install a feed-thru at transformer K305

In order to by-pass by first de-energizing TP1, the following must occur:

1. Confirm that the cable is energized at TP1 and that the tags confirm the one-line diagram.

2. At TP1, use a hot stick equipped with a loadbuster to open the cutout and de-energize the cable feeding the transformers.

3. Go to transformer K305. Using a shotgun, install a feed-thru on the parking stand.

Note: When handling cables in order to isolate or switch, limits of approach should be observed. An elbow puller used to break the seal on the elbow. Careful attention should be given to the probe angle installation.

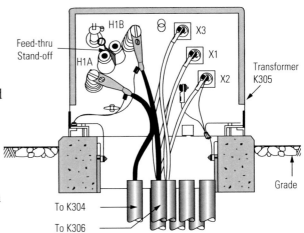

Figure 7-25. Feed-thru installed on stand-off.

4. Remove K304 elbow and install it on one side of the feed-thru. Make sure that the elbow is firmly seated on the feed-thru.

5. Remove K306 elbow and install it on the other side of the feed-thru. Make sure that the elbow is firmly seated on the feed-thru.

6. Using a hot stick, remove the feed-thru, complete with elbows, and carefully place it off to the side.

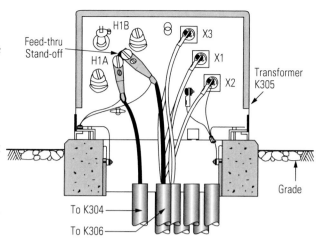

Figure 7-26. K304 and K306 elbows installed on feed-thru at transformer K305.

Use a support box, if available. If not available, lay the feed-thru down so that the elbows do not fall out (elbows should be pointing downward). Put it aside so that it does not interfere with the removal and replacement of the transformer.

7. Go to TP1 and, using a hot stick, close the cutout. This will re-energize the circuit.

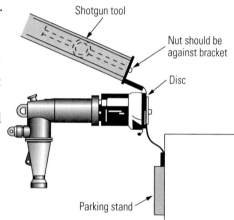

Figure 7-27. Using hot stick to remove feed-thru, complete with elbows, from parking stand.

Isolate the cables at transformer K305 from transformer K304 and K306. Install a feed-thru at transformer K305 and re-energize the isolated cables.

1. Confirm that the cable is energized at TP1 and that the tags confirm the one-line diagram.

2. At transformer K305, install a feed-thru.

3. Remove the cable (elbow) from K306 and install in the feed-thru. This will de-energize K306 and K307.

4. Remove the cable (elbow) from K304 and install in the feed-thru. This will re-energize K306 and K307.

The by-pass procedure is now complete. Transformer K305 has been isolated from the system.

303

Removal Procedure

The procedure is as follows:

- With the transformer isolated, check for potential on the primary and secondary cables. Feedback from external sources is always possible.

- After ensuring that there is no potential, isolate the secondaries and short them together.

- Now the transformer is de-energized and grounded. The secondaries are disconnected from the transformer.

- The ground connector to the transformer body is the last connection removed.

- Remove the transformer securing bolts and replace the transformer.

When removing equipment, ensure that the neutrals, perimeter ground and bonding wires remain bonded to a common point and a temporary ground is connected from the ground to the equipment. When the equipment is lifted above and clear of the feed-thru, remove the ground. Do the opposite when installing the new transformer. This will keep your equipotential zone intact.

To complete the job, remove the grounding and secondary cables from K305, unbolt and remove the transformer. The new transformer can now be installed. It is bolted in place, grounded, and the secondaries connected. The energized feed-thru is installed on the parking stand. The K304 elbow is moved to the H1A position, and then the K306 elbow is moved to the H1B position. The new transformer is now energized and in service.

Installation Procedure

When the new transformer is secured, connect the grounds, neutrals, secondaries. Using a shotgun, install the feed-thru on the transformer bracket. Return the primary cable to the original position on the new transformer.

CHAPTER 7 – System Maintenance

SYSTEM

DRAWINGS

MATERIALS

INSTALLING

SPLICING

FUSING

MAINTENANCE

TROUBLE

JOB SITE

Cable Identification

General

Checking circuit numbering tags on cables and drawings must not be solely relied on, as this is not a positive cable identification method.

Positive Cable Identification

1. **Physically Tracing the Cable Throughout Its Route**
    This method is not recommended, as it is usually impracticable in multi-circuit routes when such tracing can be confusing and lead to error.

2. **Pulling On The Cable.**
    This is generally limited to short, small cables with clear access on each end.

3. **Diode Method for Positive Cable Identification Procedures**
    To positively identify cable using the diode method, the following procedure must be followed.

    1. Test the battery of the audible continuity unit by shorting the two leads together. Use this unit to confirm the diode lead function by testing "clip to clip." It is critical that you test the lead in both directions. There must be continuity in one direction only.

    2. Check drawings and cable identification tagging.

    3. Obtain the appropriate safety permit, then under the direction of the person in charge (PIC) (unless it is level V equipment) isolate the cable following the safety permit requirement. If the termination is an elbow, the cable must be stood off on a feed-thru.

Ensure the location has a counterpoise system and that visible connections are in good condition. If the location does not have a counterpoise system, install an approved ground mat. The ground mat must be connected to a "common point of safety grounding" to achieve an equipotential work zone with the concentric neutral or sheath and ground.

    4. Check the cable for potential at the isolation point using an approved potential indicator.

    5. With no potential observed, ground the cable at the isolation point and tag with a Grounding/Blocking Protection tag if the work is being performed under a Clearance. For Self Protection, installation of the Grounding/Blocking Protection tag is not required because "worker controlled" protection is provided by the self protection tag. If the termination is an elbow, ground by installing the elbow onto a feed-

thru, then connecting an approved grounding elbow to the second position of the feed-thru. Now remove the grounding elbow and, using live line methods, connect the diode lead from ground to the cable inner conductor using a ground probe inserted into the second feed-thru position. (If the termination is pole mounted, installation of a pole band is required to create an equipotential zone and the diode lead is installed before the ground is removed).

6. Proceed to the opposite end of the cable and determine whether a counterpoise system is in place and that visible connections are in good condition. If the location does not have a counterpoise system, install an approved ground mat. The ground mat must be connected to a "common point of safety grounding" to achieve an equipotential work zone with the concentric neutral or sheath and ground.

7. If the termination is an elbow, the cable must be stood off on a feed-thru.

8. Check for potential using an approved potential indicator.

9. With no potential observed, using live line methods, check cable to ground continuity. It is critical that continuity be checked in both directions. For positive cable identification there must be continuity in one direction only.

10. Return to the opposite end of the cable, remove the diode lead using live line methods and reinstall the grounding elbow on the feed-thru.

4. **Pulsing and Tone Tracer Cable Identifiers (BCH - 2 Cable Identifier)**
This method is confined to serviceable de-energized cables.

(a) The use of the cable identifier is based upon the premise that the cable terminations are identified and can be tested for potential and be test grounded.

(b) The transmitter is connected at one end of the cable.

(c) A heavy duty diode is connected at the other end.

(d) The transmitter sends a 300 volt or more DC pulse along the cable to the other end.

(e) An identifier receiver is then taken into the manhole and all cables are scanned for the pulse. Only one cable will positively show the pulse.

(f) The transmitter is shut off when the cable is cut or alternatively, the conductors are shorted together.

Note: The use of a diode lead at one end and one in the transmitter enables the conductor identification to be done in the normal manner.

Telenex Cable Locator

Radio detection cable and fault locators provide accurate and dependable information about all types of buried (duct or direct burial) power cables. Radio detection sets are portable, battery operated instruments used to pinpoint earth return faults and locate the path and depth of the cable. The locating sets are waterproof and consist of the RD 433 HCT X-2 digital transmitter, the RD 432 PDL-2 digital receiver, an A-frame and accessory items.

The RD 433 HCT X-2 is a specially designed microprocessor controlled, multi-frequency, 5 watt transmitter used to locate cables and fault finding in congested areas and over long distances. Its operating modes and functions are selected with a push button key pad and indicated visually on a LCD panel. The transmitter is preprogrammed with five operator selected frequencies: 512Hz, 8kHz, 33kHz, and 65kHz. The frequencies are applied individually or simultaneously to the target line during locating procedures. The unit also has a multi-frequency program containing nine different frequencies that are compatible with other receivers. The signal frequencies are clamped, direct connected or induced through the earth to a target line. The transmitter also provides the following output signal strength and target line measurement functions: output current, voltage and impedance, line voltage, and line resistance to ground. The automatic impedance matching to the target line feature enables the transmitter to provide an optimum locate signal in all conditions.

The RD 432 PDL-2 is a hand-held receiver that incorporates digital signal processing with a microprocessor controlled digital LCD. These features enable the receiver to provide you with more information about the buried cables and faster processing when detecting signals on a target line. The receiver operating modes and functions are selected with a push button keypad and indicated visually on a LCD panel. The unit is preprogrammed to detect four active locating frequencies applied with the transmitter: 512Hz, 8Khz, 33kHz, and the current direction 256Hz frequency. The received signal strength is indicated on the receiver by a digital bar meter, a digital numerical display and audibly through a built in speaker. The semi-automatic push button gain control allows you to manually adjust the receiver's sensitivity either up or down to maintain a satisfactory signal level indication on the bat meter. The receiver also has a power cable mode to detect and determine the depth of the 60Hz AC signal on energized power cables without using the transmitter. The push button depth function gives an instantaneous digital display of cable depth in feet or meters and is accurate up to 14 feet.

The RD 433 HCT X-2 transmitter will test for a faulted secondary cable and the RD 432 PDL-2 receiver connected to the A-frame will pinpoint the exact location of secondary earth return faults.

For operating procedures, refer to the Radio Detection instruction book.

Underground Safety Grounding Procedures

Introduction

All high voltage lines and electrical apparatus are treated as alive unless a safety protection guarantee is held, the lineworker has tested for voltage, and safety grounding has been applied.

Even though a circuit may be physically isolated from all sources of power, it is possible for the circuit to remain charged or become charged by:

- Electrostatic or electromagnetic induction from energized circuits paralleling or crossing over it.

- Wind or fog blowing across the line.

- An electrical storm in the area.

- Induction from the earth's magnetism.

- Accidental energization from a nearby circuit becoming damaged and contacting the line or equipment, or through an operating error.

- Protection from electric shock hazard is obtained by short-circuiting or bonding together with a low resistance metallic conductor on all conducting parts (including uninsulated guy wires) in the work area. This ensures that no dangerous difference in potential can occur between various conducting parts contacted by the worker. It is necessary to connect all these conducting parts to ground to ensure that all such parts remain at or near ground potential.

When removing pothead risers, the apparatus is grounded on both sides of the riser connection before the riser is removed. In substations, risers must be completely removed. On terminal poles, the risers are removed from the pothead and then tied to the crossarm.

In some situations the risers do not have to be removed. An example of this would be in a customer's switch when installing test equipment. The pothead itself is still safety grounded and the risers can stay in position.

When cutting cables, the sheath or concentric neutrals have to be bonded across the planned cut area and then grounded.

Before working on an underground cable, the elbows are put on a feed-thru and then grounded using a grounding elbow.

Safety Permits

Before any grounding can be done, a safety permit must be in place and held by the lineworker in charge.

A safety permit is an assurance that lines (cables) or electrical and/or mechanical apparatus on the power system are isolated and will remain isolated.

There are three types of safety permit:

- Clearances (including protection extension)
- Test and work permit
- Self protection

These are enforced by three types of Do Not Operate tags.

In this chapter, a brief summary of each type of protection will be given. Remember that safety grounding refers to your personal safety as well as the public's safety.

Clearances

A Clearance is a stated assurance that a specified cable or electrical apparatus is isolated and that it is safe to apply safety grounds and to work on.

A Clearance is issued by the person in charge (PIC) of the cable or apparatus. The PIC is usually the control center. It ensures that the cable or apparatus has been de-energized, isolated and tagged with clearance tags. The clearance also ensures that the cable or apparatus will not become alive while being worked on.

When a Clearance is received it must be repeated back to the issuer immediately and his acknowledgment must be received.

Under certain conditions, a Clearance can be extended to another person by the use of a Protection Extension. With a Protection Extension, a person signs on to the original clearance by stating his or her name and time of entry. The Clearance holder informs the person requesting the Protection Extension of any hazards involved and the boundaries.

When the work is completed, the person with the Protection Extension returns the Protection Extension to the Clearance holder. The Clearance holder, ensures that all persons working under the Clearance have been advised that the Clearance is being returned and the cable should be treated as alive. The Clearance holder then returns his or her Clearance back to the PIC.

Test and Work Permit

A Test and Work Permit, like a clearance, ensures that lines (cables) or electrical apparatus are isolated and will remain isolated. However, subject to certain precautions, safety grounds may be removed for conducting tests or when it is necessary to float a cable for splicing and terminating.

Floating a cable conductor means that the conductors of the cable are ungrounded and the sheath or concentric neutral remains connected to the ground. The reason for this is that if there is a ground fault in the vicinity of the termination, the rise in ground potential would be transferred out to the work site along the grounded conductors. Leaving the grounds off ensures that this does not happen.

A Test and Work Permit cannot be extended to anyone else. Also, only one Test and Work Permit can be taken out on a line or apparatus.

In underground work, Test and Work Permits are used occasionally since feeder cables may have to be floated when they are being spliced or terminated.

Self Protection

A Self Protection is a positive form of safety protection guarantee that you can provide to yourself and your crew. It can be applied on lines (cables) or apparatus where a clearance or Test and Work Permit is not required. This could include auxiliary sources to apparatus, compressors or pumps and associated piping.

Certain conditions must exist before you can use a self protection:

- You must be a certified holder of the safety permit and be authorized by Local Operating Order.

- The line or apparatus involved does not have looped or multiple feeds.

- No more than one self protection can be held on the same cable or apparatus.

- Your name is on the Do Not Operate - Self Protection tag.

The procedure for self protection includes ensuring that the line is isolated and that it is safe to apply grounds. The line is then tagged Do Not Operate - Self Protection. After the work is completed, remove the grounds and advise all personnel to treat the line as alive. Remove tags and return the line to service.

The three types of safety protection guarantees are enforced using Do Not Operate tags. These tags are installed at all points of isolation such as the terminal pole, substation, customer vault, transformer and junction box (boundaries of the work area).

CHAPTER 7 – System Maintenance

SYSTEM

DRAWINGS

MATERIALS

INSTALLING

SPLICING

FUSING

MAINTENANCE

TROUBLE

JOB SITE

Cable Work Practices

Introduction

Before making hand contact with underground components, always follow your company's established safe work practices for isolation and grounding.

Equipotential Bonding

Equipotential bonding is recognized as the safest method of performing work on high voltage conductors and equipment. After isolation, bond together all exposed conductors and the concentric neutral, and connect them to a point of common safety grounding. This limits potential differences across your work area, so that little or no current can flow through you, even if your work area becomes energized at a high potential.

Floating Conductor

When working on feeder cable conductor, it is occasionally not practical to apply a working ground to the cable conductor at the work site. For safe work practices for feeder cable refer to your company's isolation and grounding procedures.

Only the concentric neutral remains grounded at the terminals, which provides an equipotential zone for you at the work site. This assumes that the transformer, junction, or switching apparatus has a perimeter ground or counterpoise installed, which is connected to the neutral. At other equipment, such as splice boxes, pull boxes, and mid-duct run locations without grounds, install a portable ground mat at the work site connected to the neutral. Proceed with work only, while standing on the portable ground mat.

Underground Grounding Kit

Introduction

The underground grounding kit contains all the specialized components needed for grounding and switching operations in dead front transformers and junction boxes.

Upon successful completion of this section, you will be able to identify all equipment included in the underground grounding kit and state the purpose of each component.

Color Coding

The components are colored orange or yellow, in order to immediately identify them as devices for grounding purposes.

Although the colors signify these as grounding components, the various manufacturers do not use the same colors for the different voltage components. Therefore, when ordering, you must order by stock number for whatever voltage (12 kV or 25 kV) you require.

Note: Approved grounding components must always be used.

Kit and Components

- Feed-thru tools, each with an insulating cap and grounding elbow (with grounding clamp) connected
- Stand-off plugs, each with an insulating cap connected
- Protective caps
- Two test rods
- Silicon grease tubes
- Lint free wiping cloth
- Cutout ground clamp
- Terminator cover – optional

Note: It is recommended to have a minimum of six 15 kV and six 25 kV grounding elbows available.

Kit care

To assure reliability and long life of kit components, clean and re-lubricate all components and return them to their proper compartment directly after use.

To protect the operating interfaces, all components should be connected to a matching component or to a protective cap.

Component Uses

Feed-thru	For isolation or grounding of a terminator elbow. Fasten onto parking stand. (Also used as a temporary bypass with loadbreak/make capability.) It has a bleeder wire.
Insulating cap	For insulating, shielding, and protecting the surface of the bushing well inserts and feed-thru bushings. Has a bleeder wire.
Bleeder wire	For discharging electrostatic build up. Prevent getting "bites" and prevents connector stress. Although it is grounded, it is not to be used as a ground lead.
Grounding elbow	For visibly grounding cables, transformers, or switchgear with load break insert connections. Used alone or in conjunction with a feed-thru. It also keeps the bushing free of contamination during the grounding operation. It has a stainless steel pulling eye and a 600 volt insulated, stranded, tinned-copper ground lead.
Grounding clamp	Duckbill or other approved clamp for connecting the ground lead of the grounding elbow to the grounded bus.
Ground lead	For using as a bonding jumper and connecting to the ground rod, ground bus, or ground mat. It is made of No. 2 copper flexible wire, with approved clamps on either end.
Stand-off plug	Like a feed-thru, but with only one bushing. Use to isolate without grounding, or to park energized load break elbows. It has a bleeder wire.
Test rod	For a direct connection to the contacts of the primary insert for testing purposes, e.g. application of diodes (not to be used for grounding).
Wiping cloth	For cleaning off a connector before re-lubricating.
Cutout ground clamp	For grounding primary cables at the dip pole.
Terminator cover	Used to cover terminations when floating the cable at the dip pole.
Grounding mat	For grounding, if there is no counterpoise present. (Not part of kit.)

DRAWINGS   MATERIALS   INSTALLING   SPLICING   FUSING   **MAINTENANCE**   TROUBLE   JOB SITE

Other equipment needed to perform underground grounding are:

Pole band	Used at the terminal pole to create an equipotential zone for the lineworker.
Ground leads	Made up of a length of No. 2 copper flexible wire with duckbill clamps (or another type of grounding clamp) on each end, are used to connect parts to the point of safety grounding (i.e. ground rod).
Hot sticks	Shotgun, P2 sticks, etc. are used to apply grounds, open fuses and perform other live line work.
Elbow pullers	Used to break the seal when pulling and removing elbows.

Note: Shotguns should not be used to pull elbows

Safety Factors

- Check that all clamps used in grounding are of the approved type. Fargo clamps or hot taps are not approved for grounding, but can be used in bleeder wires.

- Check that bleeder wires are in good condition.

- Do not confuse bleeder wires with ground leads. Bleeders can use fargo clamps.

- Check insulating caps for contamination.

- Check that the elbow probes are in place and in good condition

- Check for damaged or worn cables.

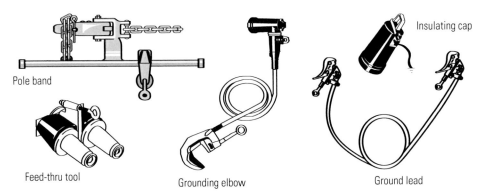

Figure 7-28. Equipment and materials used for underground safety grounding.

Grounding Cables

Introduction

This section, describes the procedures for using potential testers, feed-thrus, grounding elbows, and insulating caps to ground in dead front transformers, junction boxes, and switching units. You will also be able to describe the equivalent procedures for grounding live front switchgear.

The following procedures are done only after positive cable identification techniques, isolation and grounding procedures, etc., are in place.

Deadfront Grounding Method

1. Identify the cables.

2. Using a hot stick, mount a feed-thru with insulating caps on a parking stand – one for each phase and at both ends of the cable being isolated. Remove one insulating cap from each feed-thru, and connect its bleeder wire to the grounding bus.

3. Using approved elbow pullers, remove the load break elbow of the cable being isolated and stand it off by inserting it on to a feed-thru bushing. Cover the open bushing well insert with the insulating cap. Do this at both ends of the cable. The cable is now isolated.

4. Test for potential: Test to ensure lines and equipment are de-energized.

   a. Change the scale on the instrument (i.e. Modiwark) to the underground setting and system voltage.

   b. Remove the test cap on the elbow with a hot stick, exposing the test point. The test point is not actually in contact with the cable conductor, but is close enough to show a potential to the Modiwark.

   c. Using a hot stick, place the instrument against the test point. A steady tone or lamp indicates a live cable.

   d. If there is no tone or lamp, reconfirm the instrument is working by checking a known live elbow.

   e. Ensure the detector is turned off after use.

SYSTEM | DRAWINGS | MATERIALS | INSTALLING | SPLICING | FUSING | **MAINTENANCE** | TROUBLE | JOB SITE

Livefront Grounding Procedure

In livefront kiosks, such as Mark II switchgear, or for switchgear in livefront transformers, the grounding sets used are very similar to those used on overhead lines.

1. Verify that the alternative feed is in the Normally Open position, and the source side has been isolated and tagged. Tag the "N.O." with the appropriate safety permit in the operating handle compartment.

2. Using an instrument (Modiwark and hot stick) test potential at the fuses. Move the Modiwark, slowly toward the conductor being tested, the Modiwark will buzz if the cable is energized, until it indicates that the cable is de-energized.

3. If de-energized, use a live line tool to open the fuses and insert barriers. Ensure the other end of the cable is isolated also.

4. Apply ground leads to the ground bus and then to the terminators.

5. To float the cable for working on the cable conductor, wait at least one minute and then remove the ground leads.

6. If no counterpoise is present and hand contact is made, connect a portable ground mat to the concentric neutrals at the work site.

Safety Grounding a Cable

The isolating and grounding procedures for a faulted cable located between two transformers are:

1. Ensure a safety permit is in place.

2. Using approved live line tools, mount a feed-thru tool on the parking stand at transformer A.

3. Remove the elbow for the cable being isolated and insert it on the feed-thru. Cover the bushing well with an insulating cap.

4. Mount a feed-thru on the parking stand at transformer B.

5. Using a shotgun, remove the elbow for the cable being isolated and insert it on the feed-thru. Cover the bushing well with an insulating cap.

Note: The cable between transformer A and B is now isolated.

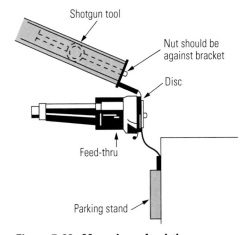

Figure 7-29. Mounting a feed-thru.

6. Using a Modiwark, test for potential (absence of voltage) at the feed-thru in transformer B).

7. After confirming that the cable is isolated (no potential), mount the grounding elbow, which is connected to the ground bus, on the feed-thru).

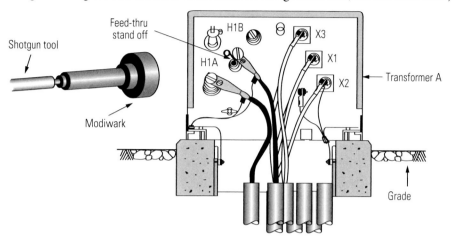

Figure 7-30. Checking for potential and the grounding elbow in place on the feed-thru.

8. Using a Modiwark, test for potential (absence of voltage) at the feed-thru in transformer A. Once the isolation is confirmed, mount a grounding elbow on the feed-thru.

9. The cable is now grounded.

If a cable is going to be made discontinuous by cutting through the concentric neutrals, a bonding jumper must be used. Its purpose is to bond the concentric neutrals across the planned cut and to ground. The bonding jumper consists of two ground leads attached to a ground rod, ground bus or counterpoise. If you are in a location where there is no ground rod, ground bus or counterpoise, a ground mat is used.

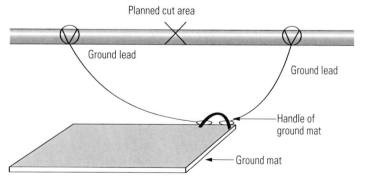

Figure 7-31. Ground mat being used to ground an underground cable across a planned cut area.

Safety Grounding a Junction Box

To safety ground a junction box, use the grounding elbows in the same manner as for the transformer.

Safety Grounding a Switchgear

A MK II switchgear or a 13/25 kV switchgear is safety grounded using grounding sets very similar to those used on overhead line work.

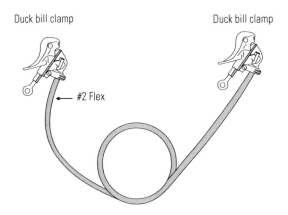

Figure 7-32. Safety ground lead. One is needed for each phase.

To safety ground a switchgear:

1. Isolate the switchgear. This could involve doing switching at other locations to ensure that as many customers as possible remain energized while the switchgear is out of service.

   After de-energizing all the switchgear's feeds and laterals (taps), open all fuses and switches.

2. Obtain the appropriate safety permit. Using a Modiwark, check the terminators for potential and buzz them before applying the grounds.

3. Go to one switching compartment and safety ground all the terminators. This is accomplished by attaching a grounding set first to the ground bus then to the terminator connection. Repeat for each terminator in the compartment.

Safety Grounding at a Terminal Pole

On a wooden pole, ensure the cutouts or switches are open and (if possible) the risers are removed. Using a Modiwark, check each terminator and riser for potential. Install a pole band below your feet and connected to the neutral. Using the shotgun, install the ground leads on the terminators and ensure that the clamps are firmly attached. Figure 7-33 shows the sequence in which to attach the ground leads.

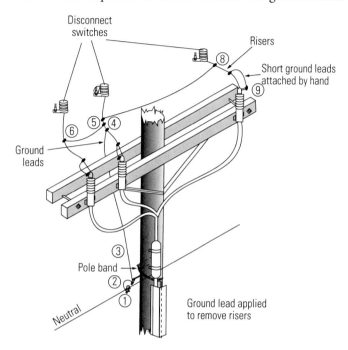

Figure 7-33. Sequence for installing safety grounding at a terminal pole.

With all the grounds in place, the risers can be removed from the potheads and swung out of the way. If any equipment has to be attached to the potheads (i.e. diode leads for testing purposes), it may be done live line method or grounded. The ground leads are removed after the equipment has been connected.

The ground leads are left attached, until the job is completed and the risers have been reconnected (reinstalled).

Conclusion

To safety ground any apparatus or cable, you must first isolate it and then safety ground it. You have to isolate and safety ground only the specific apparatus or cable on which you need to work. Remember that a cable has two ends and in order to isolate and safety ground it, you must do both ends. A safety permit must be in place before any grounds are applied.

Also, before applying safety grounds, you must check for potential and then buzz the apparatus, cable or equipment. The grounds are applied by first attaching them to a ground bus and then to the apparatus, cable or equipment.

Summary

This concludes the module underground equipotential grounding.

You should now be able to:

- Describe the procedures required to set up equipotential zones on underground systems.

- Identify the components included in the underground grounding kit.

- Describe the use of potential testers and the underground grounding kit for grounding and floating cables.

Underground Cable Cutting and Removal Procedures

Cutting

The appropriate isolation and grounding procedures must be followed prior to any cutting of underground cable.

The concentric conductors of a XLPE cable serve as the *system neutral* and may be the only connection to ground for a portion of the system. Therefore, before any XLPE underground cable is cut, the effect on the distribution system and the worker's equipotential zone must be determined.

- For cutting in open areas, the worker must maintain a safe distance.

- For cutting in confined spaces, the worker must vacate the space before cutting commences.

- A bond must be installed across any cut in the cable neutral or sheath prior to cutting, except the final cut when cable is to be removed.

- All cables will be cut by remote cutting using approved hydraulic cutters or by using approved and tested live line cutters.

- After a cable has been cut, the workers must avoid placing themselves in the opencircuit between two sections of the neutral or sheath because a dangerous potentialdifference may exist.

Note: It may not always be necessary or possible to remove an underground cable that has been damaged. If it is determined that the cable should be repaired instead of removing it, see Chapter 5, pages 188 through 194 for information on cable repair, jacket repair, and rejacketing.

Removal

A) This procedure covers the removal of level V cables (no loop, multiple feed or customer in-feed exists):

1. Confirm the equipment is level V (no loop, multiple feed or customer in-feed exists).

2. Check drawings and cable identification tagging.

3. Isolate the cable following Self Protection procedures. The personalized self protection tag provides Worker Controlled protection. (If the termination is an elbow, the cable must be stood off on a feed-thru). Determine whether a counter poise system is in place and that visible connections are in good condition. If the location does not have a counterpoise system, install an approved ground mat. The ground mat must be connected to a "common point of safety grounding" to achieve an equipotential work zone.

4. Check the cable for potential using an **approved** potential indicator.

5. With no potential observed, ground the cable. If the termination is an elbow, ground by installing the elbow onto a feed-thru, then connecting an approved grounding elbow to the second position of the feed-thru. (When the diode method for positive cable identification is to be used, remove the grounding elbow and, using live line methods, connect a diode lead from ground to the cable inner conductor using a ground probe inserted into the second feed-thru position).

6. Proceed to the opposite end of the cable (this is the "first cut" cable end) and, determine whether a counterpoise system is in place and that visible connections are in good condition. If the location does not have a counter-poise system, install an approved ground mat. The ground mat must be connected to a "common point of safety grounding" to achieve an equipotential work zone with the concentric neutral or sheath and ground. For work on pole mounted terminations a pole band is required to establish the equipotential zone.

7. Check for potential at the work site using an approved potential indicator.

8. With no potential observed, positively identify the cable by one of the following methods:

   - Pulling on the cable

   - Diode method

   - Cable identifier - A Test and Work permit is required for this method.

When the diode method for positive cable identification is being used, and the diode lead has been installed as described in step 5 above, confirm positive cable identification using live line methods. Return to the isolation point, remove the diode lead using live line methods and reinstall the grounding elbow on the feed-thru.

9. At the "first cut" end of the cable (opposite end of the cable from the isolation point) cut the cable as described in the underground cable cutting procedures.

10. Insulate the conductor and neutral or sheath by installing an insulated cover* using Class 1 rubber gloves. This will protect against a possible potential difference across the grounding system.

*For work in live front equipment, approved barriers must be used.

11. Return to the grounded end of the cable and make the final cut. If the cable was faulted mid-run, also insulate this end of the cable using class 1 rubber gloves.

12. Remove the cable.

B) This procedure covers the removal of cables defined as level IV:

1. Check drawings and cable identification tagging.

2. Under the direction of the person in charge (PIC), isolate the cable following Clearance procedures. (If the termination is an elbow, the cable must be stood off on a feed-thru.) Under the direction of the PIC, complete any switching for service restoration (relocation of normal open point).

3. At the isolation point at which grounding will be installed, check the cable for potential using an approved potential indicator. This is the "final cut" end of the cable.

4. With no potential observed, ground the cable at this isolation point and tag with a Grounding/Blocking Protection tag. If the termination is an elbow, ground by installing the elbow onto a feed-thru, then connecting an approved grounding elbow to the second position of the feed-thru. (When the diode method for positive cable identification is to be used, remove the grounding elbow and, using live line methods, connect a diode lead from ground to the cable inner conductor using a ground probe inserted into the second feed-thru position).

5. Proceed to the other end of the cable (this is the "first cut" cable end) and determine whether a counterpoise system is in place and that visible connections are in good condition. If the location does not have a counterpoise system, install an approved ground mat. The ground mat must be connected to a "common point of safety grounding" to achieve an equipotential work zone with the concentric neutral or sheath and ground. For work on pole mounted terminations a pole band is required to establish the equipotential zone.

6. Check for potential at the work site using an approved potential indicator.

7. With no potential observed, positively identify the cable by one of the following methods:

   - Pulling on the cable

   - Diode method

   - Cable identifier - A Test and Work permit is required for this method.

When the diode method for positive cable identification is being used, and the diode lead has been installed as described in step 4 above, confirm positive cable identification using live line methods. Return to the isolation point where the diode lead was installed and remove it using live line methods, then reinstall the grounding elbow on the feed-thru.

8. At the "first cut" end of the cable (opposite end of the cable to where the grounds have been applied) cut the cable as described in the underground cable cutting procedures. For XLPE cables this cut opens a system neutral loop.

9. Insulate the conductor and neutral or sheath by installing an insulated cover* using Class 1 rubber gloves. This will protect against a possible potential difference across the grounding system.

*For work in live front equipment approved barriers must be used.

10. Return to the grounded end of the cable and make the final cut. If the cable was faulted mid-run, also insulate this end of the cable using Class 1 rubber gloves.

11. Remove the cable.

CHAPTER

TROUBLESHOOTING

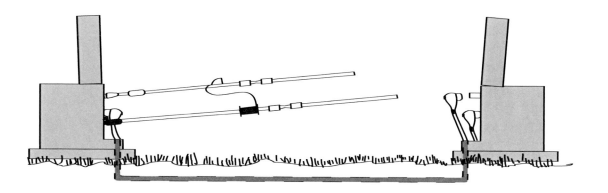

SYSTEM

DRAWINGS

MATERIALS

INSTALLING

SPLICING

FUSING

MAINTENANCE

TROUBLE

JOB SITE

Underground Troubleshooting

Introduction

Faults occurring on underground systems are generally caused by one of the following:

- Physical damage (for example, dig-ins)

- Aging failures

- Material and workmanship failures

- Overcurrents (for example, switching surges)

Physical damage can include such things as dig-ins, water infiltration or stresses caused by settling of soil. Aging failures can include increased aging due to high ambient temperatures or soil conditions (direct burial) or exposure to sunlight (dip poles).

There are many methods that can be used to troubleshoot a circuit. The methods can be simple to complex, and inexpensive to expensive. The method used depends on the situation and the equipment available.

Upon successful completion of this section, you will be able to describe and perform the procedures requires to analyze, locate, and repair underground distribution faults.

The topics covered are:

- Sectionalizing

- Line/fault locators

- Conclusion

Sectionalizing

A primary cable fault will probably result in a blown fuse on the terminal pole, while secondary trouble will normally cause an individual transformer fuse to blow. In underground distribution systems utilizing low profile transformers (LPT), a secondary fault may pass through the transformer fuse and blow the fuse at the terminal pole. For this reason, every attempt should be made to ensure there is proper fuse co-ordination between the LPTs and the terminal pole (dips). The transformer fuse should clear before the dip fuse to isolate the faulted transformer or secondary.

If a fault does occur on the primary cable, we need some method of locating the faulted section of cable and restore power to the other customers. Sectionalizing can be done in basically two ways. The first is by using fault indicators to help eliminate the trial and error of re-energizing damaged electrical equipment. The second is the systematic elimination of circuit components.

Fault Indicators

The first method is essentially the same approach but with the mechanical/electrical advantage of fault indicators placed on the cables. There are many different types available, but the basic concept of being tripped by the magnetic field of a passing fault current is the same. When a cable is energized on a fault, a red indicator is shown, indicating that the fault is beyond the point where its FI is installed. Some fault indicators are manual reset and require a special tool for re-setting back to normal. Other types of indicators will reset automatically by current or the electro-static field of the conductor.

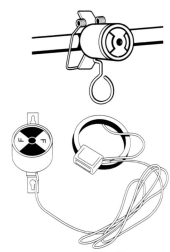

Figure 8-1a. Fault indicators.

By beginning at the first sectionalized point and visually checking the fault indicators, the problem can be quickly found between the last "fault" (trip) reading and the next "normal" reading. This section can now be isolated by standing off elbows etc. and re-energizing the loop from both directions to restore power.

Fault indicators are very useful when multiple feeds or three phase undergroundloops are involved. In older areas where there are no permanent fault indicators installed, cable mounted (temporary) indicators can be used to locate faulted cables. Many districts are permanently installing fault indicators at strategic locations. These locations are shown on the underground distribution diagram (UDD) and may also be marked on the kiosk or LPT.

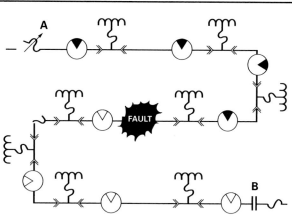

Figure 8-1b. Fault location.

The indicators are placed on the primary cable at every sectionalizing point and the fuse closed to energize the cable and activate the indicators. It is now possible to check the indicators, locate the fault, and isolate the cable.

Systematic Elimination of Circuit Components

The second method used to locate the faulted section is to divide the suspect area into two smaller areas and check each area. One area will check out OK, while the other will be broken down again and checked.

After checking the one line diagram and determining the circuit involved, divide the area into two sections. With the help of another lineworker and following the underground distribution diagram (UDD), consult with the person in charge (PIC) and proceed as follows:

1. Stand off an elbow at transformer approximately midway in the faulted section.

2. Go to the terminal pole where the fuse blew and install a new, smaller rated fuse. Close the fuse to re-energize from the terminal pole to the open point where the elbow has been stood off.

3. If the fuse blows, the fault is located between the stood off elbow and the terminal pole.

    Depending on the size of this section, find a midway point and stand off an elbow, or go to the next transformer and stand off an elbow. Re-fuse the cutout at the terminal pole and re-energize.

Note: Always wear safety protective equipment (safety glasses, hearing protection, etc.), when closing cutouts.

4. If the fuse does not blow, the section from the terminal pole to the stood off elbow is OK. Using a loadbreak tool, open the cutout at the terminal pole.

5. In this case, the next step is to go midway again and stand off an elbow, put the first elbow back in place and return to the terminal pole.

6. Re-energize at the terminal pole. If the fuse blows, the fault is located between the present stood off elbow and the transformer just before where the first elbow was stood off (Figure 8-2).

   If the fuse does not blow, this section is without fault and you should continue, doing the same procedure each time.

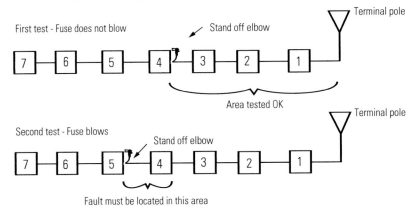

Figure 8-2. Results of two tests on two areas.

Once the fault has been located, it must be determined whether the fault is at the transformer, the primary cable, or the secondaries.

To determine the exact location of the fault, do the following:

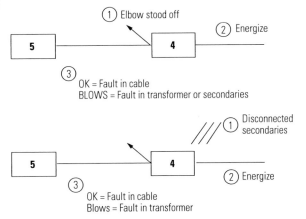

1. In Figure 8-3, the fault was isolated to transformer 4 and the cable between transformers 4 and 5. First, put the stood off elbow at transformer 5 back in place. Then at transformer 4 stand off the elbow for the cable going to transformer 5.

Figure 8-3. Determining the exact location of the fault isolated to one transformer and a cable length.

2. Go to the terminal pole, re-fuse the cutout and re-energize.

3. If the fuse doesn't blow, the fault is in the cable, not the transformer or secondaries.

   If the fuse blows, the cable is in good condition and the fault is in the transformer or the secondaries.

4. To isolate to the transformer or the secondaries, disconnect the secondaries and go to the terminal pole, re-fuse and re-energize.

    If the fuse does not blow, the fault is in the secondaries. If the fuse blows, the fault is in the transformer.

Line/Fault Locators

Many methods of fault location are in existence today. Some require relatively low cost equipment while others require elaborate expensive equipment.

Cables with metallic sheaths or coverings such as PILC, concentric neutral and shielded types usually break down to the sheath or other metallic covering. In these cases a return circuit (through the fault and the metallic covering) is available for locating the fault. In the case of non-metallic sheath cables, the fault resistance to ground may be very high. Different techniques are required for locating faults in metallic sheath cables than for those with a non-metallic sheath.

DC Hi-Pot Fault Finder

The Chance DC Hi-Pot Adapter has proved to be a valuable tool for locating faulted cables in underground systems. The DC Hi-Pot adapter is connected to the chance phasing sticks in preparation for testing the cable. The adapter is basically a diode that converts the AC line voltage to a DC voltage equivalent to the peak AC voltage.

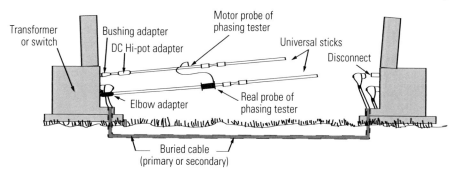

Figure 8-4. Typical underground application of the Chance DC high-pot adapter and phasing sticks.

The old method of locating faults was to repeatedly re-fuse at the riser pole and close the fuse in on different sections of cable. By dividing the undergroundloop in half and closing the fuse, one could tell whether the cable was good or bad. If the fuse blew, one divided the bad section of the cable in half, refused and closed in. This was continued until the faulted section of cable was determined.

Closing in on a fault puts additional stresses on the cable, elbows, and splices, which may result in early failure. When closing in on a fault on high current capacity underground feeder cables, the DC adapter is a preferred method. Also, the high fault currents may cause the cutout to explode violently. When re-fusing, use a smaller fuse to test energized suspect cables and limit any damage or violent explosions.

For example, on a 7200 volt AC single phase underground line, we would have approximately 10 kV DC applied on the line to test a cable. Using this system, we disconnect both ends of the cable and hook on the adapter. The cable is energized with the DC voltage. A good cable will hold a charge so the voltmeter on the phase stick will show a voltage for a second or so until the cable becomes charged. Then the voltage difference will drop to zero volts. However, when we energize a bad section of cable the fault drains of the charge and our meter continuously reads a high potential. Just as easily, the Adapter quickly tests repaired cable too. It checks that the fault repaired was the only fault on the cable and confirms that the repairs were effective. Once the cable is isolated or repaired, the cable can be re-energized without further fuse operations. This eliminates the unnecessary stresses of high-fault currents put on good cables and other equipment.

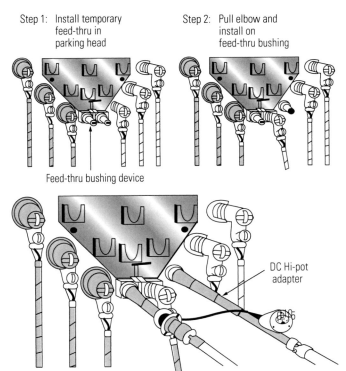

Figure 8-5. Operation of DC high-pot adapter.

Chance Line/Fault Locator

The Chance line/fault locator is for use on underground distribution lines, 115 volts through 34.5 kV, with fault location potential up to one megohm.

The Chance line/fault locator consists of four units:

- The line locator is made of epoxiglas and is self-standing for free use of both hands. It is used as a "wand" sending a null-out to the audible sound through the unit, as an indication of proximity to induced current in a buried cable.

- The fault locator, also made of epoxiglas, is designed to receive a signal from the transmitter through the two earth probes and interrupts the signal when the two probes are equal distance from the fault. 90° locations are then established from the handle of the tool to pinpoint the fault.

- The transmitter emits a 90 volt square wave and/or 115 cycle signal and one 12 volt battery installed in the carrying case.

- The receiver amplifies the signal of the transmitter and/or the 60 cycle field around a current carrying conductor.

- The unit operates on six AA batteries and includes a volume control, earphone pack and neck strap. The earphones helps to eliminate any background noise.

Telenex Cable Locator

The Telenex Cable Locator is a hand held receiver that uses radio signals to locate underground cables and pipes. The sending unit is connected to the cable (energized or de-energized) and sends a radio signal along it that is picked up and read on the LCD panel of the receiver. For more detailed information on the Telenex Cable Locator, refer to Chapter 7, Switching.

The type of equipment to be used will depend on what is available, what can be improvised on short notice, the nature of the cable installation (dry or wet ground, ducts), and the length of the cable.

Refer to the instruction manuals for fault finding equipment available in your district or area. Fault finding equipment is very specialized test equipment and require careful procedures to produce accurate results.

Conclusion

When troubleshooting, look for obvious problems before starting any fault locating procedures.

- Examine the above ground equipment for any physical damage.

- Look for signs of recent excavation which may have damaged the cable.

- Check for depressions in the ground due to settling since this may produce stress on cables.

While installing fault indicators or performing hi pot tests, visually check the equipment and components and check the area.

- Components that have failed, such as connectors elbows and conductors, will possibly be charred or burnt.

- Generally a blue-gray haze of smoke film will be found somewhere on the inside of a lid caused by a fault.

- Dead animals such as squirrels, frogs, mice, etc. which may have come in contact with energized cable

- A smell of ozone or smoke may still be present when a lid is opened. This is caused by a fault or overloaded secondaries

While isolating and switching, refer to the one-line diagram (UDD) to ensure you are working on the correct circuit.

- Consult with the PIC before doing any switching operations.

- Refer to the one line diagram during the switching procedure.

- Obtain the correct safety permit and always apply safety grounds if hand contact is required.

- When isolating by elimination with fuses, stay clear of the cutout's line of fire. Wear ear and eye protection.

- Never leave any equipment open and unattended during fault finding. You are responsible for the public's safety.

Once a fault has been located and isolated, additional switching may be required to energize as many customers as possible. Before making repairs, obtain the necessary safety permit from the PIC and apply safety grounds.

Emergency Repairs

Once the fault has been isolated, steps will be necessary to repair the damaged section. The method of repairing will depend on many variables. Components can be simply replaced, but faulted cables present a bigger problem.

If the cable is in a duct, it may be possible to pull out the cable and replace it.

If the cable is direct buried, there are two options:

1. Abandon the faulted section of cable and replace with a new one.

2. Locate the fault and repair that section only.

In order to restore power as quickly as possible in the event of an outage, some methods of emergency repairs have been developed.

Generally, components such as, terminations, transformers and short pieces of cable can be repaired or replaced on site. Special situations, such as a faulted direct buried cable, cannot be easily repaired.

Temporary Replacement For a Faulted Primary Cable

When a fault occurs on a section of primary cable, and no loop feed is available to restore full service, an emergency feed can be improvised. The temporary power cables are more flexible than normal primary cable, and has one or two layers of jacket reinforced with cotton and nylon to withstand rugged handling conditions. While this cable can be laid on the ground to bypass the faulted section of cable, it should be encased in a duct if there will be vehicular traffic. Most underground equipment, such as, transformers, switches etc. have an entrance port for an emergency cable.

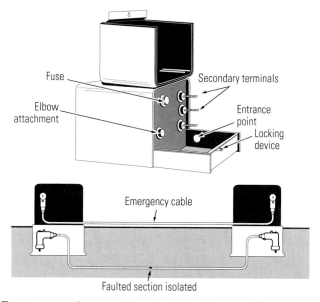

Figure 8-6. Temporary replacement for a faulted primary cable.

Temporary Replacement For a Faulted Secondary Cable

A temporary secondary cable would use the same method as the temporary primary cable. When two meters are close to each other, a meter bypass system can be used.

A meter bypass system is intended to be installed for short periods (typically a few days) to maintain power to a customer when installation of or repairs to an underground service cable is delayed. In many situations where the device is installed, the cable will be vulnerable to ground level activity such as gardening, vehicle movement, children at play, etc. If the bypass device is damaged and live parts are exposed, a safety hazard exists. It is, therefore, important that the cable insulation is in good condition, all electrical connections are well taped and the cable is placed where it is least vulnerable. The installer should perform the following precautionary measures:

- Consider suspending the cable overhead between the eaves of adjacent houses. Also, if it is required for the cable cross from one side of a house to the other, consider running the cable over the roof.

- Inspect the cable insulation thoroughly each time it is installed. Cover areas of worn insulation with a thick layer of electrical tape and replace a badly damaged cable.

- A concentric neutral service cable with a thick PVC jacket is a good choice.

- Disconnect the connections of the faulted cable in the other meter base and tape the ends. Install the temporary bypass meter base marked "load" in place of the original meter. Install the original meter.

- Be certain to connect the meter base connector marked "source" to the meter base of the customer from which power is being taken. The meter installed here will only register this customer's load.

- Avoid laying the cable across vehicular areas such as driveways and parking areas. If these areas cannot be avoided, lay some protection over the cable such as a wooden board or install the cable in rigid conduit. Place warning tape along the path of the cable.

- If it is suspected that the two loads could exceed the rating of the good service, advise both customers to minimize their consumption.

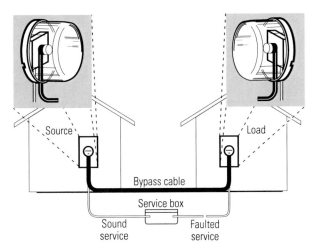

Figure 8-7. Faulted secondary cable temperature replacement.

Termination Repairs

Introduction

As a lineworker, you must be able to inspect and maintain terminating devices (terminators and elbows) found in an underground residential distribution system.

Terminating device may have to be repaired or replaced for several reasons, such as:

- Not enough care taken during the construction or installation
- Improper cleaning of the device when installed
- Improper use of materials, such as wrong dies when pressing
- Termination not protected from weather conditions during installation
- Installation procedures not followed
- Physical damage
- Faulty materials used

Note: Refer to your underground system solation and grounding procedures for safety requirements, positive cable identification techniques, isolation and grounding procedures, etc.

Repair a Terminator

There are prejob tasks that must be completed before you start the job. The first thing you should do is get the drawing (print) of the circuit to determine the area involved. If the drawing is not supplied, go to the first transformer or switchgear from the terminal pole and check inside for the drawing. You must ensure that you and the public are protected from any possible electrical hazards. Other prejob tasks include such things as switching, de-energizing the cables or equipment, obtaining the appropriate safety permit, and grounding. Every effort should be made to keep as many customers as possible energized while the repairs a being made.

First, check the terminator to determine the problem and how it can be corrected. When checking a terminator, look for:

- Burnt off neutral.
- Tracking damage may be evident.
- The terminator may be severely damaged.

Note: The appropriate safety permit and grounding must be in place before hand contact is made.

In each of these situations, the damage will normally require the terminator be replaced. Occasionally, it is necessary only to repair and reconnect the neutral. Use caution, as a burnt off neutral may indicate a more serious problem. If the terminator shows little or no damage, it may just require some cleaning. To replace the neutral, it may be necessary to splice in an extra length of the neutral and remove some of the jacket on the cable to expose more neutral for connection purposes. This is not a normal occurrence.

Replacing a terminator located on a pole differs slightly from replacing one located in a switchgear, therefore it will be discussed separately.

Replace a Terminator on a Pole

Note: The appropriate safety permit and grounding must be in place before hand contact is made.

To replace a terminator on a pole:

1. Check the other end of the cable (at the next transformer, junction box, switchgear, etc.) to see if there is sufficient slack available to cut off the terminator and install a new one.

2. If there is sufficient slack, disconnect the riser and bend it out of the way.

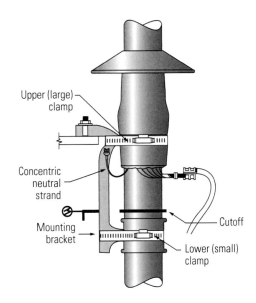

Figure 8-8. Location of terminator cutoff.

Note: If there is not sufficient slack, it will be necessary to splice in a piece of cable or pull in a new cable.

3. Use the cable cutters to cut the terminator off below the neutral bonding area.

   If there is obvious exterior damage or tracking/arcing marks on the jacket, cut the cable below this area.

4. Use a skinning knife to remove some of the jacket so the underlying layers (especially the neutrals) can be checked. You want to ensure that there was no internal damage to the cable when the terminator faulted. If internal damage is found, cut off more of the cable until undamaged cable is found.

5. Remove the terminator from the mounting bracket.

6. Remove the cable guards and cover to expose the cable.

7. Using cable pulling equipment (if necessary), pull enough slack to make the termination.

SYSTEM | DRAWINGS | MATERIALS | INSTALLING | SPLICING | FUSING | MAINTENANCE | TROUBLE | JOB SITE

8. Tie a handline to the cable to hold it in place and assist in pulling the cable (the slack) up the pole.

9. Remove the tape from the bottom of the sock holding the cable.

10. Pull the slack cable through the hanging sock. Retape the bottom of the sock and remove the handline.

11. Train the cable and feed it through the cable mounting bracket. Tighten the bracket on the cable.

12. The cable can now be terminated. Install the new terminator using the procedures explained in Chapter 6, Splice and Terminate Cable. Remember to use the correct materials and to follow all instructions.

13. Reconnect the neutral (bond the terminator).

14. Install the pothead riser with the appropriate connector.

Note: In bad weather, at night or when there is a lack of equipment, the replacement job can be done in the back of a company vehicle/van. The main caution is to ensure that the measurements are correct and that the terminator reaches its terminating position.

As previously mentioned, where there is not enough slack, it is necessary to splice in a piece of cable or pull in a new cable. Many factors must be considered when deciding what to do. For the most part, the choice depends on the size of the job, the ability to do the job, and the duration of the power outage for the customers.

If the decision is to splice in a piece of cable, the damaged terminator has to be removed and the piece spliced in. Follow the appropriate procedures to remove the terminator and to splice in the piece of cable. The location of the splice will vary depending on the job and working conditions. Once the cable is spliced, the new terminator can be installed on the end of the cable as per procedures.

If the decision is to pull in a new cable, both the damaged terminator and the good terminator (at the other end) have to be disconnected and removed from the apparatus. The cable is then pulled out and the new cable pulled in. To pull in the new cable, use the equipment and procedures explained in Chapter 4, Pull Cable. Once the new cable is pulled in, both ends will have to be terminated and connected to the apparatus.

Replace a Terminator in a Switchgear

Note: The appropriate safety permit and grounding must be in place before hand contact is made.

To replace the terminator in a switchgear:

1. Perform the necessary prejob tasks explained previously.

2. Check to ensure that there is enough slack to cut off the terminator and install a new one. In switchgears, there is usually more slack available.

3. Disconnect the terminator connection.

4. Use cable cutters to cut off the terminator below the neutral.

5. Remove the terminator from the mounting bracket (if present).

6. Pull enough slack to do the termination. Use cable pulling equipment, if necessary.

7. Terminate the cable following the procedures explained in Chapter 6, Splice and Terminations.

8. Bolt the terminator to the mounting bracket (if present).

9. Reconnect the neutral.

10 Reconnect the terminator connection.

Before completing the job, check to ensure that no other damage exists.

Repair an Elbow

When a trouble and outage report to repair a faulty elbow is received, there are some prejob tasks that must be completed, such as, ensuring that you and the public are protected from any possible electrical hazards. Other prejob tasks include such things as switching, de-energizing the cables or equipment, obtaining the appropriate safety permit, and grounding. Every effort should be made to keep as many customers as possible energized while the repairs a being made.

Next check the elbow to determine the problem and how it can be corrected. Normally, you will have to clean the elbow using a cloth and isopropanol in order to assess the damage. You may find one of two things:

- The elbow or bleeder wire is burnt (visibly damaged).

- The elbow looks fine externally, but may be damaged internally.

Replace a Burnt or Damaged Elbow

Note: The appropriate safety permit and grounding must be in place before hand contact is made.

To replace a burnt or damaged elbow:

1. Check to ensure that there is sufficient slack to cut off the elbow and install a new one. Slack is needed to allow the elbow to be parked or moved to another bushing, etc. It is important to get enough slack to allow the elbow to reach the furthest position required on the equipment.

Note: As with the terminator, if there is not enough slack, a piece of cable will have to be spliced in or a new cable will have to be pulled in. There are many variables involved, but basically the choice depends on the size of the job, the ability to do the job and the length of the outage for the customer. The procedures are the same as those explained for the terminator.

2. If there is sufficient slack, use cable cutters to cut off the elbow below the neutral bonding area.

    Check the cable for jacket damage and inspect the underlying layers for damage. If damage exists, more cable will have to be cut off to ensure that you are working on good cable.

3. Remove the elbow from the bushing. Check the bushing for damage. It may be burnt or the bonding wire may be damaged (broken). If damage is noticed, replace the bushing or repair the bonding wire.

4. Pull in the required amount of cable, if necessary. Use pulling equipment.

5. Install a new elbow using the procedures explained in Chapter 6, Splice and Terminate Underground Cable.

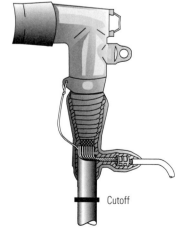

Cutoff

Figure 8-9. Location of elbow cutoff.

6. Reconnect the neutral (to bond the elbow).

7. Install the elbow on the bushing.

Before energizing the elbow, check the fuses and associated equipment to ensure that no other damage is present. If a fuse is blown, it will have to be replaced. The bonding wires on the bushings may also be damaged and may have to be replaced.

After checking all associated equipment for damage and repairing (if necessary), complete the postjob tasks. These include removing the grounding, returning the safety permit, switching and re-energizing.

If the elbow showed no external damage, you will have to do an internal inspection to determine the problem.

Replace an Elbow With Internal Damage

Note: The appropriate safety permit and grounding must be in place before hand contact is made.

To replace an elbow with internal damage:

1. Remove the elbow from the bushing and check the bushing. Replace or repair, as required.

2. Using a probe wrench, remove the probe. Clean the inside of the elbow and the probe with a cloth and isopropanol. Check the inside of the elbow and the probe for damage

3. If the inside of the elbow is damaged, the whole elbow (including the probe) has to be replaced. If the probe is burnt, melted or discoloured and the interior of the elbow is fine, just the probe will have to be replaced and the insert bushing cleaned or replaced.

Before completing the job, check all associated equipment for damage and repair if necessary.

Repair Faulted or Damaged Cables

Introduction

Most damage to cable is caused by an external source(for example, a dig-in). The next common damage is caused during installation of the cable. Finally, there is damage due to the manufacturer. Manufacturer damage takes many forms:

- Conductor not in the center of the insulation.

- Bubbles or marks in the insulation.

- Marks in the semi-con.

- Tape shield or concentrics broken or torn.

- Openings in the outer jacket allowing exposure to weather conditions.

Always follow your company's procedures for underground system isolation and grounding, and for positive cable identification, isolation, and grounding.

The equipment and materials needed to do the work depends on the type of damage and repair needed.

Damaged or Faulted Cables

There are prejob tasks that must be completed before you start the job. First, obtain the drawing (print) of the circuit to determine the area involved. If the drawing is not supplied, go to the first transformer or switchgear from the terminal pole and check inside for the drawing. You must ensure that you and the public are protected from any possible electrical hazards. Other prejob tasks include such things as switching, de-energizing the cables or equipment, obtaining the appropriate safety permit, and grounding. Every effort should be made to keep as many customers as possible energized while the repairs are being made.

Check the drawing for the circuit designations, cable length, types of terminations and type of grounding required based on the type of terminations.

Note: A Test and Work permit is required when using the cable identifier.

Check the cable to see the extent of the damage and to determine what is required to get the circuit/cable back in service. Check to determine one of the following:

- The condition of the cable.

- Will a new section of cable have to be spliced into the existing cable.

- Will the cable have to be replaced.

Repairs

If the cable jacket is only slightly damaged, it probably can be repaired. To repair the jacket do the following:

Note: The appropriate safety permit and grounding must be in place before hand contact is made.

1. Clean the outside of the jacket using a cloth and isopropanol.

2. If the jacket is slashed or cut, use a knife to open the jacket and expose the neutrals and semi-con. Examine the interior for more damage. Extensive damage will require a new section of cable to be spliced in or the cable to be replaced.

3. If there is no internal damage, use an aluminum oxide cloth or file card to roughen the outer jacket.

4. Seal the split jacket with two half-lapped layers of self-amalgamating (SAP) tape and two half-lapped layers of PVC tape over the SAP tape.

5. The jacket can also be repaired using the rejacketing kit explained in Chapter 4.

This type of minor repair is usually needed when a backhoe or working crew accidentally breaks into a pull box or digs up a cable. Sometimes the cable is not damaged and can be repositioned and energized.

Splice in a New Section of Cable

If there is serious damage to a section of the cable or if a splice in the cable is damaged, a new section of cable may be required and spliced into the cable. When a damaged section is cutout, check to see if there is enough slack to make a splice or whether a short section is required.

Note: If this damaged section of cable is in a pull box, there may be no counter-poise available for grounding. Therefore, special grounding procedures would have to be used.

Replacing Faulted or Damaged Cable

If the damaged section of cable is in a location that does not allow splicing (such as the edge of a pull box), or if too much of the cable is damaged, a new cable may be required.

To replace the cable:

Note: Refer to your underground systems isolation and grounding procedures. The appropriate safety permit and grounding must be in place before hand contact is made.

Transformer Repairs

Introduction

Transformers can be damaged if hit by motor vehicles or construction equipment. Depending on the impact, cables may be severed, hinges broken, elbows bent or damaged or the body of the transformer may be damaged. The equipment and materials needed to do the repair work depend on the situation and the severity of the damage.

The majority of the transformers that you will be working on will be dead front transformers. Since there is a possibility that you will encounter a live front transformer, you should be aware of the major differences between working on a deadfront and a livefront.

On a deadfront, the energized elbows are basically a self contained primary insulation. Contact should be avoided and limits of approach observed, but the terminations and cables are essentially dead, or at a near zero voltage potential externally. On a livefront transformer, the primary terminations are totally exposed, just like the secondaries on both dead and live front transformers. Limits of approach must be observed when working around live front transformers and step potential should be considered when damage occurs.

Isolation to repair undergroundtransformers should be done at two adjacent isolation points, such as the LPT, kiosk, junction box, etc.

Transformer Repairs

There are prejob tasks that must be completed before you start the job. First, obtain the drawing (print) of the circuit to determine the area involved. If the drawing is not supplied, go to the first transformer or switchgear from the terminal pole and check inside for the drawing. You must ensure that you and the public are protected from any possible electrical hazards. Other prejob tasks include such things as switching, de-energizing the cables or equipment, obtaining the appropriate safety permit, and grounding. Every effort should be made
to keep as many customers as possible energized while you are checking the transformer.

Now you can start to check the transformer to determine the damage and fix it. The following list shows what must be checked and how to react to the findings:

1. Check for stress on the elbows and the cables. The transformer may have moved or shifted thus causing strain (pulling) on the elbows.

Solution: Move or reposition the transformer.

2. Check the grounding and bonding. If the transformer has moved, the grounding and bonding may have been disconnected.

Solution: Reposition the transformer and reconnect or replace (if damaged) the grounding and bonding.

3. Check the secondary terminals, lugs and wires to see if they are bent or broken. If the secondary terminals are broken, the transformer will have to be replaced. If the lugs or wires are broken, they can be replaced or reconnected (if slack allows).

4. Check for outside damage to the hinge. If the hinge is damaged or broken, it can be replaced.

5. Check the hold down clamps. If broken, they can be replaced.

6. Check for oil leaks. If leaks are present, replace the transformer. Test the oil for PCBs and put the transformer in a protective bag.

7. Check the fuses with the continuity tester. It is possible that the fuse blew when the transformer was damaged. If the fuse blew, the transformer may not have been damaged.

Note: A suspect faulted LPT should not be energized by replacing its own internal fuse. Energizing to test it should be done at the first transformer or sectionalizing unit on the line side, by using the load break elbow of the primary cable feeding the faulted unit.

Replace a Transformer

When a transformer has to be replaced, obtain the drawing (print) and go through all the prejob tasks (tailboard) given for replacing a transformer.

Note: Refer to your underground system solation and grounding procedures for safety requirements, positive cable identification techniques, isolation and grounding procedures, etc.

Following proper isolation and ground procedures:

To replace a transformer:

1. Remove all items or equipment attached to the transformer. Put the primary elbows on a feed-thru or parking stand. Mark the phase and keep the elbows clean.

   Remove the secondary cables, ground bus, and neutrals and remove the hold down clamps on the transformer. Mark the secondaries on three-phase installations.

2. Using proper rated slings, remove the damaged transformer from the pad and install the new transformer. Install the hold down clamps.

3. Check the new transformer and install any bushings and grounding wires that may be required.

4. Connect the ground bus, primary and secondary cables and neutrals. Ensure that phases are correct.

5. Tag and label the transformer.

Note: Always be alert for backfeed.

Junction Box Repairs

Introduction

Junction boxes can be above ground or below ground.

In the repair and replacement of junction boxes (both single-phase and three-phase), the concrete enclosure is usually not a concern as it is rarely damaged. However, damage may occur by:

- Being hit by equipment digging in close proximity (below ground style).

- Motor vehicle accidents (above ground style).

Usually, the repairs associated with the junction boxes have to do with the elbows, J-bars, and other equipment in the enclosure (box).

Note: Refer to your underground system solation and grounding procedures for safety requirements, positive cable identification techniques, isolation and grounding procedures, etc.

Replace Below Ground Junction Box

If a below ground junction box has been hit by a dig-in or has been damaged, a major repair job may be required. It may mean that the box has moved and the duct face has not (or vice versa). The cables may be damaged or completely cut off and require replacing or repairs. Also, the box would have to be dug out and replaced.

There are prejob tasks that must be completed before you start the job. First, obtain the drawing (print) of the circuit to determine the area involved. If the drawing is not supplied, go to the first transformer or switchgear from the terminal pole and check inside for the drawing. You must ensure that you and the public are protected from any possible electrical hazards. Other prejob tasks include such things as switching, de-energizing the cables or equipment, obtaining the appropriate safety permit, and grounding. Every effort should be made to keep as many customers as possible energized while you making the repairs.

Note: The appropriate safety permit and grounding must be in place before hand contact is made.

The job may involve setting up pulling equipment and replacing the damaged cable. For procedures refer to Chapter 4, Installing Cable.

Removing the below-ground box could involve an outside contractor. Basically, the job would be very similar to a new installation.

Repair Above Ground Junction Box

This type of junction box is more likely to be damaged. The common causes of damage are:

- Motor vehicle accidents (most common)

- Weather

- Tampering

Follow the prejob tasks previously explained before starting work.

To replace the junction box:

Note: The appropriate safety permit and grounding must be in place before hand contact is made.

1. Unbolt the J-bars and set them aside. Leave the elbows on the J-bars to keep them clean.

   If the J-bars have to be replaced, remove the elbows. Clean and place the elbows in a plastic bag.

2. Disconnect all grounds and hold down clamps.

3. Install lifting bolts on the side of the box and use proper lifting equipment to remove and replace the box. Fasten hold down clamps and connect all grounds.

4. Bolt the J-bars containing the elbow in position. If the J-bars are being replaced, bolt on new J-bars. Remove the elbows from the plastic bags and install them on the new J-bars.

Repair Equipment in the Junction Box

Follow the prejob tasks previously explained before starting work.

The types of damage found inside the junction box are:

- Holes blown in a J-bar

- Bushing burned off or damaged

- Elbows burned or burned off

- Damage to the grounds or the ground bus

Replace Damaged or Faulted J-Bars

If there are holes in a J-bar, it has to be replaced. Replace it by following the procedures already explained in the replacement of an above-ground junction box.

Note: The appropriate safety permit and grounding must be in place before

SYSTEM | DRAWINGS | MATERIALS | INSTALLING | SPLICING | FUSING | MAINTENANCE | TROUBLE | JOB SITE

hand contact is made.

1. Remove the elbows. Clean the elbows and place in a plastic bag..

2. Unbolt the J-bar and remove it.

3. Bolt the new J-bar in position.

4. Remove the elbows from the plastic bag and re-install on the new J-bar.

Burned Off or Damaged Bushings

If the bushings are burned off or damaged, they will have to be replaced. There is a variety of J-bars. Some have removable bushings, some have fixed bushings and some have a combination. To replace the bushings if they are removable:

Note: The appropriate safety permit and grounding must be in place before hand contact is made.

1. Remove and clean the elbows. Store them in a plastic bag.

2. Disconnect the bonding wire.

3. Using a bushing wrench, remove the bushings.

4. Install the new bushings. Attach the bonding wire.

5. Remove the elbows from the plastic bag and re-install on the new bushings.

If the bushings are fixed permanently on the J-bar, the whole J-bar would have to be replaced. Follow the procedures explained previously.

Burned or Damaged Elbows

If the elbows are burned or burned off, they will have to be replaced. In a below ground junction box, there is enough slack available to allow the elbows to be cut off and new ones installed. Follow the procedures explained in the section on repairing cables. If a junction box does not have enough slack to cut off the elbow and install a new one, a new piece of cable would have to spliced on or a new cable pulled in.

Note: The appropriate safety permit and grounding must be in place before hand contact is made.

Damaged Grounds

If the ground or ground bus is damaged, the damaged items have to be removed and replaced. This usually involves cutting off or disconnecting the damaged wires and connecting new ones.

Note: The appropriate safety permit and grounding must be in place before hand contact is made.

Switchgear Repairs

Introduction

Normally, major repairs are not made to a switchgear. What you may do to a switchgear is:

- Check fuses

- Replace switchgear

- Clean switchgear

The most common fuse found in switchgears is the large S&C type of fuse (SM-4). When replacing the fuse, ensure the proper type is installed (i.e. 15 or 25 kV).

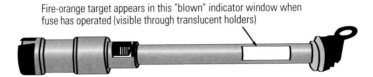

Fire-orange target appears in this "blown" indicator window when fuse has operated (visible through translucent holders)

Figure 8-10. One style of S&C type fuse.

Switchgears may need to be replaced due to damage resulting from motor vehicle accidents (MVA) or other types of accidents. If a fault occurs in a switchgear, it may be necessary to check it and clean it.

Note: Refer to your underground system solation and grounding procedures for safety requirements, positive cable identification techniques, isolation and grounding procedures, etc.

Check Fuses

When checking fuses, first try to ascertain what caused the fuse to operate (blow). If a fuse disintegrated, it could mean that there is a fault in the system. If a fuse melted, it could mean that a high load is present. If the fuses do not have the red/orange blown indicators, a continuity tester can be used to check each fuse to locate the blown one. The fuses can be removed from the switchgear using live line tools (hot sticks) and the special fuse holder tool located on the door inside the switchgear compartment. If this is not possible, the cable would have to be de-energized and grounded before the fuse could be removed.

Note: The appropriate safety permit and grounding must be in place before hand contact is made

Replace a Faulted or Damaged Switchgear

If a switchgear has to be replaced, there are prejob tasks that must be completed before you start the job. The first thing you should do is get the drawing (print) of the circuit to determine the area involved. If the drawing is not supplied, go to the first transformer or switchgear from the terminal pole and check inside for the drawing. You must ensure that you and the public are protected from any possible electrical hazards. Other prejob tasks include such things as switching, de-energizing the cables or equipment, obtaining the appropriate safety permit, and grounding. Every effort should be made to keep as many customers as possible energized while the repairs are being made.

Note: The appropriate safety permit and grounding must be in place before hand contact is made.

Now the switchgear can be prepared for replacement. To replace the switchgear:

1. Clearly identify all circuits and phases. This is important when reconnecting the new switchgear.

2. Disconnect all terminations, neutrals and the ground bus from the cabinet and remove the hold down clamps.

Note: If a cable support bracket is present, unbolt and remove it.

3. Install lifting bolts on the switchgear and use proper lifting equipment to remove and replace the switchgear.

4. Install hold down clamps and reconnect all neutrals, ground bus, and terminations to the new switchgear. Ensure all the phases are in the correct order.

Cleaning the Switchgear

If a fault occurs in a switchgear, the arc tends to leave traces of carbon on the terminations, switchgear, and inside compartments. To clean the switch:

1. Remove the switchgear from service (de-energize).

Note: The appropriate safety permit and grounding must be in place before hand contact is made.

2. Inspect the insulators for cracks or damage.

3. Using protective equipment (including rubber gloves and safety glasses) clean the insulators and terminators with isopropanal and a cloth.

4. Check all moving parts to ensure that they are operating correctly.

5. Put the switchgear back it into service (energize) and check for any arcing etc.

Troubleshooting a Three-Phase Transformer

Introduction

This section examines four different transformer electrical problems and describes how each may be detected. The problems presented are typical of those found in transmission and distribution systems, both overhead and underground. They do not present all possible transformer problems or a complete picture of transformer troubleshooting. Company procedures should always be followed for all troubleshooting.

Objectives

- Define "one leg open" and describe its symptoms

- Define "ferroresonance" and describe its symptoms

- Define "off ratio winding" and describe its symptoms

- Define "open neutral" and describe its symptoms

Troubleshooting Considerations

When a three-phase transformer malfunctions, the problem may be difficult to diagnose. Different transformer problems may have similar symptoms. The difficulty of troubleshooting a three-phase, pad-

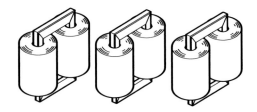

Figure 8-11. Three separate cores for each phase.

mounted transformer can also be complicated by the transformer's design. For example, the transformer's core construction can affect the symptoms. Some three-phase transformers have three separate cores, one for each phase. Each phase is physically separated from the others. This type of construction is illustrated in Figure 8-11.

Other transformers have a common core construction. As illustrated in Figure 8-12, each phase is wrapped around a different leg of a common core. With this construction, induction between the primary windings can affect the symptoms of a transformer problem.

A transformer's core construction is not usually indicated on its nameplate. However, a worker who is troubleshooting a transformer should be familiar with the core design, as it can affect voltage readings under certain conditions.

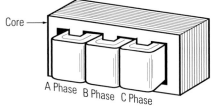

Figure 8-12. Common core construction.

The illustration in Figure 8-13 can be used to demonstrate the effects of four different problems on a three-phase, pad-mounted transformer. The illustration is a simplified diagram of a 13.2 kV, wye-wye connected, three-phase transformer. The three phases are indicated by the letters A, B, and C. Each phase has switches, a bus bar, a fuse, and windings. Each of the voltage problems discussed in this section affects the phase labeled C in the diagram.

To identify any voltage problem, it is important to take a complete set of secondary phase-to-phase and phase-to-ground readings. Depending on the problem's symptoms, other voltage and amperage, or load, readings may have to be taken as well.

The readings normally expected for the transformer in this example are shown in Figure 8-14. The normal expected secondary voltage phase-to-ground reading is 120 volts. The normal expected phase-to-phase voltage reading is 208 volts. In reality, however, normal voltages can vary within a specified range.

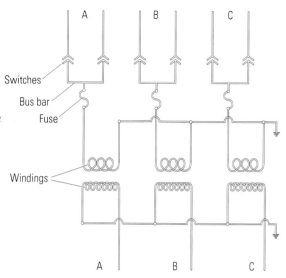

Figure 8-13. Three phase, 25 kV wye-wye connected transformer.

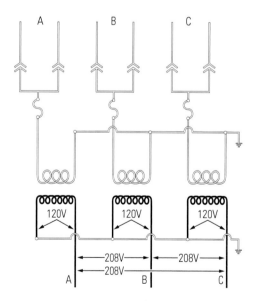

Figure 8-14. Normal voltages for three phase 25 kV wye-wye connected transformer.

One Leg Open

One possible transformer problem is an open leg, or phase. The diagram in Figure 8-15 shows that the fuse connected to the C phase has blown, causing the C phase primary supply to the transformer to be open. In this situation, the voltage expected on the secondary side of the open phase might be zero. However, for several reasons, the open phase can still show a voltage on the secondary. In this example, as shown in Figure 8-15, the secondary readings phase-to-ground are 120 volts, 120 volts, and 90 volts. The 90-volt reading on the open leg is due to the transformer's **common core** construction, which allows the leg to be energized by induction through the core.

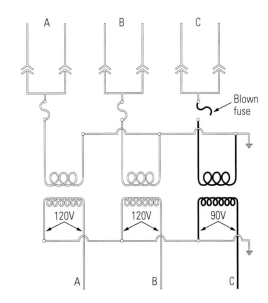

Figure 8-15. One leg open: Phase-to-ground readings.

Phase-to-phase readings show 208 volts from A to B. From A to C and from B to C, however, the voltage readings are abnormal. In this situation, voltage readings can be higher or lower than normal. In Figure 8-16, the A to C reading is 140 volts and the B to C reading is 200 volts. The 90 volt phase-to-ground reading and the low phase-to-phase readings with C seem to indicate an open leg.

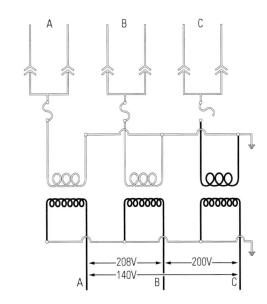

Figure 8-16. One leg open: Phase-to-phase readings.

Load readings are taken with a clamp-on ammeter on each secondary phase to determine whether the affected leg is carrying a load. There should be a load on each normal secondary leg, but no load on the open leg. As Figure 8-17 shows, for this example, the load readings are 83 amps on the A phase, 67 amps on the B phase, and 0 amps on the C phase. The 0 amp reading on the C phase confirms the open leg.

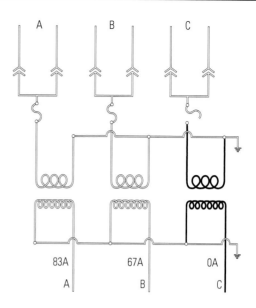

Figure 8-17. One leg open: Load readings.

If the transformer in this example had individual cores for each phase, rather than a common core, voltage could still have been detected on the open phase. This could happen if the open phase were connected to another phase through customer equipment, causing electrical backfeed. Although the open phase would not be energized from its normal source, it could still be energized by the electrical backfeed. In Figure 8-18, the B and C phases are electrically connected through customer equipment. C phase is being backfed through that equipment. The phase-to-ground reading on each phase is 120 volts, or apparently normal.

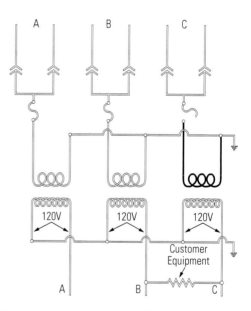

Figure 8-18. One open leg: Electrical backfeed phase-to-ground readings.

The phase-to-phase readings, however, include an abnormal voltage reading. Because the electrical backfeed originates from the B phase, the readings (Figure 8-19) are 208 bolts between A and B and between A and C, and 0 volts between B and C. With the C phase open, the phase-to-phase reading between the two electrically connected phases is 0, because no potential difference exists between them.

Load readings taken on the secondary legs should verify that the leg with the blown fuse is carrying no load. The reading for that leg should be 0 amps.

After the cause of the problem has been determined, and any faulty equipment has been replaced, a new fuse should be installed. This should energize the phase again, and normal secondary voltage should be present on all phases.

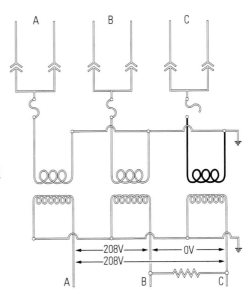

Figure 8-19. One open leg: Electrical backfeed phase-to-phase readings.

Ferroresonance

When a fuse blows outside of the transformer, at the cable pole, for example, another problem, called ferroresonance, can occur. Ferroresonance occurs when the capacitance of the undergroundcable between the transformer and the blown fuse closely matches the magnetic characteristics of the transformer core. Ferroresonance is only a concern in transformers with common core construction.

Ferroresonance takes the form of a resonant circuit consisting of the cable capacitance and the core induction. This current can cause a higher than normal voltage reading on the phase with the blown fuse. In some cases, the resonance can also produce higher than normal vibration and noise levels during operation. Cable overheating, arcing and blown fuses can also result.

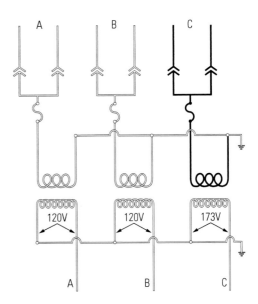

Figure 8-20. Ferroresonance: Phase-to-ground readings.

Figure 8-20 shows the phase-to-ground readings for one possible ferroresonant condition. The readings are 120 volts, 120 volts, and 173 volts. The voltage on two of the transformer legs is normal, but the voltage on the affected C phase is high.

The phase-to-phase readings for this condition are shown in Figure 8-21. Values between the ferroresonant phase and each normal phase could be almost anything. In this example, A to B reads 208 volts, A to C reads 158 volts, and B to C reads 293 volts.

The ferroresonant condition can be verified by using a phasing tool to take a phase-to-ground primary voltage reading on the C phase incoming cable through a feed-thru bushing. (Disconnecting the cable from the transformer would interrupt a ferroresonant circuit and allow a true reading of the cable.) Ferroresonance is indicated if the

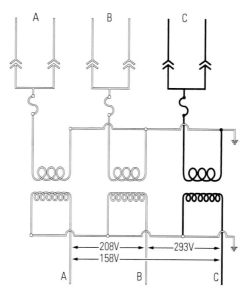

Figure 8-21. Ferroresonance: Phase-to-phase readings.

primary voltage reading is abnormal. In this example, since there are no other transformers on the circuit, the primary reading of the cable shows 0 volts instead of the normal 7,620 volts.

To resolve the problem in this example, the blown fuse must be located and replaced. The fuses on the primary cable feeding the affected phase are checked, beginning with the nearest fuse and working toward the cable pole until the blown fuse is found. After any necessary equipment repairs are made, replacing the blown fuse should correct the problem.

Off Ratio Winding

The high phase-to-ground reading associated with ferroresonance could also be a symptom of another condition, called an off-ratio winding. With an off ratio winding, a voltage surge, such as lightning, could cause several of the primary coil turns to short out leaving fewer primary turns. Fewer primary turns raise the secondary voltage on the affected phase, resulting in a high phase-to-ground reading.

Figure 8-22 shows the phase-to-ground readings for one possible off ratio winding condition. Two of the legs read normal phase-to-ground voltage, but the reading on the affected C phase is 132 volts.

The phase-to-phase reading between the affected C phase and each of the other phases is higher than normal. In Figure 8-23, its value is approximately 218 volts. Between the A and B phases, however, the reading is normal. In contrast to the ferroresonant condition, for an off-ratio winding condition, the phase-to-phase readings between the affected phase and each normal phase are equal.

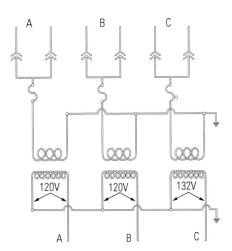

Figure 8-22. Off ratio winding: Phase-to-ground reading.

To verify the off ratio winding condition, a phasing tool is used to read the primary phase on a feed-thru bushing. The voltage reading should be a normal 7,620 volts. With ferroresonance, the primary voltage reading is abnormal.

When an off ratio winding condition occurs, voltage remains constant, and the problem usually affects only one phase. If the condition is confirmed, the transformer will have to be replaced.

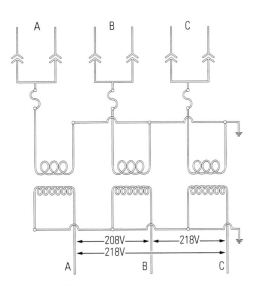

Figure 8-23. Off ratio winding: Phase-to-phase readings.

Open Neutral

The voltage problems discussed so far affect only one phase. In some cases, the entire transformer can be affected by a voltage condition. One such condition is an open neutral. With an open neutral, the transformer's secondary neutral is not solidly connected to ground because of a burn-through, a mechanical defect, or some other reason.

The diagram in Figure 8-24 shows an open neutral condition. The open neutral is represented by the X. Secondary voltages on a transformer with an unbalanced or open lead on each phase will fluctuate. Phase-to-ground and phase-to-phase voltages may be much higher or much lower than expected, and they will change as the load changes.

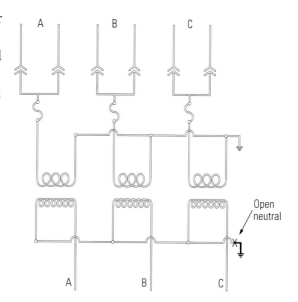

Figure 8-24. Open neutral.

If voltage readings are within the normal range or if the effects are intermittent, an open neutral could still be present. A load reading on each secondary phase and on the neutral should verify the condition. If the load is different on each phase, a load would be expected on the neutral. If there is little or no load on the neutral, the neutral may be open. The load readings may not be conclusive, however, because with a balanced load, where the load readings on each phase are the same, no amperage should be detected in the neutral. If the voltage and load readings are inconclusive, recording voltmeters may have to be installed to record voltage fluctuations over a period of time. If an open neutral inside the transformer is confirmed, the transformer will have to be replaced.

CHAPTER

JOB SITE SAFETY

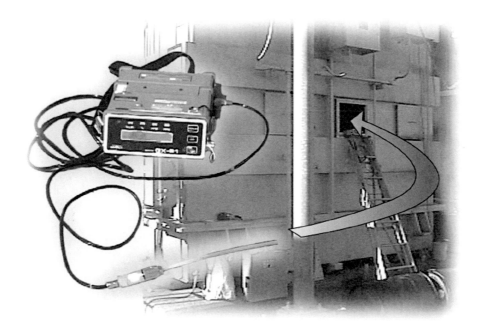

Prepare Job Site

Introduction

This section will describe how to prepare the job site so that work can be safely carried out.

Preparation of the job site includes the following:

- Reviewing the work order and drawing(s) prior to going to the job site

- Setting up traffic control at the job site

- Arranging equipment and materials around the cable vehicle at the job site

It is important for you to realize that vehicles and pedestrians travel on many routes that are also used for electric cables. Therefore, it is often necessary for lineworkers to get involved in traffic and pedestrian control when these cables have to be worked on.

Safe planning involves the actual arrangement of the traffic control devices, and also the related locations of the lineworkers and the equipment while the work is being performed. Barricading for pedestrian safety may also be required.

The topics covered are:

- Equipment and materials

- Prejob

- Traffic control

- Work location (manhole)

- Work location (other than manholes)

Equipment and Materials

The following is a list of the equipment and materials that may be required for traffic control.

- Traffic control devices may include traffic cones, flashing lights and manhole guards.

- High level warning devices are mounted on a vehicle or by some other method so that they are clearly visible from a distance.

- Traffic barricades with flashing lights.

- Ropes and signs.

- Qualified flagpersons may also be required, depending on the job, the location and the traffic flow.

Prejob

A meeting with the crew in the morning to discuss the job can help plan the job and identify any hazards. By checking the work order and the drawing(s) for the job location, it can be determined if traffic control is needed. Depending on the job site, it may be necessary to arrange for traffic control personnel. This may be arranged by the supervisor. An on site tailboard discussion must be held before the work commences.

In order to determine what traffic control is needed, it is necessary to refer applicable national, state, local, and company regulations.

Traffic Control

Traffic control, in accordance with company regulations, should be set up before the manhole is opened.

If it is not possible to set up the traffic control devices before positioning the vehicle at the job site, position the vehicle first, then walk to where the traffic control devices should start and begin positioning them. Face the traffic and walk back towards the vehicle while placing the traffic control devices (cones). Figure 9-1 shows a typical placement of traffic control devices.

The traffic control devices must also be positioned a certain distance apart. This distance depends on the road conditions and the road speed. Refer to your company's traffic control regulations for the correct spacing to use.

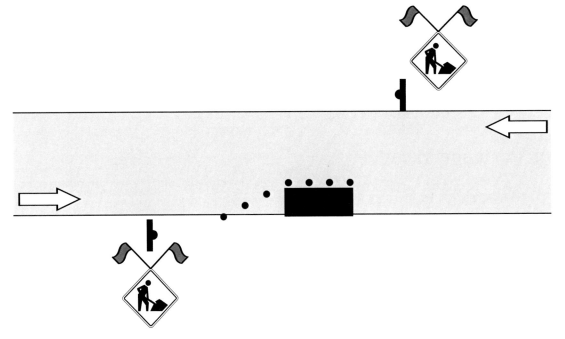

Figure 9-1. Positioning of traffic control devices.

Work Location (Manhole)

Once traffic control has been completed and manhole entry procedures have been carried out, the manhole guard used to prevent people from accidentally walking into the open manhole must be placed around the open manhole.

The area between the vehicle and the manhole must be kept clear of any obstacles. Put tools and materials to either side of the manhole and route cords and hoses to one side of the manhole. Keep propane furnaces and torches away from the manhole opening to prevent them from accidentally falling in (onto a lineworker). Ensure that furnaces are level and on a firm surface or support.

Rope off the job site or use traffic control devices to route pedestrians around the job site. It is essential that the public is protected from any safety hazards.

Work Location (Other than a Manhole)

As was the case with the area around a manhole, the area around a transformer, switchgear, junction box or terminal pole must also be kept clear of obstacles. There must be a clear path between the work area and the vehicle.

Equipment and material must be set up in a safe location. All job sites must be set up so as to protect pedestrians. Ropes and cones must be used to direct or guide pedestrians around the work area.

When working on terminal poles, ensure that pedestrians are guided around the bottom portion of the pole. Ropes and handlines must be secured so that they do not swing out into traffic.

At any job site, the main point to remember is that the public and the lineworker must always be protected from any danger.

> *Caution:* The confined spaces procedures described in the manual are for general guidance only. The confined spaces procedures for your company may be different. Always follow your company's established procedures and safe work practices.

Enter Confined Spaces

Introduction

You will frequently be required to work in a confined space, most common being a manhole. Other types of confined spaces include tanks, tunnels, trenches and enclosed or restricted work sites. These sites may be hazardous because toxic, flammable or oxygen deficient atmospheres may develop in them as a result of construction, location or content. Special precautions are necessary before and during work in these sites to ensure your safety. Entry into confined spaces must comply with all OSHA, state, and utility regulations.

Safe work practices are a vital part of the trade. Review of the appropriate safety manuals and proper training is required.

The topics include:

- General requirements

- General procedures

- Specific procedures

- Emergency entry and rescue for confined spaces

General Requirements

Safe work practices for entering a confined space are the same in all areas. Before entering a confined space every crew must ensure that there is:

- No fire or toxic hazard

- Adequate oxygen (O_2)

- Provision for rapid emergency exit or rescue

The equipment and materials required to make these checks include:

- Equipment for testing oxygen and toxic gas levels

- Manhole entry log

- Manhole ventilators

Since different types of testers and ventilators are used , be sure you are familiar with the one in your department.

Before entry, every confined space must be checked for combustibles and oxygen deficiency by a competent employee trained in the use of field testing equipment. The person in charge must also be aware of potential hazards from solvents, asbestos, metal fumes and gases such as carbon monoxide (CO) and hydrogen sulphide (H_2S).

Tests for these or other toxic gases must be made if these gases are suspected. In every case, a written entry procedure must be available and reviewed to ensure that crew members are aware of potential hazards and understand the necessary work precautions. Precautions must also be taken to ensure that hazardous conditions do not occur due to the work being done. If hazards have the potential of occurring, additional testing is required during the work period. Sometimes, in order to prevent accumulation, it is necessary to block ducts or lines that contain hazardous material.

Where hazardous air contaminants exist or may occur, they must be controlled by continuous ventilation. The results of tests done before entry and during the work period must be recorded. If difficult breathing or signs of illness occur at any time, immediately evacuate the confined space and undertake additional hazards checks.

Note: Alterations in the work procedure may be necessary to ensure safety. Confined spaces must be continuously ventilated and monitored.

For entry and work, oxygen concentrations must be maintained at 18 to 21% and combustibles at less than 20% of the lower explosion level (LEL). The LEL is the level at which a combustible is considered to be safe. If the level is any higher, there is risk of an explosion, so the LEL is a warning zone. Confined spaces must be continuously ventilated unless a variance has been issued. Toxic contaminants must be maintained at less than 50% of the maximum allowable concentrations.

Note: Normal air contains 21% oxygen. You can work safely as long as oxygen concentration is higher than 19.5%. When there is less than 16% oxygen in the air, thought processes may be disrupted, and at 12% unconsciousness occurs, followed by death.

If entry or exit is difficult, adequate precautions must be taken to ensure that safe and rapid rescue of workers is possible in case of emergency.

These requirements also apply to areas which may not be immediately obvious as confined spaces. For example, excavations, other construction sites and small rooms may become hazardous because of restricted ventilation combined with the use of noxious (harmful) substances.

General Procedures

Entry into confined spaces must comply with the OSHA and company standards regulations. A review and understanding of these rules and regulations and appropriate training is mandatory before entering and confined space. Work involving entry into confined spaces requires a minimum of two workers. If a hazard has been identified and personal protective equipment is used, at least one man must act as a safety watcher and must be ready and able to carry out a rescue. When both workers are to work in a confined space, a man check system may be used. You must always obtain supervisory authorization before entering tanks or other confined spaces that have not already been identified as part of a regular confined space work site.

The general entry procedures cover four areas:

- Testing

- Ventilation

- Provision of assistance

- Cleaning

Equipment and Materials

The Model 1214S Gastechtor Gas Alarm is a portable unit designed primarily for detecting combustible gases and oxygen deficiency in confined work spaces. It can detect and indicate gas concentrations up to the lower explosion level (LEL) and actuate a characteristic audible signal if the concentration exceeds a preset level. It also analyzes for oxygen over a range of 0 to 25% and actuates a different audible signal if oxygen concentration drops below a preset level.

The unit draws the air sample in over a combustible detector and an oxygen detector. Thus every test for combustible gas is automatically accompanied by the test for oxygen deficiency.

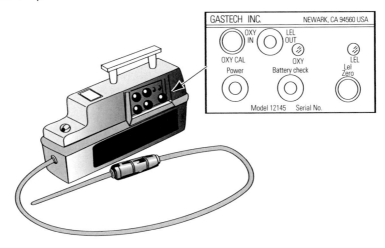

Figure 9-2. Gastechtor gas alarm model 1214S.

The controls used in normal operation are arranged on the left side of the unit as viewed from the rear. These controls are recessed to minimize the possibility of accidental operation. The controls are as follows:

- Power switch (push button). Push it in to turn the unit on. An orange indicator dot is visible when the switch is in the On position.

- Battery check switch (push button). Push it in and hold to check the charge level of the battery.

- LEL ZERO (knob). This is used to adjust the reading to zero in the absence of combustible gas.

- Alarm lights. Red (LEL) and amber (OXY) lights illuminate when in an alarm condition. The red light blinks in a combustible gas alarm condition. The amber light blinks in an abnormal oxygen condition.

- Range switch (push button). This is used to select the operating range. For combustibles (LEL), the button must be in the Out position. For oxygen (OXY), the button must be in the In position. A colored indicator dot shows when the switch is in.

- OXY CAL (knob). This is used to adjust the reading to 21% in normal air.

A probe is plugged into the unit to check manholes before removing the cover. There is a probe that attaches (plug in) to the unit.

It is advisable to test the unit before using it for entry to confined spaces. A cylinder containing a mixture of gases is located at the lineroom. To test the unit, insert the probe into the top section of the cylinder. Open the valve on the cylinder. The gas will flow into the probe and an alarm will sound if the unit is working. It may take a minute or two for the alarm to sound.

There is also an manufacturer's instruction manual that should be reviewed before using the unit.

Testing

1. Before entry, test for oxygen deficiency and combustibles. If the space is covered, test by inserting a sampling probe through any space that may be available before removing the cover. If sampling is not possible before cover removal, move the cover gently to ensure that sparks are not created. After removing the cover, test again at various locations in the confined space. Avoid friction, open flames, and sources of sparks until you are sure that combustibles are not present.

2. Test for toxic gases or substances, if suspected.

3. Record in an appropriate log book all test results, date, times, location of confined space and have the tester sign the record.

The following points should be noted:

- Combustible gas detectors calibrated for methane or hexane detect most of the commonly encountered gases accurately or within a reasonable error on the side of safety. One notable exception is hydrogen, which gives a reading approximately 25% lower than the actual amount present.

- Some interfering gases can seriously affect a combustible gas detector's reading. High concentrations of chlorinated hydrocarbons such as trichloroethane or the lead compounds in leaded gasoline may depress meter readings. These compounds may also corrode sensitive detector elements, decreasing future instrument sensitivity.

- Combustible gas detectors are not sensitive enough to identify hazardous concentrations of toxic gases or vapors and cannot be used for this purpose. If toxic gases or vapors are suspected, test using specifically developed testing equipment (such as Drager sampling tubes) for each contaminant. Detectable low-level concentrations of combustibles will frequently require respiratory protection and ventilation to control the toxicity hazard associated with the combustible standard.

Perform Test with Model 1214S Gastechtor Gas Alarm

To check for gases and oxygen, do the following:

- Connect the hose and probe to the fitting on the front of the unit. Usually these are already in place.

- Press the power switch to turn the unit on. The meter needle will normally move upscale briefly and a pulsing alarm may sound. Sometimes the LEL alarm may sound during warm up.

- Press the battery check button and note the meter reading. If the reading is close or below the BATT CK mark on the meter, recharge the battery.

- Switch the range switch to the LEL (Out) range and allow the meter needle to stabilize (about a minute). With the probe in a gas-free location, turn the LEL ZERO control to bring the meter needle to 0.

- Switch the range switch to OXY (In) range and allow the meter needle to stabilize. With the probe in a normal air atmosphere, turn the OXY CAL control to bring the meter needle to CAL (21%).

Note: This unit can be checked by blowing into the probe. The alarm should go off at 19.5%.

- To check for gas, expose the probe to the atmosphere to be monitored/checked. The meter will indicate the gas concentration. If the reading rises above the alarm setting (20%), a red light will go on and an alarm will sound.

- To check for oxygen, expose the probe to the atmosphere to be monitored/scheduled. The meter will indicate the oxygen concentration. If the reading drops blow the alarm setting (19.5%), an amber light will go on and an alarm will sound.

If any dangerous situations are indicated, follow the procedures given in OSHA and company standards.

Ventilation

When work is carried out in any confined space, the space must be ventilated continuously and tests for harmful or combustible substances and oxygen deficiency must be made and recorded at the beginning of the job and after any interruption in the work procedure. Interruption in the work procedure means any stopping of the ventilation or the crew leaving the confined space for more than 20 minutes. Full entry procedures must be used after each interruption in the work procedure.

If oxygen levels cannot be kept above 18% or combustible readings cannot be maintained below 20% of LEL or toxic substances below 50% of their maximum allowable concentration, workmen required to enter the vault must comply fully with OSHA and company standards.

The use of mechanical ventilation does not preclude testing beforehand for combustibles and oxygen deficiency. Unless specific variances have been granted, a confined space must never be entered until it has been tested for oxygen and combustibles and then ventilated for *five minutes* as follows:

1. The blower must be placed upwind of the confined space entrance.

2. The blower must force air into the confined space. Do not use it as an extractor, as the turbulence produced by blowing gives much more effective air exchange than extraction. If the source of contamination in a confined space is localized, using the blower as an extractor may provide better control of the hazard than blowing air into the confined space.

3. The blower discharge hose must be free from kinks and be suspended in the vault with a bend to make the outlet horizontal. This ensures that the blown air creates the necessary turbulence in the vault's atmosphere to remove pockets of gas.

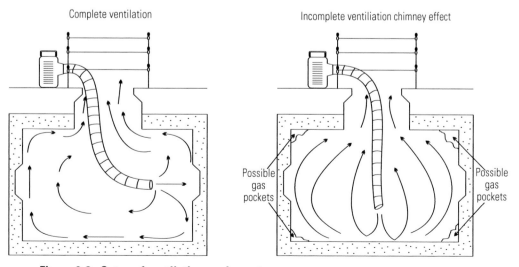

Complete ventilation

Incomplete ventiliation chimney effect

Possible gas pockets

Possible gas pockets

Figure 9-3. Setup of ventilation equipment.

4. The blower suction inlet must be clear of vehicle exhaust or other sources of pollutants and must be in an area clear of debris which could enter the blower.

5. The blower must provide adequate ventilation while work is in progress. In practice, a blower should provide a minimum of 10 air exchanges per hour. Most industrial air blowers will move 400 to 1000 cubic feet per minute (cf/m).

Figure 9-4. Type of ventilator used.

Provision of Assistance

A worker entering a confined space must be attended by or in regular communication with another person stationed at or near the entrance to the confined space. Alternatively, the worker entering the confined space must be provided with a means of continuous communication with a person outside and visually checked by a designated person at intervals as often as may be required by the nature of the work to be performed.

Where the nature of the confined space and the precautions taken result in a low risk associated with entry, local authorities may approve modified man check procedures.

Cleaning

Confined spaces where gasoline, diesel or other harmful or combustible agents have been spilled must be cleaned before entry for normal inspection or maintenance.

The confined space should be washed down with high pressure water (Oilsperce 43 or similar surfactant will assist in washing contaminants from walls). Pump washings into a suitable container for disposal.

Specific Procedures

Specific procedures apply to the following situations:

- Entry and work in street vaults and manholes.

- Entry and work in street vaults after chemical spill, explosion, fire or serious equipment failure.

- Entry into fuel tanks and cleaning.

- Work on oil and sulphur hexafluoride (SF_6) filled electrical equipment.

The above situations require special attention and the procedures should be followed carefully. If no actual procedure is given, check with your subforeman/woman or supervisor, as it may be specific to an area or district and therefore is not available for this section.

Entry and Work in Street Vaults and Manholes

The hazards of underground vaults and manholes include air contaminants and oxygen deficiency. Carbon monoxide from vehicle exhaust, methane from natural gas distribution systems, and vapors from gasoline spills are all possible air contaminants. Oxygen deficiency in tightly closed underground workplaces may result from rusting of iron or bacterial degradation of plant material. Limited and undedicated combustion can also deplete oxygen if there is poor ventilation.

Entry and work in underground locations must meet the precautions outlined under General Procedures unless specific variances or work procedures apply.

Some jurisdictions allow a variance to the ventilation regulation for entry into electrical operations manholes and street vaults for periods of 10 minutes or less where the work will not create a harmful atmosphere and no hazard is identified by the initial testing.

The procedure is as follows:

1. Hold a tailboard discussion. This must take place at the job site.

2. Using a probe, test the oxygen level. It must be greater than 20%.

3. Using a probe, test the combustible gas level. It must be less than 5% of the lower explosion level.

4. Record the oxygen and combustible gas levels on the Manhole Entry Log. This record must be kept for inspection.

MANHOLE ENTRY LOG						
		Readings		Mancheck		
Manhole No.	Date	O_2	Combustible	Entry	Exit	Signature

Figure 9-5. Manhole entry log.

5. If oxygen or combustible gas levels are not acceptable, immediately report this condition to the supervisor. ***Do not enter.*** Ventilation and/or cleaning may be necessary before you can enter. It must be confirmed that the hazard is controlled before normal entry procedures can be used again.

6. If the readings are acceptable, station a worker outside the street vault or manhole for the duration of the entry period to check on the well-being of the worker(s) who enter. Entry must never be attempted by a person working alone.

7. Enter the street vault or manhole carrying a continuous reading oxygen and gas monitor. The monitor must conform to approved standards for oxygen and combustible gas meters.

8. If at any time the continuous monitor sounds an alarm, all personnel must immediately evacuate the street vault or manhole.

A minor risk must be accepted when using only an oxygen combustible gas meter, since the meter does not measure toxic gases (e.g. carbon monoxide) or low levels of combustible substances which are also toxic. This risk is minimized by the time limit noted for this monitoring procedure. The audible alarm will warn all workers of combustibles or oxygen deficiency if an emergency occurs in the vault or manhole.

If the work period will be longer than 10 minutes or if the work will generate an air contaminant, the following steps must be added to the procedure just described above (for 10 minutes or less):

- After removing the grate or manhole cover, check all levels in the space. Record the results.

Note: See Step 5 on the preceeding page.

- If no hazards are detected, start continuous ventilation. Ventilate the space for *five minutes* before entering. Continuous ventilation must be maintained throughout the work.

- Follow established procedures for protection of workers from contaminants generated by the work process, such as solvents, lead fumes.

- If the work location is in an area where rescue crews cannot reach the site within 30 minutes, the worker stationed outside must be equipped for and capable of effecting a rescue in accordance with a written rescue procedure.

- If ventilation is interrupted or the crew leaves the confined space for more than 20 minutes, full entry procedures must again be used.

- A continuous reading oxygen and combustible gas monitor is not required once the space is being continuously ventilated.

There is an exception to the vault's entry procedure: All crew members may enter and work in the street vault or manholes provided that the following conditions are met:

- A radio man check system is used in lieu of the outside worker.

- The radio man check system is implemented a minimum of once every 30 minutes.

- All street vault or manhole entries are logged at the radio dispatch center and at the work site. A worker may leave and return to the street vault or manhole without logging in, provided it is not check-in time for the radio man check.

- The duration of the entries does not exceed a total of two hours in one work shift.

- Rescue crews can reach the site within 30 minutes.

Entry and Work in Street Vaults after Chemical Spills, Explosion, Fire or Serious Equipment Failure

Entry and work in underground locations must meet the precautions outlined under General Procedures unless specific variances or work procedures apply.

In the case of chemical spills, explosions, fire or serious equipment failure, the procedure is as follows:

1. Ensure that the circuits are isolated. This may not be necessary, based on the nature of the hazard.

2. Extinguish any fire.

3. Identify the hazards arising from the chemical spill, explosion, fire or equipment failure prior to entry. If necessary, contact your Safety Department.

4. Test for oxygen level. It must be greater than 18%.

5. Test for combustible gas level. It must be less that 20% of the lower explosion level (LEL).

6. Ventilate the street vault or manhole until 20 air changes have occurred. Continue to ventilate. The time required for 20 air changes equals:

$$\frac{\text{volume of the space is 3 cu. ft.} \times 20}{\text{ventilation fan output is 3 cu. ft./min.}}$$

Instead of waiting for the 20 air changes, tests can be carried out to measure any chemicals identified as per Step 3.

7. Retest for oxygen and combustible gas as per Steps 4 and 5. Ideally no deviation from clean air should be detected.

8. Wearing a lanyard, body harness and appropriate personal protective clothing and equipment, enter the street vault or manhole to work. A worker must be stationed outside the street vault or manhole to check on the well-being of the worker(s) who have entered. There must be rescue personnel present and ready to effect immediate rescue.

The following points should be noted:

- It may not be possible to fully control hazards that arise from fires, chemical spills, etc. by ventilation alone. It may be necessary to utilize special protective equipment, clothing and respiratory protection. Contact your Safety Department for further assistance.

Work on Oil and Sulphur Hexafluoride (SF$_6$) Filled Electrical Equipment

Toxic by-products from sulphur hexafluoride (SF$_6$) gas-filled circuit breakers, disconnect switches and bus ducts, and hazardous combustible gases formed in oil filled transformers, require special precautions and well defined procedures for opening and sampling.

Emergency Entry and Rescue for Confined Spaces

The following guidelines should be used in conjunction with local operating orders for emergency entry and rescue procedures for confined spaces. The three events that could require removal of an employee from a confined space are:

• Fire or explosion

• Electrical contact

• Accident or illness

In all cases, notify your supervisory or the person in charge (PIC) as soon as possible, giving your name, work location, type of problem and assistance required. Personnel (for example, local fire department) must be present and ready before any person enters a dangerous street vault or manhole for rescue purposes. Enter the manhole only when you are sure there is sufficient oxygen and no other risk (electrical) to your own survival and provisions for rescue are in place. Don't become a second victim!

Fire or Explosion

Extinguish fires using dry chemical fire extinguishers. Ventilate to replace oxygen, which is rapidly consumed during a fire or explosion. Rescue trapped or injured employees only when doing so will not place you at undue risk.

Electrical Contact

Do not touch the victim before checking whether electrical hazards are present. Use a Modiwark to quickly check for electrical potential. A victim's body can be cleared by using a dry rope or live line tool if voltage is present. It is preferable to de-energize all sources before attempting a rescue.

After the victim is clear, check for breathing and external hemorrhage or burns. Administer the appropriate first aid. When assistance arrives, ensure the rescuers are aware of all hazards.

Accident or Illness

In cases of accidental injury, always ensure that the victim can be rescued from the confined space without causing additional injury.

Illness may be caused by lack of oxygen or the presence of some air contaminants, so get the victim into fresh air as soon as possible. Always ensure your own safety by using adequate respiratory protection and/or ventilation if air contaminants are suspected

The oxygen and combustible gas levels must be recorded on the Manhole Entry Log after completing the probe tests. This record must be kept and made available for inspection.

It is the Safety Department's responsibility to ensure that the emergency personnel are equipped for and capable of effecting a rescue.

Gases

Introduction

The gases that you will use are usually compressed to a certain working pressure. These compressed gases are contained in specially constructed cylinders. Gases such as sulphur hexafluoride (SF_6), nitrogen (N_2) and air are usually at 100 psi while propane (C_3H_8) is compressed or pressurized until it is in the liquid state.

These gases and their containers or cylinders must be handled with care to prevent damage to the cylinder, leakage and possible explosions or fires.

This section will identify some of the commonly used gases and their applications, and highlight the safety concerns. Although the PLT does not usually come in contact or use some of the compressed gases mentioned, they have been explained, as some areas use the underground department to assist the cable splicers.

The topics covered are:

- Compressed air

- Sulphur hexafluoride (SF_6)

- Nitrogen (N_2)

- Propane(C_3H_8)

- Acceptance and handling of compressed gases

Compressed Air

Air is a mixture of gases and is composed chiefly of nitrogen and oxygen but also contains certain amounts of carbon dioxide and some inert gases such as helium, argon, etc. This air is compressed in cylinders and can be classified as a dielectric gas. At 100 psi, compressed air has a dielectric strength comparable to mineral oil. However, air promotes oxidation of other components of the system and is readily ionized, forming corona at high voltages.

Its uses vary from air breaker control to breathing apparatus to cleaning equipment. It is relatively safe if a few basic rules are followed, but many accidents have occurred in the industry due to an air hose being used for horseplay.

Never use compressed air to dust off or dry clothing. You may imbed some of the dust in your skin or your eyes. If compressed air is blown into a cut or natural body opening, it can result in bleeding, pain and/or death depending on what may have been mixed in with the compressed air.

If you are working with an air hose, before you open a valve, check the hose and the trigger or operating valve. Ensure that the hose is clear and contains no particles, and ensure that the valve is in the off position. If air is applied to a hose, without checking these points, the hose will whip around out of control, causing injury to an unsuspecting party.

Ear protection must be worn when draining off air on all high pressure air systems as the noise level can damage your eardrums and affect your hearing. When using compressed air for breathing purposes, reduce the pressure to atmospheric pressure and filter the air before breathing it.

Sulphur Hexaflouride (SF$_6$)

This gas is chemically inert in the pure state and is considered to be physiologically inert as well. To be inert means to have few or no active properties (inactive).

SF$_6$ has remarkable dielectric strength. It is classified as an electronegative gas, which means that it absorbs or captures free electrons. Its high vapour pressure, chemical stability and electro-negativity make it a very good insulator. When taken to 100 psi, it becomes a better insulating medium than transformer oil. Its dielectric strength is better than twice that of compressed air.

SF$_6$ is increasingly used as an insulating and a protective gas in electrical switchgear, transformer connections and bus-work. The gas is totally enclosed under normal conditions and an alarm is usually used to warn of a drop in SF$_6$ density. Service equipment, including filter systems, vacuum pumps, compressors, coolers, dryers and storage vessels, has been designed to handle SF$_6$ transfer, drying and purification.

Not only does SF$_6$ possess a high dielectric strength to prevent arcs from occurring, but its dissociated molecules rapidly recombine after the source of the arcing is removed. This makes SF$_6$ uniquely effective in quenching arcs.

Potential exposure to the gas is limited to those instances when maintenance to SF$_6$ filled equipment is required or when contaminated SF$_6$ has been vented to the atmosphere.

The following safety precautions should be kept in mind:

- Pure SF$_6$ is non-toxic. However, a suffocation hazard exists when high concentrations exist in areas where personnel are working.

- SF$_6$ by-products created in electrical arcing are hazardous. Refer to OSHA and local standards before servicing any electrical equipment containing SF$_6$ that has been subjected to arcing.

Nitrogen (N$_2$)

Nitrogen is an odorless, colorless and tasteless gas. Compressed nitrogen has less dielectric strength than compressed air but its advantage is that it does not promote oxidation. It can be used to create an inert (inactive) atmosphere.

It is used as a blanket to exclude oxygen and moisture from certain parts of electric systems. It is commonly used in switches (along with the insulating oil) to change the air left in the box to nitrogen. This prevents moisture build-up and also eliminates oxygen oxidation. Being a weak dielectric, it can, to some extent, control the flow of electrons (arcing). Also, the nitrogen is left at a slight positive pressure to serve as an indicator of tightness.

Propane (C_3H_8)

Propane is a chemical compound made up of hydrogen and carbon and is classified as a gaseous hydrocarbon. It is colorless, non-toxic and is artificially odorized to aid in the detection of leaks.

Propane has the property of transferring from a gas to a liquid when pressure is applied. This allows a small cylinder to hold a large quantity of liquid propane and makes transportation relatively inexpensive and easy. Propane is frequently called a liquefied hydrocarbon or L-P gas.

Propane has great importance as a fuel for both domestic and industrial uses, it is used to fuel the torches, furnaces, etc.

If you ever become aware of an propane leak, close all cylinder valves immediately, shut off all equipment being supplied by the propane and ensure that no sparks or flames occur. Ventilate or allow air flow while looking for the cause or source of the leak. Do not turn on any equipment or valves until the cause has been found and corrected.

Acceptance and Handling of Compressed Gases

The following gas cylinder safety procedures must be followed. Every cylinder must be inspected before you accept and use it. **Do not** accept or use the cylinder if:

- The cylinder is not properly tagged to identify what it contains.

- It appears to be in poor condition (rust damage, dents in the surface, etc.).

- The hydrostatic date is not current.

- The cylinder threads are damaged.

- The cap is not on the cylinder.

If any of the above problems are encountered, return the cylinder and notify your supervisor.

The cylinders must be handled with care as they contain pressurized gases. Sudden release of high pressure will result in a cylinder becoming a missile capable of being projected through concrete or brick. The following points on cylinder handing must be adhered to:

1. Never drop cylinders or permit them to strike each other with a strong force.

2. Cylinders should be assigned a definite area for storage. The area should be dry, cool, well ventilated and, if possible, fire resistant. Keep cylinders

protected from excessive temperature increases by storing them away from radiators or other sources of heat. The area should have the names of the gases stored there prominently displayed.

3. Cylinders may be stored in the open but, in such cases, should be protected against the extremes of weather and from the dampness of the ground. This will prevent damage and rusting from occurring.

4. The valve protection cap should be left in place until the cylinder has been secured against a wall or bench or placed in a cylinder stand and is ready to be used.

5. Avoid dragging or sliding cylinders (even for short distances). They should be moved using a suitable hand truck.

6. Do not use cylinders as rollers for moving material or other equipment.

7. Never tamper with safety devices. These may be located in the valves of the cylinders.

8. When returning empty cylinders, close the valve before shipment and leave some positive pressure in the cylinder. Replace any valve outlet and protective caps originally shipped with the cylinder. Mark and label the cylinder as Empty. Do not store full and empty containers together.

9. No part of a cylinder should be subjected to a temperature above 125°F. Keep cylinders away from contact with sparks or flames from torches or other sources. Do not permit cylinders to come in contact with electrical apparatus or circuits.

10. Never permit oil, grease or other readily combustible substance to come in contact with cylinders or valves.

11. Use regulators with cylinders when connecting to circuits of lower pressure service ratings.

12. Pressure cylinders, whether full or empty, should always be securely chained in the upright position. When not in use, caps should be screwed on hand tight. This does not mean that when equipment is being used on an intermittent basis in the shop that gauges and control valves should be removed and caps applied. However, if the equipment is moved by vehicle, the gauges and controls should be removed and the caps installed during transportation.

13. Never repair or paint cylinders that do not belong to the company. If the cylinder valve is leaking, move the cylinder to the outside of the building (to a safe location) and inform your supervisor.

Propane Systems

Introduction

You will often be using propane gas systems when performing your job. It is important that you know how to operate these systems effectively and safely. You should understand the basic components of a propane gas system and the safety requirements that must be considered when using or transporting propane.

Propane is a chemical compound made up of hydrogen and carbon. It is therefore classified as a hydrocarbon. Propane gas is used to fuel the torches that you use on the job.

The topics covered are:

- Propane gas system
- Cylinders
- Regulators
- Piping and appliances
- Operation of simple manual systems

Propane Gas System

The basic components of a simple propane gas system are:

- Cylinder of gas
- Regulator to reduce pressure
- Piping and connectors
- Appliances

JOB SITE

Cylinders

Cylinders for propane gas are pressure vessels made of the finest quality steel and especially designed, tested and maintained to carry propane gas only. There are many sizes and kinds of propane cylinder.

Standard 20 lbs

The size used depends on the volumes and pressures of gas required to operate the connected appliances properly. The size is always designated by the weight of propane gas it contains when filled. For example, a standard 20 pound cylinder will contain 20 pounds of propane and will weigh approximately 43 pounds when full and 23 pounds when empty.

Standard 100 lbs

Figure 9-6. A few of the many sizes and kinds of propane cylinders. The 20 lb and 100 lb are commonly used for portable, industrial and domestic purposes.

The cylinder used must have sufficient capacity to maintain proper pressures to the appliances being operated. One standard 20 pound portable cylinder will operate several large burners satisfactorily in warm weather but may be too small to give enough gas for larger appliances used in the winter. The propane distributor can advise you about the capacities of cylinders and the gas input ratings of appliances.

Standard Propane Cylinder

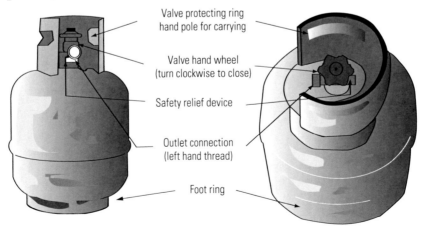

Valve protecting ring hand pole for carrying

Valve hand wheel (turn clockwise to close)

Safety relief device

Outlet connection (left hand thread)

Foot ring

Figure 9-7. Top standard 20 pound cylinder.

The valve protecting ring (sometimes called a neck ring) protects the valve and other parts from damage during transportation. The valve protecting ring has a hand hold in it to make the cylinder easy to carry. The outlet valve (or cylinder valve) is opened and closed with a hand wheel which turns clockwise to close. On one side of the outlet valve there is a safety device designed to release gas if the cylinder is subjected to temperatures over 165°F.

Never tamper with this safety device. On the other side of the outlet valve is the outlet connection, which has a left-hand thread. Turn the nut on the regulator or pigtail connection counterclockwise to make the connection.

Other types of propane cylinders have different arrangements on the top of the cylinder. All propane cylinder valves must be protected to prevent damage and possible release of gas. Any cylinder with an exposed valve on top should have a valve protection cap. This must (by law as well as insurance regulations) be in place at all times except when the cylinder is connected to a system and in use.

Cylinders should always be upright whether in storage, during transportation or in use. Laying a propane cylinder on its side is bad practice at any time. In high temperatures or during transportation, it can be dangerous. In the cylinder, propane gas is part vapor (gas) and part liquid. Each cylinder has a safety relief device (usually on the valve) to relieve the pressure if the gas gets too hot. If a cylinder is lying on its side and the temperature rises, the safety device will open and release the liquid propane.

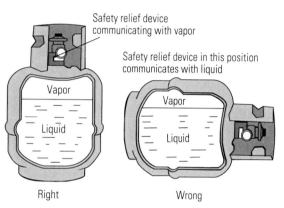

Figure 9-8. Why cylinders must always be upright.

Cylinders connected to any system must be outdoors. Every cylinder (and the regulator) should be a minimum of three feet horizontally away from any building or opening below the level of the cylinder's safety relief device. Since propane is heavier than air, any gas leaking from the cylinder may tend to collect near the ground or flow into a basement or manhole.

Never use a damaged or leaking cylinder. No cylinder should be put into service which has been involved in or near any fire, or has dents or other signs of damage of any kind. Such a cylinder must be requalified for service according to government regulations.

If a cylinder is leaking gas, stop smoking and keep all sources of ignition away. If possible take the cylinder away from all buildings to an open field and try to shut off the valve (there might be a particle of dirt keeping the valve from closing). If the leak continues, let the gas escape to the open air until the cylinder is empty. Make sure the wind blows any gas away from buildings, automobiles, etc. Once the cylinder is empty, take it to your supervisor and explain what happened.

Never try to transfer gas from one container to another. This can only be done safely by people trained in this work who have the proper pumps and equipment in approved locations and premises. It is against the law as well as insurance regulations to transfer gas from a large cylinder to a smaller one, except in an approved propane cylinder filling plant.

Close cylinder valves fully when not in use (by turning clockwise). This is necessary to prevent moisture from getting into the empty cylinder during storage and transportation. Moisture in the cylinder can cause freeze-up of the regulator in freezing weather (due to the refrigerating action of the gas in the regulator when the pressure in being reduced).

Regulators

The regulator automatically reduces the cylinder gas pressure and maintains a constant low pressure to the appliance(s).

Gas pressures in the cylinder will vary from as low as a few pounds per square inch when the gas is very cold to pressures exceeding 100 pounds per square inch on a hot summer day. The regulator reduces the high pressure by automatically closing and opening to maintain a constant delivery pressure to the appliance(s). Otherwise, if the pressure to the appliance fluctuated up and down, the flames on the burner would get larger and smaller and all sorts of problems would arise.

Regulators for portable use have an inlet connector to fit directly into the cylinder valve outlet. Remember that a special connector (male) with left-hand threads is required to fit into the valve outlet of most propane cylinders. This is for safety, since it prevents any ordinary pipe or hose from being connected directly to a propane cylinder. Most regulators are preset by the manufacturer to give the proper delivery pressure. Never try to repair a regulator. Special knowledge and proper tools and flow gauges are required.

Some regulators have inlet connections to which a pigtail is attached, which, in turn, is connected to the propane cylinder. Most regulators for permanent systems have two pigtails attached for connecting two cylinders. Again, these pigtails have the special connectors with left-hand threads to fit into the cylinder valve outlets. Such regulators are usually attached to the wall of the building with a special bracket and must always be located outside.

An adjustable pressure regulator is required for some torches and appliances. Such regulators are equipped with a pressure gauge. Follow the manufacturer's instructions and apply the correct pressure as required by the appliance.

Piping and Appliances

Piping and connectors are needed that will ensure a gas tight system. Seamless copper tubing with forged flared nuts and flared fitting are required.

Only appliances approved for propane gas are to be used in a propane gas system. If the appliances are made for use with natural or other gas, they must be modified for propane use by qualified personnel before being used.

Operation of Simple Manual Systems

The basic rules for the operation of a simple manual propane gas system are as follows:

1. Before connecting a full cylinder, open the cylinder valve for a short time and then close it tightly. This blows out any dust or moisture. Do it three times. This should be done in the open and away from any source of ignition.

2. Each cylinder should be turned so that the safety device points away from any other cylinder or combustible.

3. Close off all valves on appliances before connecting a cylinder.

4. Make sure the pigtail or regulator is screwed into the cylinder valve outlet.

5. Open the cylinder valve to its full extent. Test the connection for tightness with soapy water. Check the operation by lighting one burner.

6. Cylinder valves should be closed tight before any cylinder (full or empty) is connected or disconnected from the system.

7. If a gas leak is detected by the presence of the characteristic gas odor, all valves are to be closed immediately until the trouble is found and corrected.

8. Never under any circumstances check for leaks with an open flame. Keep sources of ignition away from the system.

Abbreviations

The following is a list of abbreviations used when describing underground circuits. While this list is not all inclusive, it does contain the abbreviations most commonly used.

In practice, there is considerable variation in the use of capitalization and periods (for example: psi, p.s.i., PSI, and P.S.I.), and stylings other than those listed here are often acceptable. Engineering drawings tend to use abbreviations in all-capital letters, abbreviations in text are more likely to use lower case letters.

In general, use capital letters for:

- Units named after a person (W for Watt)

- An abbreviation for several words (HV for high voltage)

- Phase designations (A, B, C). If a drawing shows both primary and secondary circuits, primary phases may be shown as capital letters (A, B, C), and secondary phases as lower case letters (a, b, c).

- The first letter of a chemical symbol (Cu for copper)

- Points of the compass (N, S, E, W)

A	ampere	**CL**	current limiting (fuse), centerline
A	A phase	**cmil**	circular mil
AC, ac	alternating current	**CN**	concentric neutral (cable)
Al	aluminum	**CO**	carbon monoxide
AM/FM	automated mapping, facility management	**CONC**	concerete
amp	ampere	**COND, cond**	conductor
AWG	American Wire Gauge	**CONN, conn**	connection
B	B phase	**cos**	cosine
BIL	basic insulation level	**CPSE**	counterpoise
BWP	bushing well plug	**CT**	current transformer
1C	single conductor (cable)	**C$_3$H$_8$**	propane
2C	two conductor (cable)	**CTM**	cable transition module
3C	three conductor (cable)	**Cu**	copper
4C	four conductor (cable)	**DB**	deadbreak
C	capacitance, Celsius, Centigrade	**DB**	direct bury (cable)
CAD	computer aided design	**DC, dc**	direct current
CB	circuit breaker	**DCC**	discharge control compound
CC	control center	**Δ**	delta connection (Greek letter delta)
cct, ckt	circuit	**DRSW**	dual radial switch
C.F., COF	coefficient of friction	**EDPM**	ethylene propylene diene monomer (plastic sheeting or seal)
CFC	chloroflurocarbon	**EPR**	ethylene propylene rubber
CIC	cable in conduit	**F**	Fahrenheit, farad, fuse

FCAN	full capacity above normal
FCI	fault circuit indicator
FI	fault indicator
ft	foot
FWO	field work order
FU	fuse
GA	gauge (wire)
GCA	ground clamp (or clip) assembly
GIS	geographic information system
H	(transformer primary terminal). H_0 is ground. H_1, H_2, and H_3 are phase terminals.
HS	heat shrink
HMWPE	high molecular weight polyethylene
HV	high voltage
Hz	hertz
HTS	heat shrinkable transition splice
H_2S	hydrogen sulfide
HVTM	high voltage tubing material
I	current
ID	identification, inside diameter
in.	inch
J	junction
JA	junction box above grade
JB	junction box below grade
JBAR	junction bar
JK	junction kiosk
JV	junction vault
k	kilo- (prefix for thousand)
kcmil	thousand circular mils (replaces MCM)
kV	kilovolt
kVA	kilovolt-ampere
kVAR	kilovolt-ampere reactive
LB	loadbreak
lb	pound
LEL	lower explosion level (gas)
LPT	low profile transformer
LWO	local work order
M	mega- (prefix for million)
MBSM	moisture barrier shrinkable material
MH	manhole
MK II	(a brand of padmounted switchgear)

MTS	modular transition splice
MVA	motor vehicle accident
N	neutral
Neut	neutral
NO	normally open
NPS	nominal pipe size (iron pipe)
NTS	not to scale
N_2	nitrogen
OD	outside diameter
Ω	ohm (Greek letter omega)
OPVC	oil packed varnished cambric (tape)
OSM	oil stop module
O_2	oxygen
PB	pull box
PE	polyethylene
pf, PF	power factor
PH	phase
ϕ	phase (Greek letter phi)
PIC	person in charge
PILC	paper insulated lead covered (cable)
PILCPJ	paper insulated lead covered plastic jacketed (cable)
PL	plate
PLT	powerline technician
PMT	padmount transformer
PMDFT	padmount deadfront transformer
PRI	primary
PT	potential transformer
PVC	polyvinyl chloride
r	radius
RCBN	reduced capacity below normal
RDSS	Rayflate duct sealing system
RFI	radio frequency interference
ROW, R/W	right of way
RTE	a loadbreak elbow designed by Rural Transformer and Equipment Company, now part of Cooper Power Systems
S	switch
SAP	self-amalgamating polyisobutylene (tape)
SB	service box
SEC	secondary

SF$_6$	sulfur hexaflouride
SHLD	shielded
SIC	separable insulated conductor
sin	sine
SOP	standoff plug
SRM	stress relief material, stress relief mastic (tape)
STLT	streetlight
SU	switch, underground
Substa	substation
SWBP	sidewall bearing pressure (cable inside a curved conduit)
SWGR	switchgear
3 ϕ	three phase
3 ph	three phase
θ	phase angle (Greek letter theta)
tan	tangent
TEL	telephone
TFR	transformer
TGR	tool for grounding and removal
TR	trench
TP	terminal pole, test point
UC	underground cable
UD	underground distribution
UDD	underground distribution diagram
UG	underground
URD	underground residential distribution
US	underground switch
UTS	ultimate tensile strength
V	volt
VA	volt-ampere
VT	voltage transformer
W	watt
Wh	watthour
WP	weatherproof (insulation)
WR	weather resistant
X	(transformer secondary terminal). X_0 is ground, X_1, X_2, and X_3 are phase terminals.
xfmr, XFMR	transformer
XLPE	cross-linked polyethylene (cable)
Y	wye connection
Z	impedance